To David

a fellow Smallwood Villager
and friend also dovetailed together
through our families as neighbours
— a life-long connection

with my love + fondness

Jean
(Williams)

September 2018

'Doreen'

THE
GENTLE
RIBBON

Written by
Jean Williams

*Recalling the pillow talk of a True Story
in Fictional Style*

Set during the period of 1891 to 1920

First published in Great Britain in 2008
by
Jean Williams

Copyright © 2008 Jean Williams

1st Edition Printed 2008

Names, characters and related indicia are copyright and trademark
Copyright © 2008 Jean Williams

Jean Williams has asserted her moral rights
to be identified as the author

A CIP Catalogue of this book is available from the British Library

ISBN 978-0-9558791-0-4

Printed and bound in
Great Britain by Biddles Ltd,
King's Lynn, Norfolk

Brookhouse Green

The Blue Bell Inn

To Brownlow

Cheshire

Smallwood

Hangmans lane

Higher Smallwood Farm

Chance

green lane

Forge Farm

Bowden Hall

long drive

Chance Hall Lane

Pump House Farm

Rode

Mill

Moors Farm

Ho

Townsend Lane

Church Lane

All Saints

Old

To Sandbach

Packhorse Fm

Rode Pool

Game Keepers Cottage

Church Cottages

Walled Garden + Cottage

Home Farm

Rode Hall

The Broughton 'The gap'

Rode Heath

Hall Lodge

Cricket Pitch

Tenants Hall

icehouse

Lodge

rear drive

Hall Drive

The do Hou

Lunts moss

The Gentle Ribbon - Jean Williams

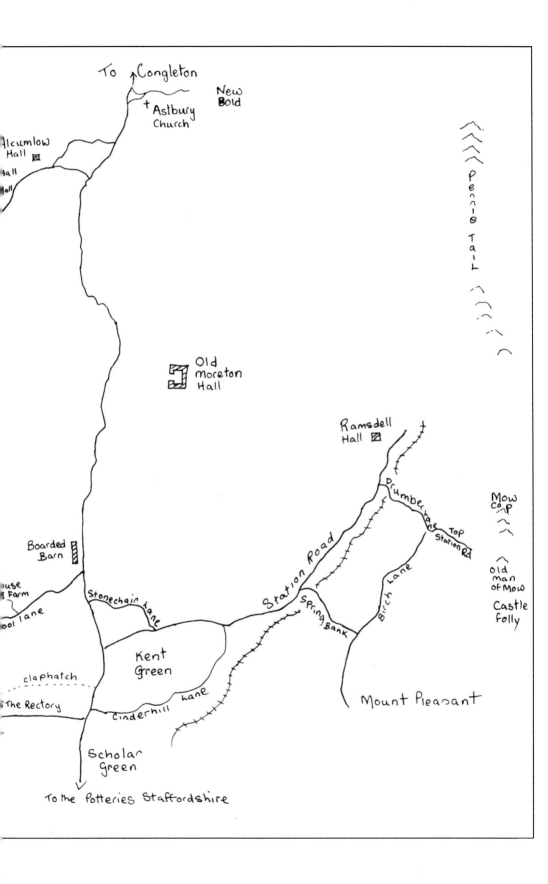

FOREWORD

Prior to my marriage I shared a bedroom with my Grandmother Mary at my parents home at Little Moss End Farm Smallwood in the County of Cheshire. I always called my grandmother Nana and I can vividly remember listening to Nana as she told me true stories while we were lying together with our heads on the white pillows and bolster in the old feather bed. These stories took me through my childhood, teenage and young woman years of my life and I heard first hand from Nana details of her younger life, whilst tenant farming at Odd Rode, couched in adult terms. Her mother Edith Helen, known as Nellie, is the heroine of my book and Nana Mary also gave me a deep insight into her mother's life hence my clear knowledge of the late 1800's.

I was fortunate enough to know Great Grandmother Nellie well through close regular family visiting and I occasionally stayed at her then home of Oak Tree Farm Betchton. Even in her latter years she had a gracious upright figure and radiated a warm smile. I was nineteen years of age when she died at the age of 94 in 1967. I was in my thirties married to Godfrey with our own children Peter and Rachel, when my Nana Mary died at the age of 85 in 1982. I feel fortunate to have received loving hugs and kisses from Great Grandmother Nellie and exceptionally sound advice from Nana Mary. Whenever life gets tough for me I long for my Nana Mary's mental strength.

My Mother, lovely Ruby the youngest daughter of Mary,

had a spell in her life when she suffered from throat cancer and she made me write down the outline of the Family story on the reverse side of a large old photograph. I already knew it from the close details Nana Mary had often relayed to me in our pillow talk. However, before dear Mum Ruby died she insisted I listened to her as well because she felt one day I would 'string it all together in words'. This book is the completion of the task she believed I could do and I sincerely hope I have done all three of my remarkable matriarchal ladies proud.

Jean Williams 2008

* * * * * *

I thank my treasured family namely my husband Godfrey, son Peter, Joanne, daughter Rachel and Michael for their encouragement to bring my work to fruition. I wish to dedicate this book to them and to my precious grandchildren Andrew, Steven, James and Robert.

The Four Generations
left to right -Nellie, Mary and Ruby
Mary holding baby Jean 1948

To be noted:

Where the story line is delicate I have altered some names to protect descendants living locally today. The setting of The Gentle Ribbon at Odd Rode Cheshire is correct but it is my dear wish not to hurt anyone and I have been in close contact with Lady Anne Baker Wilbraham of Rode Hall to guide me as I was willing to set my story on a fictitious Cheshire estate and not the present Rode Estate. Lady Anne told me my book belongs to Rode but I do declare that my reference to the Vicar of Rode or Hall staff members is pure fiction and is not to be taken in any other context. Although the incident between Nellie and a visiting clergyman is true I have chosen the fictitious title of the 'Canon of Malvern' to mask the identity of the perceived episcopal visitor of that time. I know that my reference to Rode should be Odd Rode and the Wilbraham Family should be the Baker Wilbrahams but for simplicity and lessening the length of this my book I have only referred to Rode and to the Wilbrahams. Also my reference to any of the Wilbraham family deaths are not correct as to date but it suited the timescale of The Gentle Ribbon for me to incorporate how esteemed landlords were dealt with after their demise.

CHAPTERS OF

THE GENTLE RIBBON

CHAPTER 1

A Particularly Picturesque Corner Of Cheshire

'Excellent, Sir!' Alec Bailey the Gamekeeper reverently shouted, giving praise to Sir Philip Wilbraham as two pheasants were expertly shot out of the sky. Alec always enjoyed ending a morning shoot on a good note and immediately thereafter gave notice to the Guns that it was the noon break for refreshment on that 7th day of January.

The New Year of 1891 was seeing the continuation of the exceptionally severe winter weather. Hunting to hounds had been cancelled for many weeks making the enjoyment of the shoots in the countryside much sort after, particularly at Rode Hall in the County Palatine of Cheshire, the home of the Wilbraham Family.

'Are we down on beaters today Alec?' Sir Philip enquired with a puzzled frown.

'Yes Sir. The water bailiff wishes to complete the packing of the ice house and I have released some beaters to assist him. I felt sure you would agree. You can see the hoar is here, so after three days and nights of frost the thaw will come Sir.'

'Yes, of course it will. Yes you are right to provide extra hands for the bailiff's task.'

With a relaxing of his countenance Sir Philip continued, 'We'll have a short afternoon no doubt if we are cutting out the spinneys by the Pool.'

'That's correct Sir.'

With no more to be said Sir Philip headed towards his guest

Guns, who were grouping, to usher them into the Tenants Hall for refreshment.

In the freezing still air of the hoar frost each minute particle of moisture was frozen into tiny shards of prickly white and silver forms of ice covering every portion of the landscape, mimicking the icy fingers of Jack Frost. The trees looked exquisite as if clothed in magical silver gowns. All contours of the ground were accentuated with the cold hoar mantle, the frosty crystal carpet having traced each vein and defined every edge of the dead leaves and the sleeping grasses.

Alec sharply blew his whistle twice and his beaters respectfully appeared from the frozen thickets. As they trailed happily behind him towards the coach house, each footstep crunched on the ice packed terrain and all the men were looking forward to the tasty benefit of Cook's hard work. Both the Tenants Hall and the coach house had roaring fires which were going to be most welcome on that very cold day although, apart from their extremities, in the main most of the Guns and beaters were dressed appropriately and felt quite warm.

Whilst they were walking, as if with perfect synchronisation of Alec's proficient organisation, the bell rang from the tower to confirm noon. Alec looked up to the old clock, cloaked in the frosty hue, and was pleased the bag of the morning was high, for he knew after Sir Philip and his Guns had enjoyed their food and particularly their drink, their ability to shoot and to concentrate would be severely curtailed for the afternoon sport.

Rode Hall was a sound, Georgian, understated Cheshire hall situated in the south east corner of the County owned by the Wilbrahams. The Estate pastures were pleasantly undulating and Estate land to the east was tucked into the very rise of the Pennine Ridge. At the end of the Pennine tail was a folly known as Mow Cop Castle.

Although at a distance, standing stark and looking to the casual observer like an old portion of a neglected castle, it was plain to see on closer inspection that Mow Cop Castle was a folly and merely represented ruins. The folly castle was built in 1754 by the Wilbrahams on land formerly owned by them on the high east perimeter of their estate. Originally it was erected as a picnic area, affording a supreme vantage point to look over the Cheshire Plain and on a clear day gave vision well over to the Welsh Mountains. Local old villagers often told of how, when the folly was newly built by the Wilbrahams, it was inadvertently erected slightly on their neighbours land, gentry from Staffordshire believed to be the Syneds. To appease for the siting mistake of Mow Cop folly, the use of it became joint for recreation, by the gentry families.

Equally part of local history, especially fresh in the memories of the elderly, were the huge gatherings at Mow Cop when the Wesleyan movement was gaining a wave of popularity under the inspirational leadership of the Wesley Brothers. Long rousing sermons were heard by hundreds of people particularly at Easter gatherings and the strategic position of Mow was reinforced by the preaching of Hugh Bourne.

From the high position of Mow Cop Castle looking to the west, a very large stretch of water could be seen known as Rode Pool. The Pool in the grounds of Rode Hall added greatly to the beautiful west vista of the Hall. One could be forgiven for thinking that the word 'pool' gives the impression of a round area of water but Rode Pool was almost a mile long lake covering some forty acres and containing three islands. It was reputed that the extension to the original Pool was dug out by hand by French prisoners from the Napoleonic War.

The exceptionally cold Winter of 1891 had kept Rode Pool frozen for many weeks and a good number of able bodied villagers had their own skates and were allowed to enjoy their skating on the frozen Pool. The local youth loved the length of the Pool and took part very enthusiastically in their skating races. The Villagers appreciated the free use of the Pool from the lane side to skate or spectate in happy fellowship and such a privilege embodied the feeling of well being on the Estate.

In the main, whatever the season, skating or enjoying cricket on the new pitch, the residents of Rode felt valued for their work and play, aware of the pulse of give and take as the Rode Estate represented a good and normal portion of estate life, in a particularly picturesque corner of Cheshire, linking loyal cottage and farm tenants to a fair landlord. Also a proud crown to Rode was the recently built All Saints Church. Such a village jewel was established with the over stretching monetary generosity of Sir Randle Wilbraham, started in 1864 and completed a few years thereafter.

William Bailey was a tenant farmer at Pack Horse Farm on the Rode Estate and his farm was on the Pool side almost opposite the Hall. His family had lived on the Rode Estate for several generations prior at Moors Farm and he had a wife Emily who was formerly a Barratt from Brookhouse Green Smallwood. William and Emily had been blessed with eleven children, seven boys and four girls but were rearing nine as two had died. The eldest of their children was Edith Helen known as Nellie. William was brother to Alec Bailey the highly respected and skilful Gamekeeper at Rode Hall. When William and Emily had their second child, a son, he was named after Williams's brother and was affectionately known as 'Young Alec'.

William Bailey was always one of the tenants who provided his horse and cart, without being paid, to assist water bailiff and Hall staff with the packing of the ice house. The staff had the precarious job of smashing the ice with pic axes to roughly the correct handling size from the Pool. William carried the heavy sheets of ice with his bare hands to his cart until it was full and then he took his horse and loaded cart to the ice house, where he was assisted with the unloading.

It was hard cold work and the men wore thick hessian sacks, crudely made into large aprons, to protect their working clothes from the extremely cold excess water which accompanied most pieces of the heavy ice. But it was a question of many hands, although numb and blue with cold, made light of the work and there was intermittent happy bantering between the staff at the

Hall and the tenant farmers who assisted. Such a task took place on a dry Winter's day and the surrounding fields, spinneys and woods never failed to look exceptionally beautiful, sparkling usually with the icy diamonds of a hoar frost.

The ice house, within close proximity to the Hall, was an admired brick egg shaped construction, mostly underground, the protruding top covered with soil and turf forming a smooth acceptable mound which was pleasing on the eye. Access was gained by a substantial door and pathway and the huge sheets of ice were literally thrown and packed into the remarkable storage area. Once full of the tons of ice the door was shut for months.

The usefulness of the ice came into its own during the Summer for Cook, keeping the Hall's dairy products cool and helping to enhance her presentation of delicious summer desserts, as well as the ice being incorporated into refreshing drinks. Eventually when the ice became old and stale within its house, the cleverly constructed drainage system dealt with the residue, before the ice house was totally cleared and cleaned in the Autumn for the following year's store of ice. Any Hall of significance aspired to an ice house and Rode Hall's acquisition was certainly a talking point in the Village.

CHAPTER 2

INTELLIGENCE CANNOT OUT WIT COUNTRY NOUSE

The Canon of Malvern, who was renowned for composing religious music and hymns, was suffering with chronic depression commonly known as malady. One day he and his wife received permission from the Bishop of Worcester to take leave for six months, in an endeavour to cure his condition. Joyous with the news the canon's wife suggested they should spend the six months with his sister who was the wife of the Rector of Rode in Cheshire. His sister was delighted to accommodate them at Rode Rectory and did so in a kindly spell of weather in early March.

William Bailey was grateful that Spring had come early that year as it enabled him to row his boat over the Pool in his usual manner when taking his rent to the Tenants Hall on Lady Day, the 25th March, although he had seriously worried on the 24th about his ability to pay. In general chit chat most of the gathered tenants knew of the residence at the Rectory of the eminent Canon from Malvern and news was circulating that his convalescing was going well and he had offered to assist with the training of All Saints's choir for the Easter Services.

The two eldest children of William and Emily Bailey were choir members. Nellie, their daughter, was an extremely good looking tall slim young lady with brunette hair and beautiful blue eyes, well mannered and kind. Alec their son, was eleven months younger than Nellie, was equally as tall and very popular with his family and friends.

Events were normal and progressing well for the choir as the Rector and the Malvern Canon attended to the practices. At one, the Rode Rector decided it was time to let the Canon take the practices on his own. The Canon was an excellent music teacher but at his first lone practice he felt very drawn towards Nellie, who dismissed one of his strange glances as perhaps merely imagined.

The following week the same happened, a feeling of lust by the Canon for Nellie but this time unnoticed by Nellie. The practice ended in the usual manner with everyone bidding the Canon good evening but as Nellie was leaving the Canon surreptitiously took her anthem book out of her old small carpet bag. She wandered as usual to the church gate with the other choir members but then discovered her book was missing. Upset, she asked her brother to sit and wait for her on the mounting steps, while she retraced her footsteps in an endeavour to find her book.

In the meantime the Canon had placed the anthem book back in the choir stall where Nellie had sat and took himself into the Wilbraham Family pews in the pretence of reading. Nellie innocently re-entered the church and on seeing the Canon reading walked to him and politely apologised for interrupting and she asked for permission to check the choir stall to see if she had inadvertently left her anthem book. The Canon gave her permission and walked with her, falsely offering his assistance in trying to find the missing book.

Nellie threaded herself sideways along the narrow choir stall and to her relief the book was there. As she turned to reshuffle her way out the Canon too had threaded himself in the choir stall and much to her astonishment was standing by her side, blocking her normal exit. He stood too close to her for what seemed to be an age to Nellie and her lovely flashing smile of relief in finding the book turned to a look of concern and anxiety. He said nothing but placed his lean bony hand over her hand on the book and gazed into her eyes. Nellie felt vulnerable and afraid and the uneasiness increased so much in her, she pleaded quietly, 'Please let me go.'

It was as though her words and worried look triggered him back into responsibility and he immediately threaded his way out of the choir stall and strangely and profusely congratulated her on finding the book. 'Well done, well done Nellie, you've found it.' Immense relief allowed Nellie to composed herself. She confirmed that it was the correct book and made her way out of the stall with a thanking acknowledgement of the head that he had stood back for her. His head acknowledged a return thank you. Nellie did not stop. She kept briskly walking down the aisle towards the east door and gathered herself enough to offer a polite, 'Good evening Canon.' He too kept composure within the composure Nellie had created and bid her a slow, 'Good evening.'

The fresh air of the Spring evening blasted on Nellie's face as she hit the light after the dark porch way. Quickly walking down the church path half way along, she was greeted with the unsuspecting familiar voice of her brother Alec who enquired loudly, 'Have you found it?'

'Oh yes,' she replied almost as loudly, hoping she was sounding natural and added in a semi confident voice, 'It's safe. The Canon helped me to find it. I'd left it in the choir stall.'

She did not look back but she could sense from the hooded darkness of the church porch that the Canon's eyes were on her. Her full confidence returned on safely rejoining Alec. They both commenced to walk home and Nellie did so without one glance backwards, acting as normally as she possibly could to ensure the peeping Canon nor Alec detected how uneasy she felt.

The sleepless night that unfolded for the Canon was to him excruciating and at breakfast the following morning at the Rectory with his wife, sister and the Rector he felt most uncomfortable. Immediately after the meal, when the ladies had left the room, the Canon asked for a private meeting with the Rector in the study. The Rector was quite relaxed about the request and led the way. The study was warm with the coal fire burning and the sun of the Spring morning was pouring pleasantly into the south east facing room.

Both men raised the rear of their frock coats as they took to comfortable chairs. The Canon commenced the conversation and the Rector was alarmed at the story relayed to him. The Canon told of the previous evening's incident concerning Nellie but lied by saying that Nellie had left her book. However, with profound honesty he declared he wrongly impeded her in her effort to leave the choir stall and informed of the joy, beyond belief, he felt as he touched her hand. Such expression of joy was dovetailed with the utter remorse he had suffered the whole of the night for the deep sin he had committed. The lustful desire he had for Nellie felt like sheer adultery. How could he tell his wife of his sin?

The shocked Rector begged him not to tell his wife. Was he sure the story was correct and not just in his mind? Had Nellie suspected anything? Was he really sure it had happened? The Canon bowed his head in shame and nodded confirming it had definitely happened.

The Rector rose to his feet, turned his back on the Canon and stared out of the window in deep thought for a while before returning to his seat. He continued his panicking stabbing of questions asking firmly, 'Were there any witnesses? Was Nellie alone? Did you upset her enough for her brother to detect anything untoward when she rejoined him?'

The Canon nervously answered, 'I do not think so. She sounded calm as I watched her walk down the church path and she did speak with a firmness of voice to her brother.'

After a small silence the Rector said reassuringly, 'Don't worry I will call round at Pack Horse Farm today and without giving anything away, I shall enquire in a general nature if the children are well. Nellie is a pretty young lady and she is also very mature and modest and will not willingly think ill of you. They are a poorish family but they have just and honest ways. If Nellie has not realised the gravity of your actions she will not knowingly exaggerate them into becoming an incriminating incident.

'No! No! It is no use.', the Canon blurted out uncontrollably. 'It's not Nellie that is the problem, it is me! I cannot be with her, not even in a crowded church. She draws me. I am transfixed with her. I have terrible lustful feelings towards her.'

The Rector's anger rose.

'Stop it man, pull yourself together. The clergy cannot be drawn to every pretty girl in a village. One has a sixth sense of dealing with such thoughts and you will learn to be with her without your thoughts addressing her in that way.'

Near to tears the Canon pitifully said, 'No, I am sinful and am not worthy of my marriage vows. I must tell my wife.'

In a raged voice the Rector insisted, 'I order you not to confess to your wife!'

Dejectedly the Canon replied, 'Very well, I must leave Rode today.'

'Today!' the Rector exclaimed.

'Yes right away', the Canon confirmed.

'This is not the sane answer to the situation', the Rector retorted.

'It has to be, I cannot reside in Rode any longer with the temptation of Nellie.'

'What of All Saints; the Easter Services in need of your attention?' the Rector pleaded coldly.

'It makes no difference. It pains me deeply, but worrying about my sinful act with Nellie and my sleepless night has compounded my decision', the Canon replied in a desperate acceptance.

'What on earth will your wife think?' the astounded Rector asked.

'She will think my malady has returned. Can I ask you never to tell anyone, especially my sister.'

Silence fell between them again for a while. 'Very well', the Rector answered curtly. 'You have my word. I will bid the coachman to prepare for your journey and instruct Madeline to help with the packing of your things. I will conform to your lie and inform my wife of the recurrence of your malady.'

As the Rector and his wife waved goodbye to their guests the Rector's wife, in a critical vein of sisterly thinking, lamented the re-emergence of her brother's malady and felt after making such a stalwart effort to involve himself in the church life of Rode he was making her feel that he was ungracious with his sudden departure. She also felt his ingratitude dismissed all the arrangements she had diligently made concerning his accommodation at the Rectory.

After watching the coach go out of sight the Rector turned to his wife and suggested that they pray for the Canon and draw comfort from the farmers' sad saying that within families eaten bread is soon forgotten.

That afternoon the Rector deemed it necessary to take himself to the Hall and told Sir Philip the prepared lie, that the Canon's malady had come to the fore again, hence his sudden departure from Rode. Sir Philip pretended to be interested and as a gesture said he was saddened by the news and then reverted to the usual rallying of the Rector. He felt sure the departing Canon's efforts in assisting the church choir would be noticed by the congregation in the forth coming Easter Services when the anthem was sung.

Nellie in her quiet moments pondered on the acute uneasiness she had felt when retrieving her book and was not looking forward to the Easter Services and wondered how she would rebuff the Canon's glances. Her mother had noticed she was not quite herself, a little quieter than normal.

William Bailey had purchased a load of mash to assist with the feeding of his pigs. Caleb Lea from Rode Heath Mill was making the delivery of the mash with his horse and cart to Pack Horse Farm. William had instructed Alec his son to assist Caleb with the unloading. This task was done with a good working spirit and easy chatter between the two young men.

Caleb announced to Alec, 'I've just seen Madeline from the Rectory and she says the Canon of Malvern and his good lady have left for home. In a bit of a hurry they've left. His malady has returned.'

'What about the Easter Services?' Alec enquired.

'Sorted', replied Caleb. 'I believe Madeline said the Rector was going to see Sir Philip to tell him the news.'

When the Bailey family were together at Pack Horse Farm, around the large living kitchen table eating their mid day meal, Alec mentioned Caleb's conversation about the sudden departure of the Canon. William Bailey said he did not much care for the Canon anyway and felt he was short of a good feed. Alec said he was helpful at the choir practices but made no inroads into William's point of view. Emily gently said malady was a dreadful condition and such folks were to be pitied. As she was talking she did detect Nellie was quiet and slightly wide eyed at the news. Alec stated enthusiastically, 'He was kind to you Nellie last night wasn't he? He found your book didn't he?'

Nellie did not want to answer and didn't. The men noticed nothing but Nellie's silence spoke volumes to Emily.

Washing dishes later Nellie and her mother were alone. Emily had contrived the situation by assigning duties to her other daughters Lily and Lucy, taking them out of ear shot.

Emily enquired softly, 'What troubles you Nellie about the Malvern Canon?'

'Oh, Mother, please don't ask such a direct question.'

'Nellie, you usually confide in me. What is different about the Canon?' Emily asked reassuringly.

'It was my fault. I stupidly left my anthem book in the choir stall after practice last night.'

'So?' Emily slowly encouraged.

'He helped me to find it.'

'Did you thank him?' Emily asked dutifully.

'Yes, yes I remembered my manners afterwards.'

Emily sustained a warmth in her expression to wheedle more from Nellie.

'Afterwards?' Emily questioned slowly.

'Oh mother it was horrid.'

'Nellie keep calm and tell me so I can help you.'

'When I picked up my book to shuffle out of the choir stall he was right beside me. There was no need for him to be in the stall, no need at all. Then,'

Emily did not speak wishing to keep Nellie's thoughts clear.

Nellie drew a deep breath.

'Then he put his hand on my hand on the book for what seemed to be an age and did not speak. I quietly begged him to let me go and thankfully he stood to one side. I nodded a thank you to him and left, keeping on walking not stopping. The aisle seemed a dreadful long way.'

Nellie then fell silent.

'Was that all Nellie?'

'Yes mother. I remembered my manners and bid him good evening as I kept on walking but I was rude in not looking at him again. I had the sure knowledge that he was staring at me, I sensed him in the porch way as I walked along the path to Alec.'

'Nellie you did well. Did you notice anything about him while the others were there when you were at the practice?'

'No I don't think so. Well perhaps I did. When I looked up in my singing sometimes he did seem to be looking at me strange.'

Emily praised her. 'Nellie you did very well. You are a pretty girl and you will always wonder what you have done to create these situations. But you remembered your manners and you acted in control.'

'He made me feel so uneasy.'

'Nellie you must follow your instincts, as you did. When we are uneasy with someone our instincts are vital, that's why we have them. You were right Nellie to keep on walking.'

'You don't think this is anything to do with his leaving do you?' Nellie asked anxiously.

'No. No, of course, not. Malady can re-appear, the only reason he was here in Rode was to convalesce. It re-appears sometimes.' Emily said calmly before she asked,

'Did you tell Alec?'

'No. No, I didn't.'

After a slight pause Emily kindly announced, 'No more now Nellie. On with our work. I'm proud of you. You did right not to tell Alec, it's not mans' talk. It is best we keep this to ourselves. There'll be no need for either of us to speak of it again.'

Nellie felt she was exceptionally blessed to have such a wonderful mother. Even at sixteen years of age, Nellie felt a soothing of her inner fears through their undeniable bond. Her mother often referred to such a feeling as the wonder of an invisible cord floating between two people sharing a love, like a gentle ribbon. Not all mothers and daughters share such a precious gift but Emily and Nellie did.

The Easter services were a resounding success. The Rode Rector competently covered the faint cracks caused by the Canon's untimely departure, as Sir Philip knew he would. And Nellie, well she stepped normally into All Saints with a strength given to her by her mother that she had done no wrong and indeed her mother was proud of her. She held her head high in the choir and sang well.

Nellie's confident demeanour was notice by the Rode Rector. As they left the church he complimented all the choir members equally on their singing, including Nellie. Sir Philip complimented the Rector on the choir's splendid singing during the Easter services and the circle of the Estate village life was steadied once more.

The following Wednesday afternoon, Emily packed her usual basket with baking and walked from Pack Horse Farm along the lane skirting Rode Pool for about a mile. She turned right down Home Farm drive immediately prior to the Hall drive and made her way in her brisk small gait to Keepers Cottage, which nestled to the rear of the farm. It was a beautiful April afternoon and Emily was enjoying the warmth of the vernal air on her face and was lifted with the ever faithful tonic of Spring.

The vivid green of the new grass was peppered with the contrast of the early bright yellow flowers of celandines and first dandelions. The catkin and pussy willow bushes had tell tale signs of branches and twigs broken off where the children had lovingly gathered them to take home to their mothers for Easter decoration, particularly for Palm Sunday. The rooks and jackdaws were vocal, settling to their nests and their crescendo of noise duetted with the bleating of the new lambs. It was a day when all of Mother Nature's smells, sights and sounds of Spring were perfectly canopied under pure white small clouds in the deep blue sky, giving joy to any receiving soul.

Spring meadow
peppered with bright yellow flowers

Emily
tolerant and capable

On arriving at Keepers Cottage, the home of her brother in law Alec and his wife Martha, Emily opened the little wicket gate and noticed the activity of the ducks on the pond immediately in front of the Cottage. Ducks always made her smile and that afternoon was no exception. She politely knocked on the door and entered. Martha, as always, was pleased to see Emily and had the kettle boiling on the fire. Emily, as usual, made the pot of tea for both of them and they sat together for their weekly chat.

'You are so good Emily coming every week with some baking for us. You only just manage to get by financially and yet you still find it in your heart to be generous to us', Martha commenced with solemn gratitude as both ladies were drinking their tea from china cups.

'Oh it works both ways. William and me are grateful with Alec's guidance in teaching Young Alec his trade. He is hoping to be the underkeeper one day.' Emily replied cheerily.

'We would have had our own son you know if it wasn't for my lungs', Martha said woefully.

'Yes I know. No need to explain again.' Emily comfortingly replied and added assuringly, 'Well you do have your four grand girls.'

Changing the subject Martha said, 'I've been told the Easter Services were very good, the singing better than ever. The Malvern Canon helped with the training of the choir didn't he? What a pity he left before seeing the fruits of his labour. Malady again they say.'

'Yes the services were good.' Emily replied taking care not to mention the Canon but noted Martha had mentioned the malady.

Martha proceed in mono tone, 'You are fortunate your Nellie and Young Alec sing in the choir. My girls say they can't sing but that's nonsense when you are young every one has some sort of singing voice. A little training is all that's needed but my Alec he never encouraged our girls to sing and join in. You must be proud to see your children in the choir?'

'Yes I am but your girls were in church Martha and they mix very well in the Village', Emily replied in a light way.

Martha continued her droning, 'Yes I know but Alec says he need not conform to the Estate's politics to make his children take part in things. They don't do much and he hardly takes me to anything.'

'It's difficult for you to breath. Perhaps he is thinking of you.'

'Yes, you're right,' Martha answered knowingly adding, 'He does say that. He does take me to the Christmas Eve gathering in the Tenants Hall. I can just about make it with the shelter of the walled garden and across the cobbled yard, well wrapped.'

'There you go,' Emily answered smiling, thankful that Martha had found one positive thought and enlarged, 'you don't have to travel down the snowy lanes at Yuletide like most folks.'

With a rare smile, Martha, continued with slight eagerness, 'I do enjoy seeing folks on Christmas Eve. My chance of catching up with them but no matter.' Her smile faded before she despondently proceeded, 'No one can help my lungs, they are deteriorating, Emily. I'm sure I'm heading for consumption.'

'Don't talk like that. You've done well with your health through the Winter months and now you have the Summer to look forward to and it looks like being a good one, the rooks have built high.'

'No Emily I have to climb 'May Bank' yet, you know what they say, folks often die in May. The Grim Reaper takes.'

'Oh Martha please don't say that', Emily requested earnestly.

After their weekly cup of tea and chat Emily carefully peeled back the gingham cloths from her basket containing her baking. Although Emily was a natural competent stock woman she enjoyed baking. Country womens' baking, particularly farmers' wives baking, was always individual like handwriting. Give two good cooks the same recipe it would taste slightly different. It was impossible to stifle individual baking styles and most country ladies pies, particularly apple pies, were instantly recognisable through the taste and presentation of their pastry creation.

Emily took from the top of her basket the plain scones and stored them in Martha's cake tin and from the bottom of her basket pulled out a rhubarb pie, which she put in the larder safe, away from dust and the old dog. As usual thereafter she cleared Martha's table of the dirty dishes and washed them in the worn tin bowl on the scrubbed slopstone in the scullery, putting them away on the open shelving after drying them on an old laundered flour bag. Feeling for Martha's pitiful plight Emily gave her a kind kiss and bid her goodbye and left Keepers Cottage.

As a little treat to herself, Emily always liked to make her homeward journey down the Hall drive to enable her to enjoy the pleasant view of All Saints Church and she also preferred walking in a loop before she picked the lane up again, instead of re-tracing her steps down the farm drive.

Whilst walking down the Hall drive she saw the Rode Rector's familiar carriage approaching. He knew of Emily's weekly visits to the Gamekeeper's Cottage and hoped he would meet her. Emily was inwardly pleased when she saw his carriage as she wished to speak with him and, was glad when on reaching her, he summoned his horse to stop, slackened his reins and commanded the horse to stand steady.

'How are you Emily?' he opened the conversation politely unaware that intelligence cannot out wit country nouse.

'Very well thank you Rector and yourself?'

'Yes very well, and Martha?'

'Oh about the same', Emily replied in an even manner.

'Did you enjoy the Easter anthem Emily?' the Rector enquired lightly.

'Yes very much.' Emily answered before boldly adding, 'It was a pity the Malvern Canon did not stay as arranged.'

The Rector pretended to be rather annoyed, 'Yes it was not easy for him, he had a lot to think about concerning his tuition of the choir. I wrongly thought he was capable of the duty but little things irritated him, silly little things like some choir members mislaying their books.'

'Nellie left her's behind', Emily said strongly and purposely.

The Rector realising that he was talking too harshly, and now knowing that Nellie had told her mother of the missing book had to tread wisely within a lie.

'Oh really', he quipped. 'I was merely pointing out a small irritation. I was unaware it was Nellie. Was she upset?'

'No.' Emily replied confidently backing the Rector into a corner to speak again.

Thinking quickly the Rector decided that if Nellie wasn't upset she must not have told her mother the whole story so he proceeded assuringly, 'She must think no more of it.'

Emily could detect the Rector was covering tracks, so pushed the conversation on, 'Surely she was nothing to do with his sudden departure Rector, not over leaving a book behind?'

'No, no of course not. Nothing at all to do with it, in fact you are the only one I have mentioned that small incident to. No, it was the recurrence of his malady, a terrible thing.' he replied slightly flustered within his lying.

Emily in control agreed, 'Yes Rector, a terrible thing. I always tell people they are to be pitied.'

The Rector's brain was locking and all he could do was to repeat Emily's words,

'Oh yes they are to be pitied.'

After a slight pause and a comfortable intake of breath, Emily said, 'Well just as long as my Nellie had nothing to do with it. I will pray for him.' The Rector continued his involuntary repetition, 'Oh no, nothing at all. Yes, we must all pray for him.'

Emily felt a strength within. She could sense from the Rector he thought she knew only half the story of the book incident. That was totally unimportant to her. She had heard from the Rector's mouth the story he was putting about Rode, namely the Canon's malady was the root of his sudden departure. That was very important to her. Nellie was out of the situation as far as

Emily was concerned and that was all that mattered to her as her mother. She knew there was no more to be said.

She bid the Rector good day with her usual cheery smile and he nodded politely, took up his reins and reciprocated with almost a mirror smile. He thought he had achieved much from his half planned meeting and subsequent conversation with Emily. In positive moods they both continued their opposite journeys along the Hall driveway on that beautiful afternoon. The Rector believed he had gained what he wanted from the conversation but Emily knew she had gained much more.

CHAPTER 3

YOU DO WHEN YOU LOVE THEM

Christmas Eve of 1891 arrived and almost all able bodied on the Rode Estate from the Wilbraham Family to staff and tenants and their families gathered in the Tenants Hall. The Wilbrahams as a family, with the assistance of their staff, always seemed to go to a deal of trouble in decorating the Tenants Hall and provided a warm welcome. Cook had known of the catering requirements since the 15th December and she and her kitchen staff provided a much appreciated festive fayre.

The noise level was high as friends and neighbours greeted one another, their cares cushioned within the merriment of the Yuletide.

'Uncle Alec it is good to see you. Mother doubted if you'd be here. It is good to see you!' Young Alec exclaimed as he warmly shook his uncle's hand.

'Is it Young Alec? Your mother was nearly right, I wasn't bothered about being here but my girls insisted that I should. They got a bit rebellious. Said they were not attending if I didn't. Their mother wouldn't have wanted me to spoil their enjoyment at this time of year.'

'It must be hard without Aunt Martha', Young Alec said softening his excited tone.

'Yes lad, it is but she warned me she would not climb May bank and she was right. It took her.'

'Terrible to think that she had taken good care of herself during the Winter and then to die in such a lovely month.' Young

Alec sadly commented.

Old Alec continued, 'The month of May takes a lot of folk. A lot of country folk. They call it May Bank. A struggle to climb if you are ill. The ailing oldens always fear the month for death. Martha was frittened it'd take her and it did. No matter. No more suffering for her.'

'I do feel for you Uncle Alec. She did love Christmas Eve here in the Tenants Hall beside the roaring fire didn't she?'

'Aye, she did lad. She loved people finding her for a chat.' Old Alec replied warmly and after a short pause added, 'The circle of life goes on and it will be time for you to be settling down with a fine lass with a pair of pretty ankles and a strong constitution.'

Young Alec blushing but knowing he could talk to his uncle Alec better than his own father decided to tell him of his inner thoughts.

'Oh yes I'm looking. In fact', he paused before nervously continuing, 'in fact I have been noticing cousin Lydia of late.'

'Nay lad you are wrong there', Old Alec declared. 'Nay lad, us Baileys are not money people but we do try to marry for love not convenience.'

'But I am very fond of Lydia', Young Alec ventured to say.

'That's as may be. But I can see you do not love my lass Lydia and besides it's not good to marry hoping love will arrive later. Find love before the altar. And we Baileys are not partial to marrying cousins. There is too much of it in these parts. Us Baileys are good looking enough to turn heads and sometime we are unaware it is happening.'

'Oh I don't think I do', Young Alec answered woefully feeling the wind being taken out of his sails.

'Yes you do. You'd be surprised who I see noticing you Young Alec.'

'But I thought if I married Lydia it would be noticed by Sir Philip and in the future I would have more chance of becoming your underkeeper. And she has such a pretty Bailey face.'

Old Alec replied knowingly, 'I don't think Lydia would

take kindly to your sentiments but I can tell you, you'll be the underkeeper to be sure.'

'How can you be so sure Uncle Alec?'

'I have no lad of my own and folks see I treat you as a son. I tell you it's been noticed at the Big House and you are learning a lot of my skills. I know every square inch of this Estate's spinneys and woods and such knowledge is invaluable to Sir Philip and he knows I am passing this knowledge on to you.'

'Oh if you say so, I was unaware of it', answered Young Alec unconvinced and despondent that his uncle had blown his idea of a courtship with Lydia away.

After a pause of thought he ventured to ask, 'Why didn't you have more than four children, Uncle Alec, and get yourself a son?'

'Aunt Martha, she was always delicate even as a lass but I did marry for love. I loved her on the day we wed and still loved her on the day she died. That is a gift in life, Young Alec, and I wish it for thee. It doesn't happen for all men.'

He pondered, twigling his old fingers around the George III sovereign, dangling from his gold watch chain and continued sadly, 'We wanted more children but the doctor severely advised against any. I loved her more to keep her than to try for a lad and lose her in childbirth. But it was hard, very hard I did want a lad. It wasn't to be but at least Martha and me lived to see the girls reared and that meant a lot to her before the good Lord took her.'

'How could you be with her as a husband and guard against anymore children?' Young Alec curiously asked, intrigued in his youthful mind that a man is capable of lying with a wife he loves yet keeps her from conceiving.

'With great difficulty', Old Alec truthfully replied. 'But when you love your woman, a man has to find ways round these things. You do when you love them.'

Old Alec took his gaze from Young Alec and glanced slowly round the festive room, his memories of Martha flooding his thoughts and hardly believing time in life could pass with such quickness and she was gone forever. Whilst doing so Young Alec was doing nothing but staring at his uncle's knowing expression, trying deeply to imagine his pain at the loss of a loving and loved wife.

He took to looking at Young Alec again thoughtfully, 'Hey, this be no use, I've taken too much of thee time. You get going with thee', he summoned to his almost son. Young Alec affectionately flung his arms around his tall uncle's shoulders, before eagerly saying, 'Good to see you. A healthy Yuletide Uncle Alec.'

'Bless thee lad. Enjoy your Christmas. Remember each one is precious, they will fly by in your life time.'

They hugged warmly before Young Alec drifted off into the merry crowd of the Tenants Hall. As Old Alec looked around feeling acutely lonely amidst the happy throng, he spotted the chair, the one where Martha used to sit, empty by the fireside. He stared at it for a while picturing her very clearly in his mind as his young wife, not the feeble older lady he had comforted on her death bed. He was drawn to sitting in the chair as if to be close to her once more. Whilst sitting he struggled to hold another surge of his grief as to the finality of Martha's death. He made a darting prayer that on his death, he dearly wished to be re-united with her in heaven. He knew, for sure, that there was no other soul mate for him on this earth.

CHAPTER 4

I'll Come To The Point

All was happy and normal for Nellie with her family, having spent a sparse but pleasant Yuletide at Pack Horse Farm. Nellie was quite surprised her mother had not had another confinement during the Winter months. It was two years since her mother's eleventh child was born and her mother did not appear to be showing signs of being with child again. Perhaps her child bearing years were over. Nellie did wish so, for although her mother appeared to have reasonable births compared with other village ladies, Nellie was weary of seeing her tired and heavy with carrying, and surrounded by all the worry that child bearing and infant rearing brought. She was also weary of seeing her father's face etched with worry when a child was born, knowing he was responsible for another mouth to feed.

Rode was in the grip of another severe Winter and during those months the Tenants were coping with farming, which was hard, as for all, but second nature for them to care for their stock during such weather. Too severe for hunting again but the shoots on the Estate were still taking place giving tenant farmers a chance to share fellowship in their get togethers as beaters. In fact the frozen countryside belied the pace and enjoyment gleaned by the fit citizens involved in Winter country life. Much merriment was to be had on the frozen Rode Pool, many sharing in the enjoyment of skating which took them through the drabness of those early weeks of January once more.

All seemed well for Nellie. She was feeling at ease with her church ties at All Saints and she distinctly felt an attitude from the Village that she was being accepted as a young lady. She was noticing the young men and, of course, her beauty had long been noticed by them.

Most young people met at church with the hope they could walk home together in groups and they did. Rode residents were very proud of their relatively new church and each Sunday there was a full congregation with everyone knowing where they should sit and more importantly where to sit in the pecking order of their wealth. Prior to the building of the church most of the parishioners formerly had to walk to and worship at Astbury Church and many of the inhabitants of Rode had forebearers buried in Astbury churchyard. Sir Philips's father, Sir Randle Wilbraham of Rode Hall, was most enthusiastic and instrumental in achieving the completion of All Saints in Rode in the 1860's having secured the architectural services of Gilbert Scott.

Rode parishioners were genuinely grateful to the Wilbrahams for their generosity in the funding of All Saints and the ease of travelling to their new church, instead of to Astbury Church, was very much appreciated by the foot members of the congregation and often remarked upon. Several of the old Rode tenants could remember their fathers transporting the stone for All Saints, from the nearby quarry at Mow Cop, with their horses and carts and the Baileys were one of those families. That was all nearly thirty years previous and Rode Church seemed to be thriving on such positive practical and emotional foundations.

On the Estate it was recognized that there was a lower end of tenant farmers to which Nellie's family at Pack Horse Farm belonged and tenants of a higher status, who were termed as well shod or well heeled farmers who occupied the larger farms on the Estate such as Chance Hall, Alcumlow Hall and Higher Smallwood Farm. Reinforcing the respect these higher farms commanded the occupying tenant farmers did not have to beat at the shoots and about five or six times a year were allowed to be one of the guns by personal invitation of Sir Philip. Nestling between the low and high ranking farmers were tenant farmers that seemed to bob along without feeling too much financial hardship. Everyone knew exactly which particular slot they fitted into and so it had been for generations on the Estate.

In mid January of the year of 1892 in Pack Horse farmhouse, William Bailey was taking his mid morning drink in his usual way sitting with his older working sons, whilst Emily and the older working girls dovetailed their chores with the waiting on of the 'men' and the supervision of the toddler. The between aged children were at school. The dogs started to bark and a fine horse entered the cobbled farmyard carrying a man who seemed to be early middle aged, dressed in immaculate riding attire covered with an expensive long riding coat. He alighted from his horse and walked to the back door and knocked firmly. Everyone had turned to watch this happening through the window without a word.

The knock summoned the Bailey family into action. Mother Emily whispered loudly in astonishment, 'It's George Walker! Quickly children tidy yourselves and mind your manners.' Instantly the toddler was whisked out of sight into the scullery by one of Nellie's sisters.

William Bailey walked slowly across the large living kitchen to his back door as if subconsciously he was allowing Emily and her brood time to be presentable. The boys wiped their mouths rapidly on their sleeves and the girls instinctively straightened their brunette hair and aprons, in almost one action simultaneously with their mother.

'Good morning Mr Walker', William said positively on opening the door.

'Good morning Mr Bailey.'

'Can I be of assistance to you?' William enquired.

'Yes, may I come in, I hope I am not disturbing you', George Walker said politely.

'Not at all. Please come in', William said whilst opening the door wider.

Mr George Walker was renowned for being a reserved man but was well known and respected in Rode. He took off his pork pie hat as he entered the warm room and, without particularly looking at anyone, bid them all good morning as William shut the door behind him. The remaining children in the room were standing out of good manners and reciprocated 'good morning' in unison to Mr Walker.

'I need to speak to you in private Mr Bailey if I may?' George Walker requested.

'Yes of course, please step this way into the best room', William instructed.

Emily was anxious because there was no fire laid although she felt calm in the knowledge her best room was scrupulously clean.

'There is no fire in there Mr Walker. Shall I light one?' Emily enquired.

'Thank you no Mrs Bailey. I will keep my coat on if I may?'

Emily nodded her head in acknowledgment and approval of his request.

Nellie couldn't help noticing how alike her father and Mr Walker looked in statue but very different in their attire. George Walker's starched raised shirt collar was shining white and stood out as an unusual beacon of Sunday importance on that ordinary weekday working morning.

After the two men had entered the best room and shut the door firmly behind them the children started whispering as to what the visit must be about. Emily was having none of it so she instructed them to drink up and get to their jobs, which they did without a word, including Nellie.

In the best room William asked George Walker to be seated and both men sat down in comfortable chairs. William Bailey could not think as to what the visit was about and, although he did not know George Walker well, he had always known him as a fellow tenant farmer on the Estate and throughout both their lives they had politely exchanged small talk over the years. The Walker family had farmed at Higher Smallwood Farm for several generations and were very well liked as a respected family at the Big House. William forced himself to sit with ease and respectfully offered George Walker the time he felt he deserved, pretending he had nothing pressing and had time to talk.

'I'll come to the point Mr Bailey', George said firmly. William nodded.

'I've come to ask for Nellie's hand in marriage and to ask that her hand is with the approval of you and Mrs Bailey.'

William could not act with composure and could not conceal that he was almost speechless. 'Well ! Well !' he spluttered. 'Well, well', he repeated trying to unscramble his brain.

George continued boldly, 'I know you think this request must sound to be rather hasty but I assure you, Mr Bailey, it is far from hasty, in fact I have given this matter thought for quite some time.'

William being wide eyed and stuck for words decided he would just listen to George Walker.

'I've noticed Nellie growing up in Rode and through her attendance at church, particularly at church in the choir. She is a fine tall beautiful young lady and I need a wife. I need a wife just like any other man to bear my children', George boldly stated.

William was gathering himself and joined in.

'Yes, all men do, Mr Walker, but why Nellie she's much younger than you.'

George pressed on, thankful his desired thoughts at long last were being interpreted into words.

'I know but I have often listened to the Rector, Mr Bailey.'

'The Rector, Mr Walker?' William asked thinking the situation was becoming more bizarre.

'Yes the Rector', George answered unswervingly.

'Time and again he has said your Emily, Mrs Bailey', he quickly added politely, 'she gives birth easily to fair faced healthy children.'

'That's as may be', William said in almost a self pitying way.

'That's as may be, but they all need feeding.'

'That will not be a stumbling block. I have money. Higher Smallwood Farm is a sound dairy farm of nigh on 200 acres and provides a good living', George stated positively.

'Oh, Mr Walker, I am in no doubt of that but it does beg the question why Nellie, a Bailey girl from lowly Pack Horse Farm?'

'I think you under estimate yourself and your family Mr Bailey. Your financial situation may be hard but you are rich in fine intelligent children. The Village remark on their good manners and tidy clean appearance in spite of your circumstances. And I can't deny Nellie's good looks have taken me.'

William, dropping his guard said very ordinarily, 'It isn't a situation I have ever given any thought to, none whatsoever, Nellie marrying you Mr Walker and living at Higher Smallwood Farm. What about the age difference?' She is only seventeen.'

'Eighteen this summer', George said positively. 'A marrying age, a good marrying age. That is why I am here today to speak with you, before her head is turned by a local lad and while she is still pure.'

William rubbed his forehead and asked, 'Have you no desire for a lady nearer your own age or from within your own circle?'

'I am twenty nine, only eleven years older than Nellie.' On changing his tone to one of slightly pleading but retaining his dignity George continued, 'Times of late have been hard for me. As you know my father died three years ago after a long illness and my mother left on the on-set of this Winter to live with my sister Sally at Townends Farm. She could not face another Winter up the long drive of Higher Smallwood and chose to go, especially as her infirmities are increasing with her age. You also know my elder brother John left many years ago to farm at Draycott, Staffordshire. That left me as provider for my mother and spinster sister and consequently I was made tenant of Higher Smallwood Farm. The farm is financially turning well and I don't regret what I have done, but I've kept myself too much to myself with regard to female company. My older spinster sister Polly who resides with me has been a particular strength to me.'

'Does your sister know you are here now?' William enquired.

'Yes she does.' 'Does she know you are asking for Nellie's hand?'

'Yes she does.'

'What does she think?' William asked thoughtfully.

'I don't know. I have taken her as my confidante but not asked for her opinion. I have simply told her of my intention', George added honestly.

'Well, Mr Walker, I am at a loss', William confessed.

'Mr Bailey can I ask you to discuss my request with Mrs Bailey and with Nellie, of course. Please stress to Nellie I wish to be a kind considerate husband and she will want for nothing at Higher Smallwood Farm.'

The chill in the room was overcoming both men as they looked one another in the eye. George stood, which automatically stirred William to his feet, and said boldly, 'I will return in one week for your answer.'

'Very well', William replied trying to disguise his heavy heart, adding, 'I will discuss it with Mrs Bailey and Nellie but I can't promise anything.'

They shook hands and walked out of the best room in silence, William was too stunned for small talk. Emily who was in the scullery had heard the latch go on the best room door. Immediately, she dutifully joined the men, who were standing in the cosy large living kitchen. She smiled warmly, sensed not to speak and only reciprocated his good morning as Mr Walker walked through the door to make his homeward journey.

William shut the door slowly and after watching George Walker through the window mount his horse with strength and vigour and leave the farmyard, he turned and looked sadly at Emily. She kept silent knowing William would speak without a question from her.

'Oh Emily, I have a heavy heart.'

'Did George Walker bring bad news?' she enquired in an

even manner.

'No, not as such, much however for us to ponder over, but not now. We will discuss matters late tonight when the children are all to bed. Keep the fire stoked, I think we will be talking a while. Emily nodded her understanding as William went through the door to continue his day. Later she followed his instructions.

At the end of the evening William and Emily sat either side the fire in their usual chairs and bid good night intermittently to their children. As Nellie kissed her parents goodnight she noticed the fire was unusually high and it was obvious they were going to discuss something at length.

Eventually, alone as a couple, Emily commented it had been an extremely long day and William reiterated that it had been probably one of the longest of his life. Emily knew the conversation was going to be serious but could never have envisaged what the matter was about.

William sighed and opened the conversation, 'Prepare yourself for a shock Emily. George Walker asked today for the hand of Nellie in marriage.' Emily stared into the fire and fell silent. Gathering herself she looked at William and calmly asked, 'Why Nellie?'

'He stated many reasons; to him her beauty and demeanour and like any man he needs a wife to bear him children.'

'Does he not think he is too old for Nellie?' Emily questioned purposely.

'No, he is only eleven years her senior and most of his fondness for Nellie has grown in a decent way through the church. In fact he says the Rector holds us as a family in high regard.'

Emily unmoved by the compliment enquired, 'Why Nellie? We are not a family of money standing. Has he not got a moneyed cousin somewhere?'

'I truly believe it is a decision made from George Walker's heart Emily.'

'Does his sister know of his intention?' Emily enquired.

'Yes she does.'

'Does she approve?'

'I don't know', William confessed.

'Well, his sister Polly is a very great friend of the Dowager. They have tea together each week. I wonder if the Dowager knows?' Emily said in a lighter tone, her mind beginning to race.

'No, Emily, Miss Polly is a confidante to George Walker in this matter. Besides them we are, at the moment, the only ones to know of this', William said firmly trying to keep Emily to the point.

Emily paused before saying, 'I feel he is too old for Nellie really.'

'Yes, I originally thought that but I must confess I thought he was more than eleven years older than Nellie. All day I have been going over his words and he stressed most keenly that Nellie would want for nothing at Higher Smallwood Farm and he would be a considerate husband.

'Higher Smallwood', Emily said almost in disbelief. 'Nellie from Pack Horse to Higher Smallwood.'

'Oh, Emily, what do you think Nellie will say? What will she really think about the situation? She doesn't have a particular young beau at the moment; perhaps she has a yen for an older man.'

'No!' Emily said emphatically having a flashback to Nellie's encounter with the Cannon from Malvern. Realizing she had spoken too harshly she softened her tone, 'Well, I'm at a loss.'

'Yes I was, Emily, with George Walker this morning but there's no doubt Nellie would have an easier life than most but do you think she could learn to love him?'

Emily said without hesitation, 'We could not have survived without our love.'

'I know but Nellie wouldn't need such a strong love to survive. Money would lessen the necessity for strong love.'

'Oh, William, Nellie is a Bailey. She needs to love her man.'

Silence fell between the two giving them both a little time to think as they stared at the slow red glow of the fire.'

Emily eventually said blandly, 'Sounds like some higher ups doesn't it? They marry for convenience and take a chance that they might love. It's just not our way, I think perhaps we should thank Mr Walker for his immense compliment but tell him to seek for a wife elsewhere.'

'No Emily, that is not his wish. He said he had thought about marriage to Nellie long and hard and gave me the impression that he had made his judgement on sound principals.'

'I can't see Nellie loving George Walker', Emily confessed.

'Could you see her running Higher Smallwood Farm House?'

'Oh yes. She is intelligent and articulate. She could add to Higher Smallwood particularly with her cheesemaking skill.'

Emily started to smile slightly and added, 'If Miss Polly still resided at Higher Smallwood I'm sure she would become a good friend to Nellie. She is such a lovely person, a real lady.'

A thinking pause ensued again for before Emily asked, 'What do you think William?'

'Well, at first I was at a loss to take in George Walker's words but after pondering all day; well it's like this, Emily, we have a large family and it is our wish that they marry and leave to have their own lives. It is a wonderful opportunity for Nellie, not only to go to Higher Smallwood but to be the lady of the house, she is well capable of it. There is no telling who will cross our door to ask to be betrothed to our other daughters.' Slightly sitting forward William said sincerely, 'After deep thought Emily I think we are honoured that George Walker wants Nellie's hand and she should be told.'

Emily tightened her lips. 'I see. You have had more time to think than me.' After a slight pause she continued, 'Although he is well shod he is like us a tenant farmer.'

William hastily added, 'A gun not a beater.'

Emily determined to have her say continued, 'Yes he is and at least Nellie would be local to us, still in Rode. And Nellie would not be a total lady, there is a lot of work in running a large farmhouse.'

William relieved with Emily's changing thoughts contributed, 'Nellie would be very busy organizing staff.'

'Staff', Emily punctuated with a wry smile. 'They would never be staff to Nellie, she would look upon them as her helpers.'

William returned to the matter in hand, 'He wants to know if he has our approval in seeking Nellie's hand in a weeks time.'

'A week!' Emily exclaimed.

'Yes we do need to discuss it with Nellie tomorrow but I don't know how. I think you should discuss it with her first.'

Emily's face changed to a countenance of thoughtful efficiency.

'Yes you are right William. I will talk with her tomorrow.'

Emily spent a restless night, not worrying but wondering how Nellie would react to what seemed an amazing unlikely request from George Walker.

The dreary Winter morn dawned grey and cold and immediately on saying good morning to Nellie, Emily said she needed to speak to her at length and suggested they go privately into the best room after breakfast. At the decreed time Emily and Nellie made their way into the room. Both women sensibly wore their shawls as Emily deemed it unnecessary and wasteful to light a fire. To be in a north facing room with encrusted frost on the inside of the window panes with the weak day light struggling through, throws a strange gloomy grey aura around the room, which offers no solace.

Nellie sensed her mother was going to discuss something serious. Perhaps her father's health but her instincts told her it was something to do with George Walker's visit.

'Well Nellie', Emily said purposefully.

'The time has come in your life for perhaps immense change?'

'Is father ill? Are we to leave Pack Horse Farm?' Nellie blurted out.

'No your father is quite well. It's about George Walker's visit yesterday.'

Nellie's eyes went wide in apprehension.

'Nellie', Emily softened. 'George Walker wishes for your hand in marriage.'

A stunned look of bewilderment overtook Nellie. Emily kept silent, instinctively knowing Nellie needed time to take in her words. There was no cheery fire to absorb Nellie's thoughts. She just stared at the icy window panes in disbelief. After a very long pause Nellie thought the request was as cold as the day. She looked to her mother and said, 'Father said no, of course.'

'No, Nellie, he didn't. George Walker wishes to know of your decision within a week and your father is only the bearer of the request in this situation. The answer has to come from yourself.'

'He is too old for me mother.'

'Only eleven years your senior.'

'Eleven years!!'

Nellie lost her repose. 'No! No. I couldn't. I couldn't possibly marry an old man. Oh mother please no.'

Emily smiling slightly to calm matters declared, 'Eleven years is hardly an age gap; not as much as you think. Your father is eight years older than me and we are happy. It's the arms and charms of your man that count.' Elaborating she continued, 'Perhaps running his farm has appeared to increase his years. Sole responsibility does not allow much leeway to act young.'

'Oh mother, when I think of the Canon's bony old hands it makes my flesh creep.'

'Nellie', Emily continued wanting to give her daughter support and the opportunity to consider all the facts. 'George Walker isn't at all like the old Canon. He is a fine respected man with strong broad hands that appeal to a country woman. He is exceptionally fit and it would be a huge honour to marry him and reside at Higher Smallwood Farm.'

'Honour! No mother, you were the one who comforted me regarding the Canon episode and told me to believe in my inner feelings and not to stay with anyone I was uncomfortable with. Now you are asking me to consider marrying an older man.'

'Nellie, Nellie dear', Emily said assuringly. 'George Walker will not make you feel uncomfortable. He stresses he will be a considerate husband and you will want for nothing at Higher Smallwood.'

'It's not money I want. I want to love my husband', Nellie said despondently.

'I know Nellie, and who's to say you wont love Mr. Walker. Some higher ups often learn to love their husbands a few years after marriage. Both your father and me feel you are well capable of running Higher Smallwood farmhouse, especially if Miss Polly Walker still resided there. She is a lovely person.'

'Does she know?' Nellie asked.

'Yes she does but she is a confidante in this matter.'

'It sounds as though you and father approve', Nellie stated coldly.

'Yes, Nellie, we do. We discussed the matter at length last night and feel it would be the right thing to do and you would still be close to us in Rode.'

Nellie realized her almost childish debating had to stop and she had to think solely for herself as an adult. Emily again allowed silence for Nellie to digest the marriage request.

After a while Emily said warmly and slowly, 'Why don't you allow George Walker to court you, see that he is honourable and caring and make up your own mind at a steadier pace?'

'You said he needs to know within a week', Nellie said sharply.

'Yes he does, but if we just gave him our blessing to a marriage and if we told him he had to court you before you made your own decision, that would ease matters.'

'Oh mother', Nellie gloomily uttered.

'Nellie we would not knowingly send you off into an unhappy life but your father and I, without doubt because of Mr Walker's kind request, feel you could have a much easier life than us and surely you can see that is not a bad thing for any parents to wish for their child.'

Emily paused and completely changing her tone announced, 'My mother used to say if you can't make a decision today over something don't force it. Sleep on matters and a decision will come to you in the morrow.'

With that mother and daughter rose from their chairs in the icy grey room and embraced one another. Emily knew she was holding her daughter as a woman not a child and Nellie felt the same sensation. For the first time in her life her mother's arms did not comfort her. She felt abandoned by the Gentle Ribbon.

Off both women went into the warmer living kitchen to join the others to continue their chores with no further mention of George Walker although Nellie's mind was racing with thoughts.

CHAPTER 5

SO DO I

Nellie's decision did not come to her on the morrow nor on the following morrow but it did on the morrow thereafter. She had adjusted to George's request and on a cold frosty morn purposely went to seek her father who was alone uncovering a few mangols in the croft beyond the stack yard.

Well wrapped, in her thick woollen outdoor shawl, she walked to him and said she was coming to terms with the idea of courting George Walker and apologised to her father for taking so long in speaking to him about the matter.

'Nay lass dunner worry about that. It has given me more time to think about it', William said kindly.

'Mother says you and her approve of his request of marriage.'

'Yes we do but only subject to your final decision. We will never make you marry anyone against your wish.'

Nellie said very maturely, 'I need for him to court me before I finally agree.'

'Yes, of course, you do, you have our encouragement to do that and if you should be happy with his request for your hand then I have one request of George Walker too.'

'What's that ?'

'You will not know, Nellie, that will be between George Walker and me. You nor your mother will not be privy to it.'

Nellie knew to trust her father implicitly and not to question more.

'Father, I too have a request. Will you please go to Higher Smallwood Farm to tell Mr Walker he has my approval for a courtship and your's and mother's blessing for a marriage but I wish to make the final decision for marriage. I do not want him to make another visit here until we are courting because the others don't know.'

'Have you not even discussed it with Alec?'

'No I haven't. I wanted to make my own mind up but now I've spoken to you and told you how I feel, I will tell Alec tonight.'

'I think you have been extremely sensible and I will go to Higher Smallwood Farm in the morning and deliver your message to Mr Walker exactly as you wish.'

Nellie felt much calmer, after discussing the matter with her father, as she left him to continue her chores in the farmhouse.

Very late that January night, after everyone was in bed at Pack Horse Farm, Nellie slipped a shawl around her shoulders over her night clothes and leaving her sleeping sisters, she crept along the landing and very quietly entered the boys bed room. She shook Alec holding her flickering candle to her face so not to alarm him.

'What's the matter Nellie?' he whispered as he awoke.

Nothing Alec, I just want to talk to you on the stairs. Shush, put your coat around your shoulders.'

Alec trustingly followed Nellie's instructions. The bedrooms were very dark because of the closed curtains but the curtains on the landing usually remained open. The landing window was south facing making it awkward for Jack Frost to keep his icy fingers across the panes of glass. The full moon looked exquisite in the sparkling galaxy and the silver moonlight cascaded through the portions of unfrosted panes and filtered on to the staircase. Nellie carefully blew the flame of her candle out, appreciating that the strong moonlight was making the candle light redundant.

Alec did not feel perturbed because of Nellie's calmness. Nellie pulled Alec's sleeve indicating to him to sit down with her side by side on the staircase and whispered to him, 'Alec I want to tell you that father is going to see Mr Walker tomorrow morning at Higher Smallwood Farm with a decision from me.'

'A decision from you Nellie', Alec whispered in a puzzled tone.

'Yes, George Walker has asked for my hand in marriage and mother and father have given their consent.'

'George Walker!' Alec whispered loudly in disbelief.

'Yes George Walker', Nellie replied almost smiling, covering Alec's mouth for a moment with her gentle hand indicating to him to keep his whispers quieter.

'Oh Nellie. What a shock.'

'I have not agreed to marry him but I am agreeing to a courtship with him before I make my decision.'

'Oh, Nellie, he is a gun at the Big House.'

'Yes I know he is', Nellie very quietly answered thinking that was totally unimportant.

'Oh you at Higher Smallwood Farm and to be married to a gun as well. This could put me in very good standing at the Big House to be the underkeeper.'

'Alec. Alec. I haven't agreed to marry him, just to enter into a courtship with him.'

'Oh Nellie!' Alec gasped, totally unable to contain himself. 'He breeds the finest spaniel dogs around. If I save very hard do you think he would sell me one of his pups? I'm sure he would if he was courting you.'

'Alec, stop it', Nellie whispered firmly. 'I thought you would react totally different and be perhaps cautious for me.'

'Cautious! Cautious Nellie.' Alec stated in the loudest whisper he dared to make. Slightly softer he continued. 'What is there to be cautious about? I think it's wonderful news. George Walker is one of the best shots around. The Walkers are highly regarded by the Wilbrahams. I think it is marvellous that George Walker has asked for your hand. I hope you say yes. Uncle Alec said on the last shoot what an eligible bachelor Mr Walker was and one day some young lady would be very fortunate when he wants to marry.'

'He's eleven years older than me though Alec.'

'That's nothing. He is very fit. You will have lots of children.'

'Alec that's enough', Nellie whispered indignantly.

She took her gaze to the perfect moon and reflected deeply on her grandmother's words. 'Think clearly about your life at a full moon. Have the realization that your span of life, in comparison to the heavens, is but short on this earth and how many of your moons have already gone? Are you making good use of your time?'

She turned her head to Alec, who had the smuggest of Cheshire Cat smiles and as she pulled her loose dark hair off her face she whispered wistfully, 'We'll see.' His smile was infectious and she broke into her first smile about the situation and was pleasantly surprised with his emphatic approval.

'To bed again before we go cold', Nellie whispered sensibly.

They stood and Alec squeezed her tightly in his glee. Nellie smiled, ushered him back to his bedroom door and warmly whispered before parting, 'Thank you. Your opinion means a great deal to me.'

William had been disturbed naturally by the call of nature and he had heard the two voices whispering, he perceived of Alec and Nellie, on the stairs but could not decipher what they had said. As he slid into his bed again the slight commotion outside their room had roused Emily in an instinctively motherly way, like any good mother sleeping lightly through the night hours on subconscious duty over her precious family. William detected Emily had woken and he slipped his arm around her as they lay together.

'What was that?' Emily whispered.

'I believe it was Nellie and Alec. They've been whispering on the stairs. I think she has been telling Alec privately about George Walker.'

'What has he said?'

'I don't know. I couldn't quite hear their words but both voices sounded happy. I think he approves.'

'So do I.' Emily spontaneously whispered.

William gave Emily a fond kiss. He knew he was making his journey to Higher Smallwood Farm in the morning for all the right reasons and sound sleep soon overtook them both.

Sleep utterly deserted Alec in his excitement. Nellie lay awake most of the night feeling that she had thrown a pebble into her pool of life and she did not know where the ripples would end.

The following mid morning William made his journey to Higher Smallwood Farm in the pony and trap, although he thought the conditions were rather treacherous for the pony and would have preferred to walk. Emily felt such an important decision by Nellie had to be taken in some sort of style and William had bowed to her wishes.

William turned left off Chance Hall Lane by Pump House Farm on to the drive of Higher Smallwood Farm. He had forgotten how long the drive was and how many bends it contained so he cautiously slowed his pony down to a walk. Although a very cold day it was a bright morning and as his pony steadily rounded the last bend, he took care with the reins to keep his pony on the drive and not to allow it to go off down green lane that leads directly to Bowdon Hall.

He also recalled how his father had told him stories of another lane known as hangman's lane. This lane was well beyond the farmhouse of Higher Smallwood over the brow nearer to Noah's Ark adjacent to the small lane nearing the Blue Bell Inn at Smallwood. Occasionally his father as a boy, along with a few other Rode boys, would sneak to hangman's lane and they would be able to see the dangling legs of a body recently hanged with a hood over the head. The eeriness of that vivid recollection made William shudder. He was glad public hangings had been abolished. However, William did have fonder memories of walking the small lane to Smallwood, when he used it as a short cut to Brook House Farm, Brookhouse Green, whilst courting his dearest Emily.

In the last hundred yards of the drive rise the farmhouse of Higher Smallwood was visible and William thought what a proud house it looked lit by the languid Winter sunshine. He guided his pony and trap into the immaculate farm yard and bid his pony to stop. George Walker swiftly appeared from around a corner and was surprised but pleased to see William Bailey.

William complimented George Walker on a fine tidy farm and apologised for making his visit unannounced but said it was Nellie's wish that he should personally bring her message. Without small talk and declining the offer to go inside the farmhouse William immediately put George at ease by telling him that he and Mrs Bailey had given their blessing for George to marry Nellie but it was Nellie's wish to enter into a courtship with George and after a suitable time of courtship it would be Nellie's ultimate decision if marriage was to follow.

George Walker being a reserved man, just wanted to marry Nellie and have done with matters but was pleased that the Baileys were working towards his wishes. He thanked William graciously that Nellie was considering a courtship and suggested that the courtship should commence after morning service at All Saints on the following Sunday morning. George also suggested that he would bring Nellie after the service to Higher Smallwood Farm to share a meal with him and his sister Polly. William thought it was a sensible way of commencing the courtship and expressed his agreement. He said he would inform Nellie of the arrangements and thanked George Walker for his time. George nodded a reciprocal acknowledgment and both men bid each other good day.

As George Walker watched William Bailey, sitting in the trap, walk the pony down the drive rise he felt nervous at the prospect of courting Nellie and he too felt a pebble dropping into his pool of life.

Morning service at All Saints the following Sunday was

tense for both George and Nellie. They exchanged weak smiles as Nellie sang in the choir and George was in the Walker family pew near to the front of the church. Neither had discussed their imminent courtship and arrangements with anyone in Rode and after the service the congregation spilled down the church path in the usual way. The Walker family, because of their required sitting position in All Saints, were always one of the first of the congregation to exit the church and Nellie, being a member of the choir and having to disrobe, was always one of the last to pass through the porch to the path way. George was attending to the escorting of his sister to his landau.

He and Nellie were some considerable distance apart and Nellie was quite unsure of the next move as she hovered by the porch. There was a hushed silence as George retraced his steps down the pathway to Nellie and offered her his arm. He walked her down to the lych gate and gently assisted her to board the Walker landau with Miss Polly already sitting in the gleaming carriage.

The mingling onlookers were quite taken aback as George Walker took Nellie Bailey, one of their fairest young maidens, from their midst. Silent questions tumbled in their minds, in the shock of the moment. What about the age difference? What about his reserved nature? Was Nellie good enough for such an encounter? As the landau moved away under the competent hands of Alfred, the Higher Smallwood groom, Nellie gave no eye contact to anyone, neither did George. His sister Polly was too busy making small talk and putting Nellie at ease to notice prying eyes. The landau soon disappeared down the lane and the crowd standing like statues cast their eyes to William and Emily who were acting normally and appearing calm on the church pathway.

The Rector had witnessed the episode from the porch way. He had hoped to see George Walker stepping forth for Nellie one day but was quite shocked it was so soon. He had encouraged George to follow his heart and the Rector had every confidence in Nellie, feeling her natural maturity would give her the platform to rise to being the lady of Higher Smallwood, but would she be able to give her heart to George?

Sunday dinner went much better than Nellie had ever thought. Polly was very warm and welcoming and equally so was Higher Smallwood farmhouse. Not one roaring fire but a fire in each room. Nellie felt slightly uneasy when she was waited on by Rose, a former school friend, but Rose acted professionally and efficiently and Polly and George detected nothing during the meal.

George treated Nellie very much as an adult, in fact, she thought it was the very first time in her life when she could act as a total adult and did so with remarkable ease. She even surprised herself. She found George's conversation very stimulating and she had to admit to herself that he did look and act younger in his own home.

Polly interjected conversation perfectly at the table. Nellie was truly impressed with some of the things she said. Polly informed Nellie and George that apparently Kaiser Wilhelm was a very disagreeable man and almost despicable. He visited the Tollmaches at Peckforton Castle from time to time as a house guest for the hunting and the shoots. Because of his affliction of a withered arm, he had issued strict instructions to the Tollmaches that if any of their servants, however loyal and true, cast their eyes on his arm they were to be dismissed instantly. Nellie lamented that he did appear to be a despicable human to weald the highest of conceit and power particularly over good folks' livelihoods.

Nellie even had the confidence to express herself freely on the subject dear to her heart, votes for women. Polly whole heartedly agreed with Nellie's sentiments and all three laughed with ease. George added to the discussion and said he strongly felt no women should vote. However, if women gained a vote in the current light of female thoughts on politics, it should not be for all and certainly a married woman should not have a vote. The man was the head of his household, therefore a vote for his spouse was an unnecessary duplication. Smiling he naturally acknowledged as a couple they would have areas where they would agree to disagree. Nellie for a split second realised George was not wavering from his determination to marry her but she managed to keep smiling because she did not want to dampen the warm fellowship all three were sharing.

Nellie had no recriminations about George's strong feelings against votes for women for after all that was how her own dear father felt and so did most good men she knew. It was the man's domain in life to be head of his family and the bread winner and to have the sole responsibility of the vote was the man's duty and this was a natural general view held by both men and older women within the countryside. It was felt the issue of votes for women was too radical and would erode the strength and characteristic of a man's role in society. It was thought to give women the vote would undermine stability particularly between man and wife and consequently would be bad for family life and furthermore for the Nation.

After the meal George encouraged the ladies to retire with him to the drawing room. Nellie thought it was a beautiful large south facing room, catching the maximum of light even on that Winter's day, and could not stop looking at the ornate decor and perfect situation of each ornament and photograph. She was unaware that the only beauty George could see in the room was her. He was totally besotted with her and adored seeing her sit so regally in his mother's once favourite chair. He felt Nellie positively blossomed away from her parents. The fortuitous time he was spending with her in his own home was serving to deepen his desire and affection towards her.

The few hours flew and George indicated it was time for Nellie to return to Pack Horse Farm in the mid afternoon before the light faded. Polly was so lovely and tactile escorting Nellie to the door, personally buttoning Nellie's coat and tying her bonnet in a very friendly and motherly fashion. Once in the gig George tucked the woollen rug over Nellie's knees as he climbed in and took the reins. Polly gave instructions to hold the horse. At that moment Rose ran from the door with a large bag and handed it to Polly. With pleasure Polly took out of the bag a beautiful brown fur muff and put it on Nellie's knee. Nellie instantly felt the extra warmth as she submerged her gloved hands in the muff. She thanked Polly and said she would return the muff with George but Polly told Nellie it was not to borrow, it was a gift from her. Nellie was overwhelmed and instinctively bowed very low from the gig and both women kissed warmly on each others cheek as Nellie thanked Polly profusely for her extreme kindness. Polly said it had been a privilege to share a meal with Nellie and hoped to share time with her again before too long.

George gave instructions at that point for his proud young horse to trot on and as they were travelling along the drive Nellie told George how kind Polly was and said she had one of the loveliest smiles in Cheshire. George with a faint laugh said that most people seemed to like Polly but in his opinion he felt Nellie had the loveliest of all smiles, which made her blush slightly.

Riding home in the gig close to George she thought how different for the better Rode looked even though grey clouds had drifted slowly across the sky. One or two local folks took a second look at George and Nellie in the gig sitting with ease together. Nellie told George she had enjoyed herself much more than she had imagined and thanked him for his kindness and particularly for extending his hospitality in providing the meal, which she had appreciated. As she was speaking to George she did perceive a lovely shy twinkle in his eye that did not displease her.

George was a perfect gentleman and took Nellie straight into Pack Horse farm yard. Emily had issued strict instructions to her children to stay indoors and keep well away from the windows. Alec was the only one who disobeyed orders. Alone he sneaked up to the attic window and scratched a little frost off the window pane to see Nellie return with George in the gig pulled by the immaculately groomed horse. He felt so elated the courtship had begun, he had to see them together.

George held Nellie's hand as she alighted from the gig and as they stood together he took her other hand. Pushing her muff slightly up her arm he held her two hands with one of his. He fumbled in his pocket with his other hand and then pressed a small navy blue velvet box into Nellie's hands. She opened the box very carefully to see a delicate gold and pearl bow brooch. She couldn't help smiling and showing her gratitude to George but both correctly with-held from a kiss before he left.

Nellie cheerfully entered the farmhouse where both William and Emily were awaiting her return sitting at the table with a pot of tea. Nellie immediately showed them her two beautiful gifts of the brooch and the muff, explaining when and how they were presented to her. Nellie herself, William and Emily thought the gifts far too generous although Nellie's happy gratitude was obvious to see.

Nellie sat and joined her parents as they drank tea and Alec ventured into the room and drew up a chair to be included in the homecoming. Nellie relayed almost every detail of her visit to Higher Smallwood Farm in an unusually excitable manner to the wide eyed trio. When she had exhausted her comments without interruption, Nellie took her presents, for safe keeping, into the best room. Emily, William and Alec took their chance to make eye contact accompanied by friendly tight lipped smiles and nodding, to confirm pleasantly to one another that the commencement of the courtship had evidently gone very well.

Gold and Pearl Bow Brooch
George's gift to Nellie

CHAPTER 6

IT MUST BE JUNE

The end of Winter ran its natural course, as in many ways too did the courtship. Nellie's affection for George was growing with ease and he was totally in love with Nellie. In his mind he had decided on a May wedding and intimated to Nellie his chosen month for the wedding.

Very shortly after his intimation Nellie walked with her mother on the Sunday afternoon of the 4th March through the meadow to the spinney where the wild daffodils, known as lent lilies, were swaying. They rested sitting on an old tree trunk.

'Mother, he wants to marry me in May', Nellie blurted out with a troubled countenance.

'Yes, of course, he does but it can't be May. It is such a bad luck month for a wedding, very pagan. You know what they say 'Marry in May and rue the day.' It must be June. Tell him you prefer this June.'

'June! June!' Nellie said slightly annoyed.

'I don't want to marry him this year, perhaps next.'

'Nellie you can't do that it must be this year or not at all', Emily replied anxiously.

'Mother I am too young. I don't want children yet. In fact one child will be sufficient for me and I hope I bear him a son at the end of a confinement.'

'Don't be coarse. Don't speak like that', Emily instructed firmly.

'Mother, it's the truth I don't love him yet and you have had such a hard life with too many children.'

'Nellie!' Emily indignantly rebuked. 'I have always loved your father and we have had what children the good Lord has sent.'

'Oh, mother, I am not doubting your love for father it's just; well a new century will soon be upon us and things are changing. I'm not a woman who wants to bear many children and I do want to vote for my future.'

'Nellie, stop it. That won't happen. You will have many children and you will never vote. All this looking forward to a new century with new ways is futile. History tells us the watershed of a century does not happen at the beginning, it is very often half way through. A woman's priority is to find a kind man to support her in marriage.'

After a small pause, Nellie purposely said, 'He's exceptionally kind but I don't love George.'

'Oh Nellie', Emily warmly answered ' you do, everyone sees you are happy together.'

'Yes, I have an affection for him but it's not love.

'Oh that will come.'

'Will it mother, real love?' Nellie asked searchingly.

'Of course it will.'

'I'm not too sure. I want to be older before marriage.'

Emily took on a tone of dishing out advice, 'You are eighteen this year Nellie, quite old enough for marriage and to be a mother. It could pass you by if you are not careful. I've seen a few of my friends become old maids because they were too choosey or things were not quite right and all they have found is unhappiness. A woman has no security without a husband.'

'Miss Polly is a spinster and she is not unhappy', Nellie debated.

Emily's exasperation rose, 'I forbid you to speak of Miss Polly in that way. She is lovely. She will have a very good reason for not taking a man. Very often the older girl is forbidden to marry by her parents. Selfishly they want her to help rear her siblings and look after them in old age.'

'But she is not the oldest, even though she is ten years older than George. She has a sister Esme who is older.'

'Nellie you are being awkward now for awkward's sake. You should be thankful your father and me have no desire to curb your future as the eldest girl and wish you to take a husband.'

Nellie smiled and agreed in a brighter way, 'You are right as to Polly. She has a wonderful nature. However, don't worry about me as to motherhood. I do wish to be a mother some day but I don't want many children.'

Emily thinking the conversation had returned to sensible tracks continued, 'Well what are you going to tell George?'

Nellie replied slowly, 'My preference would be June of next year or even the year after.

'Don't be silly', Emily said lightly.

Nellie teasingly continued, 'I remember you have always said that true love is sealed under a November moon and George and I have only courted since January.'

'Oh that's an old wives tale', Emily retorted with a chuckle at the fact that Nellie was backing her into a corner.

Nellie persisted in her teasing, 'The November moon is the most beautiful of all the Year's moons, the true lovers' moon. That is what you always say mother.'

Smiling broadly at feeling verbally trapped, Emily agreed lightly, 'Yes, the November moon is the lovers' moon and after your marriage to George in June I am sure you will fall in love in November.'

An easy silence fell between them before Emily broke it by asking, 'Well what are you going to tell George?'

Nellie smiled a small puzzled smile announcing, 'I'm not sure. I can't seem to make a decision so I'll have to wait for the morrow.'

In bed that night Emily told William of Nellie's conversation and about her indecisive mind. William to Emily's surprise agreed with Nellie's fear, particularly over child bearing. Emily, having bourne eleven of William's children, could not see his line of thought and expressed her irritation with it. William calmed her down by saying it was up to the good Lord as to how many children Nellie would have but did say that he would prefer her to embark on a large family after the age of twenty one. Emily was totally lost and told William, seeing that Nellie was a Bailey, she was quite sure that no matter what her age, when married she would conceive in her first year of marriage, probably on the first night. William allowed Emily to go to sleep with those thoughts.

The following day William purposely found Nellie stitching hessian sacks on the granary steps with her sister Lucy and asked to be alone with Nellie. He told Nellie that her mother had spoken of perhaps an impending marriage in the June. After a pause he also told her that her mother had said Nellie wished to be older before she bore children. Nellie slightly blushed that her father knew the intimate details but acknowledged with her head that it was true.

He comforted Nellie by telling her he too agreed with her sentiments and had in fact the same inner thoughts on the first day when he and George Walker talked in the best room. Nellie was astounded when her father told her in a kindly way to leave matters to him. She was embarrassed but could see her father was positive and she knew instinctively to trust him without any questions. She felt her father had such a valiant point of view and understanding that it was almost a duty now for her to marry George in the coming June of her eighteenth year. Her mind was made up for marriage.

William paused and held out his hand to Nellie. She clasped it warmly with both hands and in a low voice and with bowed head told him the wedding could be in June. William placed his other hand over Nellie's young hands and as she raised her head and looked into his loving eyes he comforted her by saying that he would speak of her intention of a June wedding on the morrow to George and for Nellie to worry no more about matters.

The following March morning was such a fresh Spring day

and, although William's pony trotted with ease up the mile long drive to Higher Smallwood Farm, William felt more nervous than on his previous January journey to see George. When he entered the tidy farmyard George appeared instantly and welcomed William. He knew the visit would be about the proposed May wedding.

'Do come into the farmhouse Mr Bailey.' George quickly instructed.

The activity of the bustling farmyard afforded no privacy so William took George up on his offer. George walked briskly through to the drawing room with William dutifully following and indicated that they should both sit. William noticed how clean and immaculate George Walker's boots were, confirming in his mind he was a true gentleman farmer. He was relieved he had taken Emily's advice to wear his best boots. George lit the ready laid fire and the flames burned up nicely.

William opened the conversation calmly, 'Nellie tells us you are hopeful for a May wedding.'

'Yes', George replied anxiously. He had never envisaged he would feel so nervous awaiting Nellie's answer.

William proceeded, 'Well May is an unwise month, our preference is for June.'

George was relieved and spoke his thoughts aloud. 'May, June no matter just as long as it suits Nellie.'

'Well, that's just it', William answered.

George's nervousness resurged.

'Is Nellie not happy with June?' he asked.

'Oh yes, June as a month is fine for Nellie to marry you but her preference would be for June of her twentieth year of age.

'George's heart sunk.

'I can't court Nellie for two more years. Will she not marry me this June?' he asked despairingly.

'Yes she will', William answered clearly.

'I'm at a loss to understand', George announced bewildered.

'I'd better explain', William said purposely, 'It's children.'

'Don't tell me she won't bear me children?' George questioned desperately.

'No.' William said hastily. 'No don't worry Nellie has a dear wish to be a mother. But Nellie is a woman of modern times', he continued awkwardly. 'Her preference would be to be married for a year or two before bearing a child for you and I wish for her to give birth to her first child in her twenty first year. She is a Bailey and all Bailey women conceive straight away. I perceive Nellie would think it kinder on you if she wed in two years time.'

George hurt. He literally hurt. 'I need Nellie now', he said pleadingly.

'I know you do but can I ask of you not to be a complete husband to Nellie for two years if you marry this June?'

George tried to compose himself but even in his composure he looked emotionally bedraggled. He slowly answered pronouncing each word singularly in mono tone and with clarity as if William was almost deaf, 'Have you any idea of the gravity of your request Mr Bailey?'

'Yes I have', William confirmed.

George asked in despair, 'How can I lie with someone as beautiful as Nellie, who I deeply love, and yet not be a complete husband to her? I have never heard of such a request.'

'If you love your woman ways can be found', William offered in a guilty way, well aware that George knew William had sired many children.

'Could I?' George asked helplessly.

'Yes your love is evident. Yes I think you could', William confirmed sensitively.

George fell silent. He knew if he courted Nellie for a further two years the chances were her eyes would wander to perhaps someone younger, nearer her own age. Although she was affectionate he could sense she did not love him but he knew he would be taking a grave risk in delaying the marriage. On the other hand how could he lie with beautiful Nellie as his wife and stick to Mr Bailey's cruel request. His mind was trying to balance like scales.

'Does Nellie know of your request?' George asked firmly.

'No. Not as such. We have talked and she is trusting me to take her to the altar in the right June.' William replied in a manly manner.

George took to his feet and paced up and down the large room, his shiny boots squeaking slightly. He stopped and glared at William who was still sitting and asked curtly, 'If Nellie and I married this June would she take her vows seriously bearing in mind she would remain a virgin for a further two years?'

'Not quite a virgin', William replied embarrassingly. 'There are ways like I have intimated. I do not expect of you that my daughter remains a virgin when married, just not with child until her twentieth year.'

'And of her vows?' George enquired strongly again.

William answered very positively, 'Oh yes. I can assure you Nellie's marriage vows will be devoutly kept by her. When she walks down All Saints' aisle to become your wife she will always be loyal and faithful. I have no doubt on that. She will never waiver from her vows.'

George paused, almost spoke but fell into a longer silence to fully digest William's words deeply before he replied firmly, 'Very well. We will marry in June of this year and I will honour your request.'

William stood with relief in his veins and thanked George for his understanding and told him he had made the correct decision and he had his and Mrs Bailey's blessing for the June wedding. 'Will you tell Nellie all of this?' George enquired in an embarrassed manner.

'No. No. Not as we have talked as men', William answered quietly before adding kindly and slightly louder, 'I shall give her the assurance that she will enjoy a couple of years settling in to the running of Higher Smallwood Farm before she is likely to become a mother.'

Both men gave a slightly awkward smile, knowing the

intimate details discussed were to be kept confidential. William shook George's hand firmly and changing his tone to a lighter manner announced, 'I shall tell Nellie and Mrs Bailey to commence preparations for this year's June wedding, knowing we will all be looking forward to the happy occasion.'

George watched William out of the farmyard and down the drive in the trap. His over riding thought that Nellie, beautiful Nellie, was soon to be his wife. Perhaps if he was the considerate husband she required and children came into the marriage in Nellie's time it would put him in good stead for her love. He felt in his heart that was a prize worth waiting for.

CHAPTER 7

ABOVE HER STATION

Village conversations often drifted to the new courtship and betrothal of George and Nellie. Older men, with a twinkle in their eye, thought George had done very well to take such an exceptional beauty from their midst whilst the older ladies were not sure if Nellie could rise to being the lady of Higher Smallwood Farm and felt George would rue the day when he made his choice. The fresh faced youths of the Rode lamented Nellie being betrothed so soon and wished they had taken their chance of a stolen kiss or two. The young ladies contemporary in age to Nellie thought she was daft even to consider an older man as plain looking as George.

On the Wednesday morning of the wedding in June all the Bailey Family had risen early to attended to their farm duties. Nellie had fetched the cows from long lane meadow before six o'clock for milking in the shippons at Pack Horse Farm and butterflies had started in her tummy. Emily later prepared a special cooked breakfast with several slices of her best bacon carved from the large joint which hung from the beam on the iron hook. Everyone had rushed their jobs giving them the chance to sit together around the big old pine table in the farm house kitchen and linger over the final breakfast with Nellie. It was a happy occasion tinged with sadness at the same time.

Emily, trying to ease Nellie's nerves, commented on the lovely perfect weather and then reminisced on the day she and William became man and wife and recalled that although they had a June wedding they awoke to fine misty rain. She further informed everyone that it was one of those days 'rain before seven sun after eleven' for eventually the rain did pass off and the welcome sun shone. As Emily was occupying needed conversation Nellie was glancing round the whole of her family at the table and although she had always felt she loved them she seemed to love them more that breakfast time, even the cats and dogs lying contentedly around felt very dear to her.

Happy family chatting continued until Emily thought it was time for everyone to change out of their working clothes and start getting washed and changed into their best clothes for the wedding. At that point William took to his feet and in a very fond manner thanked Nellie for all her hard work at Pack Horse Farm and lamented the fact that he had never been able to pay her any wages. Nellie profusely assured him that wages were of no consequence as good food had always been on the table and everyone clothed. Nellie also said that being the eldest she fully understood the enormous financial pressure on her father in finding the rent and rearing a large family. She thanked her mother and father dearly for rearing her in such a loving caring home.

Tears of pride and gratitude were in William's eyes as he fumbled in a drawer and took out a shoe box. He was about to place the box in front of Nellie when Emily announced in a raised voice, 'It's bad luck to put new shoes on the table.' William nodded in acknowledgement and placed the box on Nellie's lap. She opened the box and carefully unfolded the tissue paper. Nestling perfectly inside were a pair of cream kid leather shoes with a kitten heel.

Nellie was overcome and flung her arms around her father's neck and kissed him several times on the cheek and uttered a huge thank you. Emily interrupted by informing her to be careful when putting on the shoes as she had already placed in one of them a silver sixpence for good luck. William added that, because George was insisting on sending Alfred with his landau to drive

Nellie to All Saints, she did not need the usual new stout brown boots to walk to church so her mother and him wanted to treat her to the cream shoes, which they thought would look nice when she alighted from her carriage. After listening intently to her father, Nellie rushed to her mother, sitting at the table, gave her a kiss and a huge hug and there it was the bond of the Gentle Ribbon surrounding them both in a halo of happy gratitude.

Within an hour all the Bailey family were in their best bib and tucker and Nellie was ready in her simple cream wedding dress. The cotton voile ankle length creation, made by her mother, with slight leg of mutton sleeves and tight deep cuffs fitted Nellie perfectly. Emily had found a few pearls in a drawer, the remnants of necklaces in better times, and had stitched them intermittently around the small ruff lace collar. The fact that the pearls were of various sizes was of no matter. She had also delicately plaited new cream satin ribbons to form a small belt and running through the plait was a sky blue strand of silk which accentuated Nellie's tiny waist and the balance of the ribbons and silk flowed freely at the rear of the gown. Nellie proudly borrowed Emily's small gold bracelet for her wedding day.

Quite a few older villagers had turned out to view the wedding and were pleasantly surprised to see how the bride and groom seemed to enjoy their day. The matriarchs of the Rode were suitably pleased when they could detect that Nellie's dress had been hand made from some old cotton voile but were a little disgruntled that Nellie was not wearing sturdy substantial boots and felt she was acting fanciful and above her station by wearing cream shoes.

The Rector, although knowing Nellie's beautiful face, was stunned to have such a radiant bride before him. He was impressed not only, as usual, with her natural prettiness but with her demeanour which added to the importance of the occasion and he was genuinely moved by how strongly she said and took her vows. He had no doubt she would be a loyal wife to George but his inner feelings told him Nellie was another bride before him who did not love her man.

Following the church service one concession to the normal pattern of the wedding did take place. Instead of the wedding breakfast being held at the bride's home at Pack Horse Farm George had insisted on the celebration taking place at Higher Smallwood Farm. This was an offer readily taken up by William Bailey in his relief at being spared the cost of the occasion.

Polly Walker did her utmost to make the whole Bailey family welcome. All the rooms at Higher Smallwood were put at their disposal. Nellie's sisters, Lucy and Lily, particularly enjoyed ascending the beautiful staircase in their bridesmaids dresses on such a happy day. In one of the upper rooms they were able to have a good look at Nellie's new wedding ring and they were quite spell bound by it.

Amid the noise of happiness, George, in one of his snatched moments, gave instruction to Young Alec to go into the yard to find Alfred who would show him the spaniel dogs. Alec was elated with such an offer and before the wedding breakfast, hurriedly went to see the dogs behind the granary steps.

Thirty eight happy guests sat down in Higher Smallwood's large living room for the wedding breakfast. The Baileys particularly found much enjoyment in the day. George and Polly had invited some of their Staffordshire relations, their widowed elder sister Esme with her two grown sons Cuthbert and Samuel Pointon from Aston Lodge near to Stone, also George's good friend and cousin Edgar who admirably gave his services of best man and approved graciously of George's choice of a beautiful young bride.

Polly had such expertise in entertaining, displayed by the exquisite starched white lace cloths, the best china and a new stylish green, burgundy and gold tea urn. Small vases of fragrant roses were dotted intermittently along the three long tables with the silver cutlery shining and perfectly laid. The top table was crowned with the traditional wedding cake of two tiers, one tier for the wedding breakfast and one for a hoped for christening reception. Emily had gladly baked the cake for her daughter and Polly had iced it with amazing skill.

The New Tea Urn

After the meal the guests spilled out on to the large lawn at Higher Smallwood enjoying the sunshine and the merriment of the occasion. At four o'clock in the afternoon they gathered and Nellie threw her small bouquet backwards over her head into the hands of one of her excited sisters. The happy throng waved goodbye to the newlyweds as they left in the gleaming open landau, with Alfred proudly at the reins, to catch a train at Mow Cop Station for their honeymoon.

Victorian Southport was the venue for their honeymoon chosen by George. It was very much enjoyed by both and they returned to Higher Smallwood Farm on a beautiful summer's afternoon and yes George did carry his darling bride easily over the threshold to the ripple of applause from the welcoming staff and Polly.

The married couples' spacious bedroom which had been competently arranged by Rose, was a joy to behold. There was immaculate starched white linen on the bed showing the delicate crocheted edges of the pillows and bolster. The modern wooden bed finely inlaid, adorned with new feather bedding, was crowned with a hand stitched pink silk summer counterpane. Pleasing floral satin cotton curtains were perfectly hung. The windows were wide open to capture the slight summer breeze which very gently teased the fresh roses on the bedside table to emit their fragrance.

The whole room was light and airy and much to Nellie's liking and not a bit like she had imagined George's bedroom. When commenting on it George said it was not his bedroom but previously the bedroom of his parents, hence dowdy and unused for several years. It had been recently decorated under Polly's instructions as to choice of decor, so he was pleased it received her approval.

At tea time Polly listened smiling as Nellie relayed her evident enjoyment of Southport and could just imagine her promenading along Lord Street. George had been most generous and had encouraged Nellie to purchase a new wardrobe of clothes for herself. Nellie took the lid off two huge hat boxes and placed on her head in turn two striking expensive hats. How beautiful Nellie looked in a hat. She did suit a large hat and both of them were up to the minute in style and fashion. Nellie impishly said her mother would disapprove of the hats as she strongly thought women should always wear a bonnet to save the ribbon industry, especially the jobs locally at Congleton.

Polly took her opportunity to discuss her future in leaving Higher Smallwood. Nellie was visibly shocked at such a statement and in a very genuine manner insisted she should stay. Polly confessed to preferring to stay but felt her bedroom would be needed for any children which might come along. Nellie said that was nonsense as George's room was empty for a nursery and she really did not think she would have a large family. Polly felt slightly embarrassed at such intimate talk and George, under Nellie's prodding glance, continued in the attempt to persuade Polly to stay. He added that perhaps there would not be any children for a year or two. With that Polly agreed to her continued residence at Higher Smallwood with the reservation of reviewing her situation as and when the hoped for children were born.

Polly allowed George and Nellie to take themselves into the drawing room without her for their privacy. On almost resting in his favourite chair George rose sharply and told Nellie she had not had her wedding present from him. She claimed she had already received too much but he continued by taking her hand and escorted her across the room to a fine walnut bureau which he unlocked to show Nellie that it was empty and then he gave her the key.

George's Wedding Gift to Nellie
His Bureau

He told her that the bureau was a present to her from him, informing her that farmers usually gave housekeepers cupboards or a useful oak dresser for household purposes. Higher ups preferred giving paintings. He intimated that perhaps they were some where in between so he wished for her to have the bureau not for household use but for her private use. He added that it had been his grandmother's and her mother's before her and although it was old he had put new handles on and he hoped she liked it. Nellie was overcome with his thoughtfulness and at the beauty of the piece of walnut furniture. She promised to take very good care of it and use it with pride. That was enough for George as he kissed her gently on her forehead. He was a happy man.

Days unfolded well for Nellie and George in marriage. Nellie worked hard with the cheese making and soon increased production and moved equipment around to make the process more efficient. Polly was a real treasure and was always on hand to guide, encourage and generally ease Nellie's role of knowing where everything was at Higher Smallwood Farm and assisted her constantly.

After a year Nellie did notice that George was totally in charge of his finances and never once committed her to any worry over money and more astoundingly to Nellie rent day came and went without any comment. How different she thought to the finances of Pack Horse Farm where her father was always sharing his money worries with her mother and the 25th March, Lady Day, was a huge worry when her father had to muster his rent money. He always seemed a pathetic figure on Lady Day morn in his boat rowing from Pack Horse slowly across Rode Pool in his clean tidy clothes. Each stroke of his rowing seemed to emphasise every effort he had put into his farm to raise his rent. Her mother always anxiously watched him hoping he would keep a bright countenance even though she knew his heart would be heavy as he sat to the round table in the Tenants Hall and saw his hard earned money put into one of the rent draws by the Land Agent.

The fields and meadows of Higher Smallwood were lovely and Nellie did enjoy a walk with George to learn about them at any time of the year. George had such a natural eye for pointing out to Nellie the lie of the land, each of his favourite views, the different varieties of trees, flowers and birds. He was particularly good at identifying bird song and trees in their winter silhouette. In fact he used to say often that folk did not know their trees properly until they could identify them in Winter. Although Nellie thought she was quite knowledgeable on country matters, in George's company she became well aware of her ignorance and found it a pleasure to learn from his amazing mind. She also found it pleasing to hold his hand, link arms with him and enjoyed his wonderful strength when he sometimes caught her by her waist on alighting from a stile and teasingly whizzed her around.

One particular Autumn evening after such a happy field walk they settled in their usual way in the living kitchen, George enjoying his whiskey and Nellie a rare glass of elderberry wine, listening to the crackling of the fire. Nellie broached the subject of George's finances.

'Do you require any help with your accounts George?'

'No', he replied in a friendly way 'I have been doing the books for several years since my father died in 89. They are no trouble to me, in fact I enjoy attending to them.'

'How will I know when things can be afforded in the household or for our clothes?' Nellie enquired in a puzzled manner.

He smiled and replied, 'Just purchase what you want when you need them.'

'I cannot possibly do that', Nellie replied almost in disbelief.

'Of course you can, I know you are very prudent. I admire your cheese making skills and there has been a difference already financially with that enterprise. Apart from your needle and threads you have no expensive hobbies. I assure you, Nellie, I spend far more on shooting enjoyment with my dogs and guns. Carry on as you are, everything is fine financially.'

'I feel indulged', Nellie sighed. 'I know how my father and mother struggle.'

'And so do I', George forwarded in a kindly manner. 'Give them little treats if it makes you feel better.'

'I know they would not accept them, their pride would not allow them', Nellie lamented.

'Well invite them to Higher Smallwood more often. At least we can assist with feeding them, whilst enjoying their company.'

Nellie appreciated George's understanding and distinctly felt that George was at ease with his money matters but made a mental note never to abuse his generosity. George interrupted her thoughts. 'By the way cousin Edgar is becoming a dab hand with a camera. Apparently he has up to the minute photographic equipment and I want him to come here to Higher Smallwood and take a portrait of you. In fact I hope he takes many pictures in the years to come, Nellie, as you have added greatly to the brightness of this home. It has become a happier place and I want that recorded.'

Isn't that extravagant George? Nellie questioned, having never had a portrait done.

'No of course not, please take in what I have already told you', he stated slightly irritated.

Nellie thought she did not want to rock the boat and nodded in agreement and decided to change the subject.

'There has been a John Walker at Higher Smallwood for centuries I'm told. No wonder you are a good farmer', she pleasantly forwarded.

He answered warmly, knowing Nellie was genuinely interested, 'Yes that's correct. It is reputed that one John Walker buried a considerable horde of coins here during the onset of the Civil War. Apparently they are still in the ground, their whereabouts lost in the mists of time', he added wistfully.

He continued without a break, 'However, the name Walker tells us our roots were not always in farming', whilst teasingly raising his forefinger. 'The word 'walker' informs us that our original families had something to do with the fullers, calenderers and tenters and therefore were involved with the cloth trade.'

Nellie was amusingly bewildered but loved it when George was being generous with his knowledge so she could learn and Nellie was blessed with a quick learning brain if not as educated as George's.

Slightly more seriously he proceeded, 'Working class known as fullers were skilled and responsible for whitening cloth from its raw stage, particularly linen. The tenters with equal skill stretched the cloth on special delicate hooks on a square frame to keep it in shape. The hooks had to be fine enough not to mark the cloth and strong enough to take the pressure of the stretching. You know the phrase when anxiously awaiting news 'to be on tenter hooks', well that's where it comes from. Somewhere within that trade a section of further workers were involved called the walkers. I don't know if they were high or low in that trade. All I know is they were part of the fine cloth industry.'

Nellie nodded and smiled and implicitly trusted George that the information was correct. George was oblivious to Nellie's appreciation of his knowledge. All he could see was her diamond smile. He gently took the empty wine glass from her hand and placed it with his own empty glass on a nearby table. Moving lovingly back close to her he took his opportunity to enjoy a divine kiss and a heavenly embrace.

Nellie
The Lady of Higher Smallwood Farm

CHAPTER 8

WISE BEYOND YOUR YEARS

Polly　　　　　*Esme*　　　　　*Cuthbert*　　　　　*Samuel*

Polly was visiting her sister Esme at Aston Lodge in Stone and Higher Smallwood always felt slightly melancholy to Nellie when Polly was away. Esme had been widowed for several years but kept herself cheery and counted her blessings and was usually a tonic to visit. She was rightly proud of her two fine sons Cuthbert and Samuel who, since their father's death, had competently continued farming at Aston Lodge on their mother's behalf. The brothers, although subservient to their mother, kept with modern times and dressed in stylish gentry type clothes and both sported the new style thick bushy moustaches.

The grey October morning seemed to reflect Nellie's mood in missing Polly as she walked across the farmyard at Higher Smallwood, wearing her cream working blouse and ankle length navy blue woollen skirt. Her long white starched apron emphasised her extremely trim waist.

The postman peddled into the yard and very pleasantly greeted her. 'Morning Nellie. Oh I beg your pardon Mrs Walker.'

'Never say that Billy, I will always be Nellie to you', she answered in tones that hinted at a ticking-off.

'I have a letter here for you addressed to Pack Horse Farm, bearing your real name, Miss Edith Helen Bailey. Why are Edith Helens referred to as Nellies?'

'Oh I don't know Billy. For as long as I can remember I have been known as Nellie even though it is not my real name. Besides you are really a William.'

'Yes I am', he agreed and added, 'and Miss Polly's real name is Mary isn't it?'

'Yes that's right. Strange how it has all come about. Marys are often referred to as Polly or Molly', Nellie confirmed.

Back to business Billy announced importantly, 'Well this letter says 'private and confidential' hence I am delivering it here rather than leaving it at Pack Horse Farm. I hope I am doing right.'

'I'm sure you are. Thank you for your thoughtfulness.'

After enquiring as to Billy's health and well being Nellie bid him on his way, put the letter in her apron pocket and continued with her morning work.

When the men had been fed at dinner time and the maids were undertaking the clearing away and Nellie had given distinct details of their afternoon chores, she retired in her usual way to her bedroom. Each afternoon she took off her working clothes, washed from her jug and bowl, combed her brunette hair, re-clipped it high with her mother of pearl combs, dabbed her ear lobes and wrists with lavender cologne, changed into an elegant afternoon gown and generally made herself befitting of a lady should there be any afternoon visitors.

On folding her apron she had felt the bulk of the letter in her pocket and taking it out of her pocket placed it on her side table. After re-dressing she picked it up, graciously descended the lovely stair case and took it into the drawing room to read before she attended to her afternoon sewing. Sitting in her favourite chair she opened the letter and read:

Malvern Rectory

Dearest Nellie,

I am full of remorse. I am a devout Christian and, as all Christians desire, I desire to enter the Kingdom of Heaven after my death. I often feel I am not far from death and I have given clear instructions to a confidant that after my death, whenever that may be, this letter is to be forwarded to you one week after my funeral. My guilt and sinfulness here on earth needs to be addressed, giving me a thread of a chance to be reconciled with God, although I pray for his forgiveness daily.

Nellie, I wronged you in Rode Church that fateful evening. You did not leave your book. I stole it from your bag as you were leaving and put the book in the choir stalls in the carnal hope that you would come back alone to find it and you did. I was woefully sinful Nellie. I wanted to be close to you as I was in the stall and the joy I felt when I touched your hand on your book was beyond belief. I am old and you are young but it wasn't just your beauty in the bloom of youth that entranced me it was your whole demeanour. You have such a presence.

To have the lustful feelings of an old man forced upon you must have been unbearable. Yet despite your tender years, you were the one who created the dignified way out of the torrid situation and to your credit told no one of your violation. You taught me much, dear girl, more than any theology book.

To add to my sinfulness and the gravity of the situation I lied to the Rode Rector and told him you had inadvertently left your book. How could I have compounded the dreadful situation with a blatant lie? I am now confessing that I did. As some sort of defence, I want you to know I did inform the Rector of my lustful feelings towards you in an endeavour to suppress any further encounters. I cannot ask you not to feel ill of me but I want you to know the truth. You were in no way to blame about the book incident or for my sudden departure from Rode.

Every day that passes I wish to beg your forgiveness. Please don't think of me as that old man who must make your shudder if you ever re-live that evening; I wish you to think, if we had known one another contemporary of age and in correct circumstances, we would have shared a friendship, a dear trusting friendship that forms between two good people.

I am full of remorse and somehow I do believe you will forgive me. Even in the short time of making your acquaintance it is obvious you are of special character. You are wise beyond your years. I realize a letter of this nature has to be read several times before one fully digests the contents and I trust you and know you will destroy this letter in your own good time.

Nellie you will marry one day and I pray the Lord will provide you with a kind husband for you to love and to treasure. I know he will love you dearly and I pray for you to be the mother of many fine children.

Once more I implore your forgiveness for my wrong and sinful doings. Please pray for my soul to rest in peace. It is all I will have left as you read this letter.

Fraternally and pleadingly yours,
The Canon of Malvern

Nellie was stunned. She re-read the letter and two big tears uncontrollably emerged from her eyes. She was treated like a lady at Higher Smallwood Farm and as such she could experience her feelings in uninterrupted privacy and all the more so in the coincidental absence of her dear sewing partner Polly. She read the letter slowly a third time after which her turbulence of mind lasted a good half hour, before she slowly placed her silver thimble on the tip of the middle finger of her right hand. Thereafter she checked her needle was threaded with sufficient coloured silk before commencing her embroidery in her usual afternoon manner on that bland October day.

A polite knock on the door before Rose entered with the tea tray disturbed Nellie.

'There being no visitors I have your afternoon tea.'

'Yes of course Rose. My! Is it really four o'clock?' Nellie asked in a bewildered tone.

'Yes. Haven't you noticed the light fading?'

'No I can't say I have today Rose. I can't say I have.'

Rose put the tea tray down on the fireside table, lit the oil lamps efficiently, placed coal on the fire and left the room in her usual way. Nellie folded the letter purposely and replaced it in the envelope before putting it in her bureau. Rose had jolted her into the tracks of normal life and Nellie appreciated her cup of tea more than usual that afternoon. Sitting and drinking Nellie pondered on the Canon's revelation but having had time to take in the magnitude of the letter she was deeply moved by the words of the penultimate paragraph. It made her heart feel heavy. Two more tears fell on to her pretty cheeks.

CHAPTER 9

NO MARK OF RECOGNITION

The month of May was in her fullest exquisite green gown and Rode looked particularly delightful with the added mantle of the cascading cream hawthorn blossoms. In her farmhouse on the 25th of May Nellie was deciding how many of her cheeses were ready for turning when Rose came into the cheese room. 'Yes Rose', Nellie said politely.

'The Rector is here and wishes to speak to you privately', she announced efficiently.

'Please show him into the morning room. I will be along in a minute.'

Nellie quickly finished her cheese turning, washed her hands and checked her hair was neat and her apron straight in the manner which was second nature to her. Although in her morning working attire she felt tidy and comfortable enough to meet the Rector.

She entered the morning room with her lovely smile and the Rector thought how beautiful she looked even in her working clothes. He also thought she well deserved being lady of Higher Smallwood Farm. He cut short her welcome and asked if they could move into the drawing room. Nellie removed her starched apron and folded it neatly before placing the garment on the table and indicated to the Rector to follow her.

When both were seated in the drawing room with the door firmly closed the Rector proceeded. 'Nellie I do thank you for seeing me without prior arrangement but I have a grave situation in the Village and I dearly seek your help. Eliza Thimbleton is with child and her aunt feels utterly disgraced and she no longer wishes her niece to reside with her.' Nellie was sad with the Rector's news as she had a fond regard for Eliza and it worried her to know that Eliza had to face such a pitiful plight.

The Rector confessed his disappointment in Eliza. Since being an orphan she had received a good home with her aunt Gertrude and he felt it was the worst of ways to repay her aunt's kindness, adding that Eliza had been extremely foolish. Nellie defended Eliza saying she was a good young lady and the responsibility of being with child was not all Eliza's. 'Do you know who the father is?' Nellie enquired.

'Yes I do', the Rector answered firmly.

'Perhaps it is none of my business', Nellie added politely, slightly backing off and remembering her manners.

She took on an air of maturity and folded her hands nicely as she sat perfectly upright waiting for the Rector to elaborate.

'I need your help to save Eliza from Arclid Workhouse and I will tell you that the village gossip seems to be that Eliza has been frequented by the company of a soldier from Talk O'th Hill, much to the defiance of her aunt and he must be the culprit.'

'Where is he now? Can they not be married to provide stability for the child?' Nellie sensibly enquired.

'No', answered the Rector positively. 'I believe he sailed some weeks ago to serve in the Boer War and regrettably Eliza has kept her calamity of being with child to herself until', he slowly paused, 'well until the issue cannot be concealed any longer.'

Nellie stated caringly, 'Perhaps Eliza can be nurtured and allowed to marry her soldier on his next leave?'

'No', answered the Rector firmly. 'Matters are so far on that the babe looks imminent perhaps within six weeks, two months I would say at the most. No Mrs Thimbleton wishes to be rid of her niece within the course of this week and has requested me to make arrangements for Eliza to be taken to the Workhouse promptly.'

'No', Nellie firmly stated, adding, 'She would be parted from her baby.'

'Well', said the Rector coyly, 'perhaps it would be of preference for Eliza to be free to work and the child to be reared well away from Rode.'

After a slight pause Nellie proceeded curtly, 'The girl is always thought ill of. Many conceive on the first time of being with a man. It is such a high price to pay to be with child after such an encounter.'

'Nellie!' the Rector retorted as if embarrassed to hear such a forth right opinion of a delicate subject. Nellie was not embarrassed and continued, 'It is true Rector.'

'That is as may be Nellie', the Rector replied quite taken aback as to how easy it was to talk to Nellie on the intimate matter and counter debated, 'Eliza has been foolish. It is the responsibility of the young lady. Gentlemen, especially young gentlemen, always reach a point of no return and an infant is conceived. It is always the young lady's fault. It is imperative that a girl keeps her head to remain a virgin. Look at Eliza's predicament now. She should not have been so reckless and thoughtless.'

Nellie further debated, 'No, Rector, the soldier, if he loves Eliza, will be reunited with her on his return and then they can be as a family. Does he know?'

'I doubt it, the chances of him knowing are remote. He will probably be killed in South Africa. You are looking at life from your blessed position with the love of George. I tell you the soldier has probably never given Eliza one more thought and Eliza seems to be in a daze and will not name him despite endless requests.'

To create a thinking pause Nellie stared out of the window for a few moments before she re-glanced at the Rector and with purpose proceeded, 'Well how are we going to help Eliza this week and spare her from Arclid Workhouse?' The Rector full of respect for Nellie's attitude replied in a calm manner, 'Those are exactly the words I hoped and prayed you would say as I travelled here. I was thinking, subject to your's and George's agreement, of imposing on your good nature and bringing Eliza here for her confinement. She would of course work for you before and after her confinement and I would see to it that the child would be moved on, hopefully to higher circles. There are, sadly, good Christian couples who do not receive the blessing of a child and would welcome such a child as this with open arms. That would be best all round.'

Nellie pondered on his words for a few moments, re-straitened her back commanding a perfect posture and announced, 'Very well bring Eliza this afternoon with her belongings.'

The Rector was stunned. 'Today!'

'Yes right away, Eliza must be supported immediately', Nellie said maturely.

'Well!', the Rector exclaimed, 'Don't you need to discuss matters with George?'

'No', she declared positively adding, 'he trusts me implicitly over my cheese helpers. The business is growing and I can afford to employ Eliza. I can find light duties for her and it will be a pleasure to teach her the skill of cheese making.'

'No', the Rector interrupted. 'You are not expected to pay Eliza. Just a roof and food for her will suffice.'

'She will be paid like my other helpers', Nellie confirmed positively.

The Rector respected Nellie's assertiveness and decided to move the situation on while Nellie was offering such immense kindness.

'Very well', he said gratefully and rose to his feet. 'I will deliver Eliza here this afternoon.'

He recognised that Nellie, although young and from lower Bailey status, through her marriage to a Walker, had grown into the role of being the lady of Higher Smallwood with competence. As she stood before him he took the liberty of gently socially kissing her on her cheek for the first time. Nellie received the kiss graciously being neither flustered or flattered by it.

'We must part now Rector. I have much to do to make Eliza's quarters comfortable.'

'Yes of course. I will return later with her. Shall we say at three o'clock?' Nellie just nodded in approval.

On watching the Rector riding out of the farmyard in his landau Nellie waved her snow white handkerchief by way of farewell but she used the time in her brain to formulate a plan of action for Eliza. When he was out of sight she immediately found Rose and took her into the morning room. She relayed accurately and kindly Eliza's predicament to Rose and for arrangements to be made for Eliza to join the other cheese helpers Ellen and Ada in their bedroom. As usual Rose added to Nellie's plans with sensible points over the arrangements and Nellie knew Rose had totally grasped the situation without shock or fuss and Eliza's quarters would be prepared efficiently before her arrival.

Nellie also informed Rose that she did not want Eliza to be shut away and that she should make further arrangements with the helpers at Higher Smallwood to include Eliza in the attendance of Evensong at All Saints on the forthcoming Sunday. Nellie knew with Rose's magnitude of character she would put Eliza under her wing and the comments of the congregation would be much lessened about Eliza if she was seen in church at Rose's side in a pew.

And so it was; Eliza when residing at Higher Smallwood, although evidently grateful to the Walkers, found her shame of being with child kept her very quiet and withdrawn. She made a valiant effort to learn cheese making skills and thought Nellie was an excellent teacher.

One fair June evening Eliza took her usual solitary stroll around the fields of Higher Smallwood Farm. At eight o'clock, the maids' suppertime, she did not appear. Rose immediately was concerned and ran to politely interrupt Nellie and George in the drawing room to inform Nellie of the matter. Nellie asked if she thought Eliza had run away but Rose thought not as she had already checked and Eliza's belongings were still by her bedside.

Rose really did think there was something amiss. Nellie trusted Rose's intuition and instructed her to gather as many helpers as possible to look for Eliza and assemble in the farm yard.

George on hearing the conversation joined in the rescue operations and suggested that Nellie should stay at the farmhouse and make preparations for Eliza's return. Nellie watched them in the farmyard as the gathered group of eight were sensibly making arrangements to split up to search the fields. George went one step further and commanded Rose to fetch Eliza's cheese making bonnet which she did instantly. George took it over to his two best spaniels and encouraged his dogs to take the scent from the bonnet. He also commanded Alfred to stay on the yard following his words with an anxious wink, which silently informed Alfred to be ready to harness or saddle a horse if need be. Alfred raised his finger slightly touching his head indicating to George he had understood his silent instruction. Off George and the remainder of the Higher Smallwood staff went in separate ways calling Eliza's name loudly.

Nellie was very agitated in the farm yard and in a pause between calls she heard a faint distressing scream. The scream was deeply familiar to her, the undeniable scream of a woman suffering in labour. She had heard it many times in her mother's confinements. Nellie listened again and, yes, the scream came again from the pasture over the brow near to green lane. The screams had alerted the rescuers and they were all running in that direction with the dogs on the scent already out of sight in the direction of Bowden Hall.

Nellie at that time understood exactly what George's wise words meant when he had bidden her stay at the farmhouse and make preparations for Eliza's return. She flew into positive action. She shouted Alfred and commanded him to quickly take the trap and fetch Nurse Spencer the midwife from Stonechair Lane. As Nellie ran into the kitchens she was relieved to see dear Polly already attending to kettles of boiling water. Polly had read the situation better than anyone. Nellie dashed up the maids' stairs to the linen cupboard and started ripping the old sheets.

She then returned to the farm yard to see her strong George hurriedly carrying a distressed Eliza in his arms. Even in his dirty boots he carried her gently up the maids' stairs and this time, on Rose's instructions, Rose insisted on Eliza being taken to her bedroom for privacy. Nellie followed with the sheets, Polly with the water and thankfully Nurse Spencer arrived. Everyone returned to their duties. George decided to walk his excited dogs and Nellie, Polly and Rose assisted with Eliza's confinement.

On George's return at twilight Nellie came downstairs and said things were not looking good and Nurse Spencer said Doctor Latham was needed without delay. George immediately saddled his own horse and rode off at speed. Nellie was relieved after a very tense wait when she could hear two horses returning and the Doctor took over the situation.

Nellie sat with George for two long hours and knew things were bad when Rose appeared in the drawing room doorway looking very pale and quietly sobbing. She stared with shock at Nellie before sadly uttering, 'The babe's gone.'

Nellie held her face in her hands and then pulled her fingers away slowly. She tentatively enquired of Eliza. Rose composed herself and said the Doctor had mercifully stemmed her haemorrhaging and felt with care she would pull round. He said age was on her side. Rose did not want to talk further and Nellie gently put her arm around her and led her back into the comfort of the helpers' kitchen where the other girls were awaiting news. The Higher Smallwood household went to bed late, some with tears but all with a heavy heart.

Before breakfast the following day the familiar landau of the Rector made a hasty entrance into the farm yard. Nellie met him at the door knowing he would have been informed by Doctor Latham of the sadness of the stillbirth, hence his early visit. He apologised profusely for the extra trouble that had been caused by Eliza's situation and for the additional work for the Walker household. Nellie was quite drained but said the situation was not trouble but life and had to be faced. The Rector's profuse gratitude was too much for Nellie at that time and she skilfully guided him to Eliza's bedside via the maids' stairs to comfort her with prayers, which he dutifully did after Nellie left them alone.

About fifteen minutes later the Rector descended the gracious staircase, not the backstairs, and Nellie was waiting for him in the morning room. She was composed and purposeful, sitting at the oval table which was perfectly set for breakfast. Showing her manners Nellie offered the Rector a seat at the table and intimated that he was welcome to share breakfast in a while but he politely declined.

However they both sat to the table knowing business had to be discussed. Nellie opened the conversation, 'About the little funeral Rector.' The Rector's eyes opened wide. 'Nellie there will be no funeral or marked grave. There never is with a stillborn. You surely know that small point of church etiquette.'

'No I don't Rector', Nellie answered sternly and proceeded, 'The Lord has been good to my parents. They have reared nine of their eleven children. My brother George and sister Minnie died as infants and they are buried at All Saints.'

The Rector was astonished by Nellie's words and continued hastily, 'Yes, of course, I remember well, Nellie, but I had attended to their christenings. You do know stillborns cannot have a funeral service or marked grave because they have not been christened.'

Nellie continued firmly, 'Yes I suppose I am aware of that but Eliza has suffered enough and wants her babe in a marked grave in All Saints churchyard.'

'Nellie you know I can't do that.'

'Well what about the father's church?' Nellie persisted.

'Oh that is out of the question. We don't know where that soldier is. The Boer War is taking a lot of life. He is probably dead as we speak.'

Nellie started pleading, 'There must be a way of having the dear little soul in a marked grave at All Saints. George will pay.'

'There isn't a way Nellie. There just isn't.'

'There must be', she persisted.

Shaking his head he said despairingly, 'The best I can do is to put the little body within the churchyard wall in the paupers' section in an unmarked grave.'

'Paupers' section!' Nellie announced indignantly. 'This is so wrong. The poor little mite has no father probably here on earth and we are denying him knowledge of his Father in Heaven.'

'Don't make it difficult for me please', the Rector begged.

Nellie paused and the Rector felt a swell of hurt at seeing her beautiful blue eyes sad and pleading but he was helpless; he had no power to change the laws of the Church. Nellie loathed being up against a brickwall of protocol which was utterly wrong in her mind. Alas, she realised that really was the best the Rector could offer.

'Very well', she said with a heavy heart.

With deep relief the Rector instructed, 'Paupers have to be buried by men, no women, under the cover of darkness. We are nearing mid Summer so send a trusted man servant with a good spade, with the wrapped infant corpse and I will attend to the burial within the paupers' section in the church yard tonight around midnight.'

Nellie sadly knew there was no more to be said and nodded a feeble acceptance. They both rose and moved to the doorway. The Rector stepped forward and whilst kissing Nellie on the cheek, he lingered as their cheeks were together and whispered a grateful, 'Thank you.' She squeezed his hand slightly in acknowledgement of his dilemma and they parted with no more words.

At noon of that Thursday Nellie was exceedingly touched as George took her hand and led her into the laundry room. In the centre of the scrubbed top table she could see his beechwood gun cleaning box. He opened the lid and inside the box was neatly lined with clean muslin and a beautiful white crochet trimmed small soft pillow was slightly squashed into the base. He told Nellie that Polly had attended to the lining and pillow and asked

Nellie if she thought it was suitable for Eliza's dead baby boy. Nellie was overcome with George's and Polly's thoughtfulness. She leaned on his strong shoulder and nodded her agreement with tears in her eyes.

By 2 o'clock in the afternoon Polly had laid the darling infant, lovingly dressed in some old baby clothes of the Walker family, in the small improvised coffin. The babe looked perfect as though just sleeping peacefully in blissful comfort. The lid was kept open for the rest of the day and, as and when the busy staff had an inclination to view the deceased infant, they were allowed to do so at any time. Nellie had placed a vase of flowers on the table by the makeshift coffin. The vase contained red campion picked from the edge of the croft mixed with a few rose buds from the garden.

George attended naturally to the unsaid rules of country life; women attend to births and men attend to deaths. He had instructed Alfred to have the horse and gig ready at fifteen minutes to midnight. Thankfully the village lantern shone brightly in the heavens giving sufficient light for their sad assignment. George personally rode in the gig carrying the stillborn's small coffin on his knees as Alfred took the reins. Nellie sent the flowers as a token of condolence. George insisted that the rest of the household should take themselves to their beds including Nellie and Polly. Everyone followed his instructions. Nellie remembered hearing the gig return but must have fallen asleep in her exhaustion before George joined her in their bed.

The following morning Nellie was upset when she saw the flowers she had sent with the baby's coffin on the morning room table. When George came in for breakfast without asking he knew Nellie was saddened by the returned flowers. 'I'm sorry Nellie', he said with understanding and added, 'When I put them over the shallow grave the Rector insisted on no mark of recognition of the grave and handed me the flowers to take away.'

Nellie was angry inside. Not with the Rector but with the church system that would not change. She nodded understandingly to George trying not to cry and knowing he had done his best.

Mercifully Eliza, as Doctor Latham had decreed, was making good progress in health resting in Rose's bed. Polly kept her Friday afternoon tea rendezvous with the Dowager who was the widowed mother of Sir Philip Wilbraham. Her Dower House was within close proximity to the Rectory and the two ladies had much to talk about.

Often when a lady from a hall of status becomes a widow her son takes over the title of the family and residence of the hall and he provides his widowed mother with an eminent home in the village. Maids and liverymen help to keep the widow in a lifestyle of certain standing which suits her needs. The cost of such upkeep is borne by her son who becomes entitled to the income off the estate in the form of rents from the estate lands, farms and cottages. Once informally being made a dowager by her family, the widow in question accepts she will not remarry, hence the family wealth remains with her family and in particular with her eldest son. This practice is widespread throughout rural England and a gentry widow often takes the mantle of dowager by choice, reinforcing her decision by calling her home the dower house.

Polly on arriving home from her weekly visit to the Dowager, punctually as always at seven o'clock, interrupted Nellie and George in the drawing room. George could see it was going to be a womans' conversation so he excused himself to go and train his spaniels. Polly told Nellie that the Dowager knew the Tollmaches at Peckforton Castle were in need of a wet nurse and suggested that Eliza should be encouraged to draw and keep her milk so she could take the position when she would be in full milk in three days time. Nellie was horrified announcing, 'No, Polly, I don't think that is a good idea. I think her breasts should be bound and she should cut down on her fluids to stop her milk, so she can resume her cheese making training.'

Polly continued gently, 'But it would be such an important well paid position for her at Peckforton Castle and she could rear a child at this most distressing time and start a new life away from Rode.'

Nellie replied firmly, 'She will only have good wages while she has good milk. When her lactation is ended so will her job.'

'No, the Dowager knows that the Tollmaches will offer her further employment with other duties.'

'No', Nellie answered again firmly. 'Her soldier may return and she could resume her life with him.'

'Oh he will never return', Polly lamented.

'Well if he doesn't she would make a good farmer's wife with her cheese skills.'

Realising her conversation had to be more convincing Polly made the admission, 'Eliza will never marry in these parts. It's made no matter to you of Eliza being with child here at Higher Smallwood but the Village is ashamed of her actions and her aunt has bore the shame so deep she stays indoors and has not attended All Saints for weeks. No local man will ever want Eliza and she will never be desired by a good man as it is very evident she is no longer a virgin. She is impure, Nellie, we have to face that fact.'

Nellie pondered Polly's words knowing they were true and despairingly replied, 'This is so unjust that Eliza has to bear this shame alone. If her soldier ..'

Polly interrupted strongly, 'Nellie there is no soldier'.

Nellie froze, instantly knowing that Polly had privileged information.

'No soldier', Nellie repeated giving herself time to think.

'No', answered Polly firmly.

'Do you know who is the father?' Nellie asked.

'Please don't ask me that direct question Nellie.'

'Polly you do don't you, the Dowager has told you today hasn't she?'

Polly found it difficult to answer knowing the Dowager's information was always confidential and Nellie never stopped reading between the lines.

'Please, Nellie, I am a confidant of the Dowager. I simply cannot say. I will tell you in confidence that thankfully it is not a villager but the terrible conceivement did happen in Rode.'

'Where, Polly, Where?' Was it against her will?'

'Yes', Polly softly confessed.

Nellie felt extreme sadness tinged with anger and she uttered loudly, 'How dreadful for poor Eliza to have suffered all this and none of it of her own making. How pitifully dreadful!'

Polly proceeded, 'The tragic experience has left Eliza almost mute about her conceivement. A neighbour has told her aunt that some soldiers from Talk O'th Hill were seen down 'claphatch' talking to a group of girls including Eliza. They wrongly put two and two together when Eliza's stomach grew and in her shocked state she did not deny it, so it fuelled the wrong conclusion for village gossip.'

Nellie paused slightly before boldly asking, 'Does the father know he is the father?'

'Yes he does but he said it was just one act of gratification to him.'

Nellie's exasperation resurged. 'Gratification! gratification! All the suffering and life long shame Eliza will experience just for one man's evil act of rape! How can men get away with such a violation so lightly. What a terrible price women pay. Will it always be like this for women, Polly? Have we no rights or recognition?'

Polly knew Nellie's anger was not directed towards her but the situation of the injustice to women and kept silent. Nellie declared, 'We must gain the vote for all women, Polly, we must, we must! To address some sort of balance.' In a lamentable tone Polly replied, 'Even with a vote unconsenting mistreatment and rape of women, leading to inevitable births, will always happen. It is overlapped with mans' immense desire to be dominant to sire or to force their sexual pleasure regardless of consequence.'

'Nonsense!' Some men are very understanding', exclaimed Nellie, thinking of George's responsible attitude towards marital actions without siring.

Polly could read Nellie's mind and instantly dropped her glance downwards and in so doing indicated clearly to Nellie, without words, that she did not wish to know anything about the Higher Smallwood master bedroom activities.

Nellie took a different tact and enquired, 'Does the Rector know the father?'

'He thinks he does. He wrongly believes it was a soldier.'

'Can the nature of the conceivement showing Eliza's innocence be revealed to the Village?' Polly simply nodded in the negative.

'Can she reveal her violator's name to a trusted few?' Nellie pleaded.

Polly took an intake of breath and proceeded calmly, 'Apparently the episode was extremely violent. She fought long and hard not to allow the rape. She is in trepidation and too tender in her mind even to relive her catastrophe in words. I feel she never will divulge his name.'

Nellie withdrew from her questioning, sat back and sighed loudly and sadly declared, 'I have no choice for Eliza, have I? Eliza is finished in Rode because of shame, prejudice and the injustice of her not being able to declare the truth.'

Polly answered kindly but firmly, 'I cannot and must not say anymore. Please trust me and the Dowager. It is for the best now, to ease Eliza's shame, for her to leave Rode.'

'Who am I to go against the Dowager', Nellie answered blandly.

Polly stated slowly and with immense loyalty, 'Nellie you nor many others do not know of all the kind and thoughtful deeds the Dowager attends to behind the scenes in Rode, done solely for the welfare of people in need. Eliza is now the Villager in need.'

Two days later Eliza stood in the farmyard at Higher Smallwood with her whole belongings in one small carpet bag. She was wearing some old boots found and highly polished by Rose and a smart cast-off jacket previously belonging to Polly.

Alfred held the horse and trap firm and still. Nellie stood with Rose and Polly to bid farewell to Eliza who was in a pitiful dithering state.

Nellie stepped forward and gave Eliza a comforting sad hug. The hug was unheeded and as Nellie withdrew all she could see in Eliza's tormented eyes was shock and fear. Alfred stretched out his arm to assist Eliza into the trap and, when she was safely seated, commanded the horse to trot on. Eliza did not acknowledge the gathered womens' slow waves and drifted out of sight, in full milk to an unknown world, to take up her appointment with the Tollmaches at Peckforton Castle as a wet nurse to suckle one of their young.

CHAPTER 10

IT IS YOUR DUTY

Cameo brooch
The 21st Birthday Gift

In the Summer of 1895 it was apparent to all that Nellie had settled exceeding well to life at Higher Smallwood Farm. She expanded the cheese making and quickly learned which pastures were verdant producing the best grass for the cows to eat, thus ensuring through their milk which cheeses were superior. She had a fairness of tongue and articulate working hands which commanded respect from her helpers, producing a healthy atmosphere for all in her employ at the farm house, whether in domestic or cheese duties.

Emily sitting with grown daughters
Lucy, Nellie and Lily
with faithful Pack Horse Farm Dog

On the 25th July, Nellie's twenty first birthday, George gave her a fine cameo brooch, a gift she spontaneously treasured. Polly happily presented Nellie with an engraved gold propelling pencil to mark her milestone birthday. However the villagers, particularly at church, were mystified as to why Nellie, a fecund Bailey, had not produced a child for George within the early years of their marriage although it was evident that they were happy.

Just when the village gossip was reaching a crescendo Autumn revealed she was with child.

The news quickly spread of a forthcoming Spring baby at Higher Smallwood Farm and William Bailey noted that his daughter was in her twenty first year of age. Although a hard task, George had kept his secret gentlemen's agreement with William and in a sense both men thought they had achieved what was best for Nellie. George could hardly contain his excitement at seeing his beautiful wife blooming with the mantle of forthcoming motherhood.

One Sunday afternoon in the early March of 1896 Emily and Nellie walked their usual favourite haunt the Poolside spinney, adjacent to Pack Horse Farm, to see the wild daffodils often known as lent lilies. Nellie looked the picture of health even heavy in her pregnancy and both mother and daughter rested on a stout felled tree trunk to enjoy their time together after necessary Sunday chores and away from the presence of other family members.

Emily in her ever caring manner opened the conversation. 'You have carried this child well, Nellie, so you will have a good confinement. Have you got everything ready?'

Nellie just nodded in the positive. 'What's the matter?' Emily enquired slowly perceiving concern.

'I'm anxious mother. No confinement is good. I remember vividly your pain.'

'Oh, Nellie, don't be anxious, it is aptly named 'labour', the hardest work you will ever do but it is soon forgotten once the babe is in your arms. Beside the love you share with George will pull you through.'

'I'm not sure I love George yet. You said I would but I'm still not really sure. The conceivement was not,' Nellie paused and sighed, 'well it wasn't, I don't think, like it should have been.'

'Stop it!' Emily insisted. 'You are happy with George. Of course you are.'

Nellie almost crying continued, 'I am happy, yes I am at Higher Smallwood and George is a good and generous man but.'

'No buts', Emily interrupted. 'A woman's mind is all at sea when with child. We don't see things logically.'

'Please listen', Nellie implored. 'I do want to be a mother but I hope this babe is a boy for George. You know how a farmer always wants a son. I don't want to be with child again.'

Emily clasped her hands around Nellie's lovely face.

'Now, now Nellie. You will love this child no matter what and you will have lots more children. You are a Bailey. It will be impossible not to have more being a married woman.'

Nellie began to cry but in her snivelling boldly announced, 'George is a good husband and does not trouble me if I care not to be troubled.'

Emily's eyes grew large and anxious. She took both Nellies' hands and held them on her knees.

'Nellie listen to me this is extremely important. If a man does not find his 'robin' with his wife he will look elsewhere. They always do. Your thoughts are very dangerous, you must lie with your man. It is your duty.'

Nellie crying further passionately declared, 'No, mother, I can't! I don't want a lot children.'

Emily assuredly persisted, 'You wont have lots Nellie. You have been fortunate and had a few years of married life without giving birth. George must have been an exceptional husband for you to only just be with child. He'll take to those ways again no doubt and you will perhaps have only five or six children at your pace. I'm sure that's how things will be.'

Nellie fell silent to allow the vernal breeze to soothe her face as she stared into the distance but the soft wind actually caused her faint discomfort as the salt in her tears was slightly stinging her beautiful skin. She knew that her mother was not understanding exactly what she thought but on the other hand she instinctively knew her mother was right. The realisation of the inevitability of many more children hurt Nellie's feelings deeply.

Emily lovingly leaned across and with a corner of her best Sunday apron dabbed away the tears on Nellie's cheeks.

'Come on now, Nellie, you are getting things out of proportion in your mind. Life unfolds, it always does.'

Mother and daughter wandered slowly back to Pack Horse Farm, linking arms naturally encompassed within the Gentle Ribbon.

On the 24th March 1896 Nellie gave birth to a healthy daughter at Higher Smallwood Farm. George was taken into the bedroom after the confinement by Nurse Spencer the midwife and was left alone with his lovely wife and new daughter for that special first family moment, which was strangely more emotionally awkward for Nellie than George. He was relieved to see her looking well, to the point of being surprisingly radiant in view of her ordeal in giving birth. He was attentive and kind towards her and after gently kissing her he stepped to the crib.

He had purchased the new crib and Polly at the correct moment had taken it into the bedroom and it looked such a pretty acquisition to the spacious room. It was on a metal frame allowing it to rock and was covered with tiers of exquisite hand sewn frilled white cotton embroidery anglaise which cascaded to the floor. Attached to the ruche lawn cotton trailing hood were the prettiest of pink satin bows. The whole creation had been skilfully stitched and arranged by Polly for the new babe.

George gently picked the new infant out of the crib and cradled her in his arms in a natural paternal way. 'She's a darling, Nellie, a perfect little darling', George said proudly as he sat holding his first born along side Nellie on the bed.

After a few moments Nellie ventured to ask, 'Aren't you disappointed it's not a boy, George?' Her big blue eyes looked almost child like with innocence as she posed the plaintiff question. Trying to comfort her George answered sincerely in an easy manner, 'Of course not, there's plenty of time. I'm sure our daughter will have many fine brothers.'

He stared at Nellie and enquired, 'Do I detect perhaps you bear the bigger disappointment. Did you want a son?'

'No', Nellie declared regaining her womanly dignity, 'she's

beautiful. What shall we call her?'

'That's your choice', George graciously replied.

'Well she is a Higher Smallwood girl, a Walker', Nellie said purposely. 'Shall we call her Mary after your sister Polly?'

George broke into a broad grin and enthused in genuine gratitude, 'Polly will be delighted, absolutely delighted.'

'Well Mary she is', Nellie confirmed positively, as she leaned forward and tenderly stroked the fine silken hair on her precious new baby's head.

CHAPTER 11

What Had I Done?

One warm September afternoon in 1899 the Rector made one of his frequent visits to Higher Smallwood Farm, for he enjoyed his conversations with Nellie in the comfort of her splendid drawing room. He had to make a few unsavoury visits within his parish and when his pastoral worries were building up he always felt the better for spending time with Nellie. He was particularly pleased that she had risen to the responsibility of running Higher Smallwood well, especially in the light of the fact that he had actively encouraged George to marry Nellie and he felt the decision for marriage had turned out to be a sound one.

Nellie that afternoon, as usual, was suitably changed into a gown and was ready to receive visitors in the drawing room. She extended her welcome with ease to the Rector. After the politeness of the welcome and with the accompaniment of the tea tray Nellie enquired of the Rector's health.

'I am quite well, Nellie, thank you. And your good self?'

He was hoping to hear that Nellie was with child again. Little Mary was three years old and he was slightly anxious that Nellie was not fulfilling her duty in providing a son for the good of George and Higher Smallwood Farm.

'Yes thank you, Rector, I am enjoying good health.'

Their friendship was deepening and he felt he knew Nellie well enough to be open and, with a smile, proceeded in a slightly teasing way, 'I was hoping you were going to tell me some news and I would be in need of preparing the baptismal font.' Nellie immediately took to her familiar pose of sitting very straight like a ram rod.

'Really Rector. Are the village tongues wagging again?'

'I don't have to tell you, Nellie, you know they are. It is all meant for the best as there has been a John Walker at Higher Smallwod Farm, I believe, for a couple of centuries and we would wish for that to continue wouldn't we? Besides it is the duty of a farmer's wife to bear a son,' adding with particular emphasis, 'and it would be prudent to produce a son under our Queen.'

'Oh really, Rector, what a strange reason to give for a birth.'

'I'm serious Nellie the Prince of Wales is of insincere character. He is unfaithful to his wife and fraternizes with people of undesirable circles.'

'Isn't that how royal men behave, only taking their vows to sire? It is normal for them to be unfaithful, having a mistress seems second nature to them.' Nellie could not resist saying, indulging herself in royal tittle tattle.

The Rector, knowing their conversation was confidential, proceeded further. 'No, Albert and our Queen were devoted; you surely know that.'

'Yes I do', Nellie agreed warmly, 'and what were your thoughts about our Queen and Mr Brown from the Highlands before he died.'

The Rector enjoying the conversation replied, 'A strong friendship I'm sure. A totally genuine friendship and there was no harm in the Queen finding solace in her widowhood.

After spontaneously removing a fleck of cotton from his jacket sleeve his mood became rather sombre as he continued, 'However, your remark about some male royals does bear credence as throughout history princes who wait a long time for the throne do not have the ability to be loyal to their spouses and disregard their marriage vows. It appears, because the opportunity is never theirs to share the throne at an early age with their spouse, they seem to fail to see their wife's love, strength and companionship. The devil makes work for idle hands and a prince waiting for the throne often succumbs to temptation and becomes a tool of the devil. The biggest folly for any man, prince or pauper, is to marry his mistress if the circumstances arise. Rarely does a mistress have the inner quality to become a good wife. History does repeat itself.'

'Well if history does repeat itself,' Nellie announced assertively 'then I am sure there will be another John Walker here at Higher Smallwood.'

'Lets hope you are right', the Rector replied.

'Good heavens Rector I'm glad I belong to your church and I don't have to go to confession like the Catholics do.'

The Rector thought Nellie was being flippant but on a second look into her beautiful blue eyes he could see she was serious. He continued cautiously. 'If there is anything troubling you I would hope, through the goodness of the church of course, that we could discuss it. You are wise beyond your years, I am sure we could talk.'

'Don't use that phrase lightly Rector', Nellie retorted.

'You are Nellie. I do not use it lightly', replied the Rector with firm emotion.

Nellie rose to her feet and as the Rector was about to do the same, thinking he had handled the son issue badly, Nellie put a very calm hand on his shoulder to indicate that he should remain seated. She then elegantly walked to her bureau and pulled out the supporting lopers before bringing down the lid. The Rector was watching attentively as she purposely took an envelope from one of the small drawers and returned and sat again before him. She passed the envelope to him and asked him if he recognised the writing. Although he did recognise the writing he kept his eyes down for a while, giving himself time for composure, knowing he was going to receive some very searching questions from Nellie.

Eventually he raised his head and faced her piercing eyes. After clearing his throat he answered, 'Yes, I do. I do recognise the writing.'

'Do you know the contents of the envelope?' Nellie

demanded.

'No I don't. My job was to be a confidant and post the sealed envelope at the correct time.' Still in control Nellie took out of the envelope a letter and handed it to the Rector.

'I want you to read it Rector', she said firmly.

'It says private and confidential', the Rector said, trying to protect himself from reading the contents, before asking, 'Has George read it Nellie?'

'No. No one but me. Please continue' Nellie instructed firmly.

The Rector felt most uneasy and had a foreboding that after reading it he would come out of the situation in a bad light. However he proceeded to follow Nellie's instructions, because somehow, when Nellie gave a firm instruction, punctuated with the raising of her index finger, it was adhered to with no more deliberation.

He read the letter very slowly, digesting every word, knowing he would be hard pressed to debate thereafter. He read the words 'wise beyond your years'. He then understood what had triggered Nellie's presenting of the letter to him. After reading it he tentatively handed it back to Nellie who folded it and purposely replaced it in the envelope.

Their eyes met. 'I'm so sorry, Nellie, I really am.'

'You knew the Canon had lustful thoughts for me and he had taken my book didn't you?' Nellie retorted.

'I won't lie to you Nellie, the Canon did confess to me, before he left Rode, his intense desire for you but I had no knowledge that he had taken your book.'

'Why did you not tell me and protect me? Why are the men always protected? What had I done?' Nellie asked severely.

The Rector deliberated before pleading, 'Nellie don't think ill of me, I enjoy your company and treasure our friendship. I did not know you as a friend at the time, you were but a grown child.'

'In need of protection Rector. Answer me why?' she commanded firmly.

'Nellie, I beg of you don't ridicule me in this way. It is a very lonely furrow I have here at Rode. As Rector I have to please the Big House and be seen to be pleasing the lowly.'

Do they know at the Big House?' Nellie pursued.

'No! No I assure you they don't.'

'Well at least Polly will not know if the Dowager does not know.' Nellie stated in hollow gratitude.

Re-gaining his usual control he forwarded his words slowly with passion. 'No, I contained the situation within my study at the Rectory, not even my own wife or the Canon's wife know. I make pastoral mistakes, Nellie, I get weary of trying to cover my tracks, but I assure you I am telling you the truth. On the Lord's name I swear no one knows. As to your protection my duty was then towards the Canon and there was no other way but for me to fall in with the lie of his malady. Men do feel lust for women for years but at least your incident was mild and he did leave the Village instantly and to some degree you were protected with the course of events that unfolded with his leaving.'

Nellie sat still and pondered on the Rector's defence for quite some time. Eventually without words but with the clearest of statements she leaned to the fire and threw the envelope and letter on to the flames. In silence and in unison they watched until the last remnants were but ashes on the embers.

They glanced once more at one another, the Rector rather drained with emotion said, 'You have done right Nellie.'

In a friendlier tone she answered, 'Yes I know I have, so we will mention it no more but one day Rector, mark my words, women will be protected more, perhaps through a vote.'

The Rector was relieved that he could see and feel that he and Nellie were still friends, but felt in his heart that the world would not change and women would continue to be subservient. However there was a womanly strength Nellie possessed, within the bounds of dignity that truly was tangible and had to be experienced to be understood. He was quite bewildered that he knew her strength and that she drew him. He could feel the truth in her even though that surprised him as a man. His whole upbringing told him that the male should always be dominant, women had to be subservient, that was how societies survived. If he even contemplated Nellie's point of view regarding votes for women he believed the whole fabric of society would erode.

The Rector was thankful for a few more sentences of easy polite conversation after which they both rose to their feet and before he left the drawing room he and Nellie almost caressed. Not in an unacceptable way but they did linger in one another's arms with their cheeks tightly together and both felt the power of the comfort they gained by holding one another. The genuine comfort, found in a close and understanding friendship when life takes a couple to the bounds of sharing confidences and knowing that each confidence is completely safe. As they continued to hold hands after their close embrace they naturally exchanged warm smiles before one last understanding squeeze of their hands before parting.

After formal tea with George, Nellie met Polly with a basket of mixed flowers in the morning room and offered to help to fill the house vases. When finishing their pleasant task and the competent killing of two earwigs that had crept out of the dahlias, Polly could sense Nellie was slightly heavy hearted.

'It is such a lovely evening. The dark nights will soon be upon us, shall we go for a walk?' enquired Polly.

Nellie was grateful for the thought of walking with Polly and catching the opportunity of much needed fresh air. She left instructions with Rose to attend to the bathing of young Mary and said that she and Polly would be back well in time to tuck Mary in her bed and read her a story.

The two ladies walked in the fair evening across their favourite meadows mantled with splendid autumn colours and took rest by the pond near to Green Lane. Each detected they were not in a jocund mood but still felt solace in each others company. 'It is particularly beautiful by this pond', Nellie stated. 'I always like the view of Mow Cop from here especially when visibility is as good as it is this evening. Doesn't Mow Cop look close Polly?'

As she sat by Nellie, raising her eyes, Polly smiled and nodded her acknowledgement of how beautiful and close the old man of Mow looked, before replying, 'I do like it here from this aspect but I am not over comfortable with the proximity of Green Lane.'

'Many would agree; I suppose because of its association in their minds with public hangings, but I believe they were beyond the farm house in Hangmans Lane well over on the Smallwood side, not here in Rode', answered Nellie.

'No I have my own private reasons, Nellie. Very private reasons.'

Nellies eyes went bigger. She could sense Polly was going to continue into a conversation she did not want to hear, but Polly was such a giver in life perhaps it was time for roles to reverse. Nellie had received much kindness from Polly and she realised the time for her to listen to Polly was long overdue and may be she should give something back.

Each of the ladies made a conscious effort to make themselves comfortable and looked at one another. Polly proceeded with precision, 'I was thirteen at the time, a member of the church choir, as I did love singing. I seemed to be the only child of mother's who had a decent singing voice and she encouraged me to be in the choir at All Saints.

After practice one May evening, when the chestnut blossoms were in full form, large storm clouds were gathering. There had been a young curate with us for the practice but I did not know his name. The Rector suggested that the curate put me on his horse and take me home to escape the on-coming storm. He had a disagreeable countenance and did not at the time seem to accept the Rector's request with good grace. However, the Rector helped me on to the back of the his horse, with a word of caution to him about the bends on the long drive of Higher Smallwood and gave him clear instructions not to make a mistake by over shooting the top of the drive on the last corner and ending up in Green Lane.

The young curate never spoke to me and the homeward journey was most uncomfortable. I was trying to hold around his waist and the saddle was pushing into me as I was on the bare back of his horse. I thought he was riding too fast and was ungentlemanly as he never spoke, not even to enquire as to my comfort, but at the time I thought he was doing his best to get me home before the onset of the storm.

On reaching the last corner on the driveway he turned his horse off into Green Lane. I think I said something about him having taken the wrong direction and all of a sudden he brought his horse to such an abrupt stop that I had to cling on to him extra tightly so not as to fall off. The next thing he was off the horse as roles seemed to reverse in that he was then holding both my arms very firmly and dragged me off the horse. I felt I had annoyed him greatly by not giving him clear instructions on the last bend on the drive and I was at a loss as to how to apologise as he acted aggressively and with force.

He took me roughly, causing me pain in my arms and threw me backwards with great force against a tree. I was so afraid. Then he abused me. He abused me with such force, I remember vividly the severe pain in my back. It was as if I was irrelevant to him and nothing, absolutely nothing, was going to stop him until he had achieved to some sort of gratification. It seemed to carry on almost to the point where I thought I was going to faint, his horrible strength was increasing and my breath was leaving me. Up to that time in my life my brain and body had been as one but in that terrifying situation my brain started to dismiss my body from my pain as if in an endeavour to help me to survive the appalling repulsive ordeal.

When my terror was reaching the limit of my bodily strength, he strangely went still and just seemed to let the weight of his body hang on mine, both of us upright against the tree. His restraining of me had ceased. I was too afraid to move. My body was rigid with fear.

I remember, somehow, his hair was entangled in my face;

his hat must have fallen off. My tears were streaming and I was sobbing violently. Immediately afterwards he moved quickly from me and stood about four yards away with his back to me. I remember the moment when my brain and body reconnected and I hastily straightened my dishevelled clothes and I ran and ran.

I ran out from Green Lane and up the rise of the drive to home. Fortunately my parents were out socialising with my brothers and sister and the maids were off duty. I ran to my bedroom and continued sobbing as I washed myself and wiped my clothes.

I didn't understand what had happened to me. What had I done? Remember, I was still a child and the thought never occurred to me that I could have been impregnated. I hadn't started my menstrual cycles, so I was unaware of life as a woman. Thankfully no woes of that nature entered my mind but what did deeply engrave itself on my mind was his brutal violation, violation by a stranger who spoke not one word to me. I knew profoundly I had been caught up in a vile act of immense evil and, because somehow I felt the cause was perhaps my doing, something told me I must not disclose it to a soul.

I can't remember if there was any evidence of the violence on my coat as I was almost impaled on the tree. I seemed to have blotted out from my mind all the practical things I must have attended to. I do recall that I immediately stopped my choir activities and this was a source of aggravation to my mother all my church life but I never told her the reason.

When I was sixteen and my menstrual cycles commenced and I was made aware of women's role of child bearing, I could then recall my washing at thirteen and only then did I realise what the substance was I washed away. The realisation ate away at me. I was not sure how he had violated me as a child. I didn't know. My mind had done such a good job for me in my fear such details were totally blotted out. I couldn't even remember if the storm came. At sixteen I tried endless of times, to think back to my blur of tears for myself as a thirteen year old, to recall if there was any smear of blood in my washing but I couldn't, I really couldn't.

With this profound uncertainty I knew that I must not take a husband. I could not deceive a good man into marriage only for him to find out I was perhaps not a virgin. I could not have borne the shame of being impure, so I made a conscious decision never to court or marry.

Thankfully, I never saw the young man in question ever again. I have learned to count myself fortunate that my evil violation was only the once and I was not at child bearing age. I have never had to meet my violator, unlike some unfortunate local women who have to see their violator frequently. And the good Lord has presented me with a privileged and useful life in Rode.'

Tears were rolling down Nellie's cheeks as she gently held Polly's hands. She was totally overcome with Polly's story. Polly gave a slight smile, a nervous smile, and took her handkerchief and dabbed Nellie's tears.

'Well', Polly said resolutely, 'Well I have said it now. Nellie I trust you never to tell a soul especially George.'

Nellie buckled with the emotion of it all and leaned on Polly's shoulder and cried more tears. Polly allowed her to but Polly's eyes were dry. After a minute, guilt over took Nellie as she raised herself from Polly's shoulder and her crying subsided.

'Oh dear. Dear Polly it is I who should be comforting you.'

'Don't worry, Nellie, with the strength of the Lord I have not cried over the incident since that day and you have comforted me. I feel strangely better for telling you.'

Nellie composed herself but said with immense sadness, 'That is tragic Polly, such a tragedy. You would have made a wonderful wife and mother. The world has lost a good mother through one man's brutal selfish violation. That is desperately unfair.'

Polly was beginning to lose her composure, within Nellie's comforting and was trying hard not to cry. Her welling tears weren't for the horrible incident but for Nellie's profound understanding of how she really felt.

Nellie took the high ground of strength and said passionately, 'Polly, you will never leave Higher Smallwood. I always want it to be your home and more than anything I want you to be another mother to any children I may bear George. Mary, although only three, already adores you and you are the lady of Higher Smallwood.'

With intense love and loyalty Polly clasped Nellie's hands.

'Oh, Nellie, you are such an angel. You have given your first daughter my name and now you wish me to be at hand to help to rear her. That is my dearest wish and I will, but always remember you are the lady of Higher Smallwood.' Nellie and Polly hugged tightly knowing they had comforted each other deeply.

The chill of the heavy dew falling took them to their feet. Looking to the west the low early evening bright sunset revealed the incredible sight of the meadows and pastures couched in millions of fine cobwebs; the setting sun highlighting the silver gossamer strands cast like waves of an endless magical sea. To witness such a happening is a marvellous pulse by Mother Nature to a country heart, as the vivid vision of the shimmering delicate threads is soon lost to human sight, with the total setting of Pheobe. The two soul mates linked arms as they walked gracefully back to the farm house within the supportive bond of the Gentle Ribbon.

Later, as Nellie closed the book of the bedtime story she had read to her precious Mary, she felt a sense of balance in her mind. Her upsetting episode with the Malvern Canon was much less important than Polly's terrible time and in turn Polly felt that many more women had suffered worse than her in Rode. As Mary gently drifted off to sleep, Nellie knelt by her little bed, and in prayer thanked the Lord for all the blessings in her life. She also prayed for her daughter to have strength of character to face life's troubles, be an equal to men and never have to suffer at the hands of an evil man.

CHAPTER 12

BEST WE CAN SHARE

George *Nellie*

In the January of the new century Nellie realised it was time for her to be totally subservient to George for him to perhaps father a son. Her tenseness and agitation was building and she made several abortive attempts at giving herself to George. Finally the deed was done.

As they lay together George sadly informed her, 'I hold your body Nellie but not your heart. I had hoped that you would have learned to love me by now. You are all I desire but you do not desire me. I suffer without your love.' His voice started to sound bitter as he removed his arms from around Nellie and lay slightly away from her. 'Our married life is always at your pace not mine. That is wrong and undermines me as a man. It is your duty to be a full wife.'

He left the bed and whilst pacing the room he started to raise his voice. 'Nature has been good to you, Nellie, and you have received fairness of face and body. I feel I am ugly to you.'

Nellie sat up right in their bed and for the first time in her marriage she was fearful that her thoughts were going to be forced into words.

'No, George. You are a good man and generous.'

'Is that all that is important to you?' he snarled.

'No you are a good husband and a good father', she replied with sincerity.

'But you don't love me !', he shouted.

Nellie could not say she did and tried to divert the conversation.

'Shh the maids will hear you George.'

'The maids, the maids, I might as well go and lie with them!' he said with venom. 'Is that what you want, Nellie? Shall I?'

Nellie started to cry, 'No, please don't talk like that, please.'

Intermittently wiping her tears with her fingertips she continued, 'I have tried my very best to work hard with the cheese making, be kind to the staff and to be the lady for you here.' George stalked to the bed and in uncharacteristic temper shouted in her face, 'That is not enough! Polly could be the lady here and I could employ staff for the cheesemaking. You are not a true wife! You don't love me or accept me in a marital way as you should. I am the only man I know who has to dance to a woman's tune.'

Nellie was upset and embarrassed by his shouting and felt the whole household must be awake and listening. She started to tremble and pleaded, 'Please be calm, please. It was you who wanted my hand from Packhorse. You knew I wanted time to adjust.'

'Time! Time!, George roared. 'How long? Next year, the year after, never!'

A shocked silence enveloped them both. George had never shouted in such a way before and each of them found the experience disrespectful and distressing.

After a minute or two Nellie mustered the nerve to quietly announce, 'I have tried, George, really I have, and sometimes I think I love you but then I don't think we share a deep love, a true love. We just don't.' His rage had subsided and in a slow low voice he declared, 'Have you any idea how hurtful those words are to me, Nellie?'

'I have borne you a daughter and I have probably just conceived a son, that's what you want isn't it?' she ventured to reply.

'No I want you to love me. Don't you understand?'

Even in Nellie's trembling state she could not lie to him.

'I will love our children George and run your home. I have a very deep affection for you. Can't that be enough for you?', she implored.

He stared at her and in a toneless voice sadly asked, 'Is that it? Is that the best we can share?'

Nellie fixed her eyes on his and in a more controlled voice said with sincerity, 'I cannot lie to you George. Yes, that is the best but I will always be faithful to you and true to our marriage vows.'

A short silence fell between them before George with a bewildered look slowly stated, 'You are the very essence of love to me yet you hurt me deeply.' With no more words he gathered some clothes and left the bedroom, banging the door loudly, as if defining his anguish.

Nellie felt hollow, totally hollow. She buried her head in her pillow and sobbed uncontrollably until exhausted. Eventually the numbness of sleep released her mind from her unhappiness, as she lay alone for the first time in her bed.

Ten months later the consecrated water was being trickled into the baptismal font by the Rector at All Saints when he heard the first horse and carriage arrive at the south gate, the gate normally reserved for the Wilbraham Family. Good timing, he thought, and he proceeded to the church doorway to greet the Walkers and the Baileys.

Everyone seemed well on that chill Sunday afternoon of the 2nd of October as Nellie carried her well wrapped new infant along the path, the trees resplendent in their Autumn colours. George had insisted on a private baptism. The Rector was rather disappointed that his parishioners could not share in such a special occasion, particularly as he thought it good to show the union of the Walker and Bailey families as a fine example of what a village could achieve by encouraging local marriages. However, that was not to be and in no time at all the church was nicely filled by the whole of the happy Bailey family and many members of the sedate Walker family.

George and Nellie stood with their new born, facing the Rector at the font, flanked by the proud god parents. Nellie, Polly and Emily had dutifully and with little fuss perfectly presented the infant, the two beautifully knitted shawls opened to reveal the starched, pure white, cotton pin-tucked Walker christening robe. The Rector proceeded with the service and at the appropriate moment held out his arms to receive the babe from Nellie's arms. He took the infant and with the sign of the cross of holy water on the babe's forehead pronounced with certainty, 'I name this child John Walker. In the name of the Father, the Son and of the Holy Ghost.'

The love and devotion the Rector saw in Nellie's eyes towards her son was profound and there was an equal love in George's expression as he gazed at his longed for son. The Rector handed the babe into the waiting arms of his god mother Polly. The godfathers Old Alec and Young Alec stood with honour and immense pride, with full understanding of their duty as godfathers in the sight of the Lord, knowing that should a catastrophe befall George and Nellie they would rear the child as one of their own.

Everyone returned after the christening service to Higher Smallwood Farm, including the Rector and his wife, in a cavalcade of horse drawn landaus, gigs and traps. The Walkers entertained effortlessly and perfectly. A fine table was spread in the large living kitchen for a formal sit down tea and after grace was said by the Rector the guests enjoyed the delicious food, which was served efficiently and pleasantly by the maids.

The Baileys, for their part, always made people at ease and each family member had the knack of being a good conversationalist and visibly enjoyed other people's company. The Rector couldn't help admiring their qualities of adding to a room or function, rarely taking away. Put them in high or low company the Baileys had the natural ability to cope equally well with both. The Rector also knew before the happy occasion faded away singing would take place as Nellie was surprisingly accomplished at playing the piano forte and the Baileys had fine singing voices and harmonised well.

The Rector was proud of Lunt's Moss School for Rode boys but he was not over keen on education for girls. However he did have to admit to himself, by educating the girls at Rode Heath Girls School, it was producing good knowledgeable mothers in Rode; mothers like the Bailey girls, particularly Nellie, who could read and write well. He also recognised that many local young ladies did seem to treasure and make wise use of their school education. Obviously the time spent by Lady Wilbraham in exercising an over-seeing eye was an enormous blessing to the girls and the generosity of the Wilbraham family, in financing the building of both schools, plus paying the teachers fees was invaluable. However, even with this tangible example of Nellie before his eyes, the Rector had a strong feeling, that, in the main it was wrong to educate all girls of lower birth as it compelled him to think that in doing so it would tip the balance of society and would eventually be detrimental to the craft of motherhood.

Young Alec had risen with competence to his nurtured position of underkeeper to Old Alec and much to Young Alec's extra delight George had set him up with his own breeding spaniels. He was elated with the opportunity to train his own dogs to the gun and he knew his skill was being noticed at the Big House. His favourite bitch had whelped and, after the christening tea, he discussed the progeny in depth with the interested male company.

The ladies, including the Rector and his wife, retired to the drawing room to dote on the son and heir and laughed at the antics of little Mary who was acting rather precociously in front of her large audience. Before tea, several coins, florins, crowns and the occasional sovereign or guinea, had been pressed into the infant John Walker's tiny palms by the male guests. In the drawing room Nellie was carefully putting the coins into a velvet draw string pouch and then she put the pouch in her bureau for safe keeping.

As the Rector was watching her he could recall the reason for this tradition of crossing an infant's palm with silver, as it had been passed down through the centuries. At one point in history there had been a monetary tax on a new infant's head of one silver crown and poor families were helped by other family members by the giving of lesser silver coins to assist the parents to pay the detestable tax. Thankfully on that day the Rector knew the giving of the coins by the guests was just a quaint custom and the money would be the start of young John Walker's own wealth.

After a while the Rector, although sure the happy gathering would carry on until supper time, felt it was time for him and his wife to take their leave. Nellie personally took them to the front door and apologised for George being with the men. The Rector insisted she did not disturb him but passed on their farewells. He commented on the perfect day and congratulated Nellie on the achievement of producing the longed for son at Higher Smallwood Farm. His words easily tripped off his tongue in a genuine way and he added that he welcomed many more christenings as and when Nellie had further children. Nellie said nothing. She gracefully kissed the Rector's wife on the cheek and held both hands with the Rector in her usual way. However, there was no smile from Nellie to the Rector and more importantly the Rector detected an unusual limpness in her grasp, forwarding no familiar warm squeeze which was normally characteristic in their partings.

Married life unfolded, in the next weeks and months, better than George and Nellie could have imagined. Both sensed a relief in the gift of a son at Higher Smallwood Farm and, with equal pride, both constantly saw the wonder and enjoyed the natural changes in their growing children. However, George kept his emotions hidden very deeply as to expanding his family. Nellie appreciated George's air of consideration in trying to make each family day happy and worthwhile in a very much count your blessing way. This enabled Nellie to mirror the same actions but she was well aware she was blotting out George's desire to father further offspring.

Neither raised the sensitive issue of more children but Nellie acknowledged to herself that she felt content and fulfilled with her two children and definitely did not want any more. George came to the conclusion he had to accept her dictation in the bedroom, no matter how selfish he perceived her feelings.

The scar of her mother Emily's many confinements was etched in Nellie's inner being and she sadly realised she could never convey that scar to George for him to fully understand. It was also a self preservation matter for Nellie, as she had a strong instinct, not a fear, she would lose her life in another confinement. There was the air, which Nellie believed was around falsely, that Bailey women had good confinements. Certainly, in the main, they did, but odds were stacking against that theory. It was common place in every village for a few women to die in childbirth and Nellie felt it was only a matter of time before a Bailey woman would die in such circumstances. She never told a soul about her feelings but it left her with a strong belief that she should trust her instincts and be guided by them.

A very large national matter arose in 1901 and was the talk on everyones' lips, the death of Queen Victoria. It seemed a momentous point in history. However, the national mood of mourning for the deceased Queen soon changed to one of gladness in 1902 in anticipation of the forthcoming festivities for the coronation of King Edward VII. All the talk in Rode about national affairs banished the topic of Nellie not being with child again. Perhaps also it took away that delicate marital note between Nellie and George which may have reached a crescendo once more.

Together with all the household at Higher Smallwood

Farm, Nellie enjoyed the Rode and Rode Heath Coronation tea parties and gatherings. Most villages looked extra presentable because of the celebrations. Lanes and roads were mended with the piles of small stones broken by the men and youths from the workhouses. The lengths men had attended well to the scything of grass along the lane sides and completed the neat badging of the copses. The farmers had taken a pride in cleaning their lane and road side ditches and dubbed their hedges with extra precision. Union jacks swayed in many nooks and crannies and bunting was highly visible over high streets in the busy market towns. Everywhere was throbbing with a sense of community entwined with national pride.

Fortunately village commemorations were spread over a period of time giving a chance to enjoy more than one function. Indeed the Coronation had to be re-arranged because of the future King's sudden bout of ill health. Nellie felt particularly privileged to receive a personal invitation from her friends, the Yates family of Hassall Hall, to join in more festivities along with the villagers from Hassall, Hassall Moss and Hassall Green. George declined the invitation and Polly went in his place, knowing she would be a good help to Nellie with the children.

St Mary's Church Sandbach

Lodley Church
Strangely and sadly unglazed and unfurnished

And guide us when perplexed,
And free us from all ills
In this world and the next.

All praise and thanks to God
The Father now be given,
The Son, and Him Who reigns
With Them in highest heaven;
The One Eternal God,
Whom earth and heaven adore,
For thus it was, is now,
And shall be evermore.

(First verse in Unison.)

CORONATION PRAYERS to Offertory Sentences.

BLESSING.

NATIONAL ANTHEM.

GOD save our gracious King,
Long live our noble King,
God save the King.
Send him victorious,
Happy and glorious,
Long to reign over us,
God save the King.

O Lord our God arise,
Scatter his enemies,
Make war to cease.
Keep us from plague and dearth,
Turn Thou our woes to mirth,
And over all the earth
Let there be peace.

Thy choicest gifts in store,
On him be pleased to pour,
Long may he reign.
May he defend our laws,
And ever give us cause
To sing, with heart and voice,
God save the King.

ORDER OF
Official + Coronation + Service
FOR SANDBACH.
IN ST. MARY'S PARISH CHURCH.
June 26th, 1902, at 11 a.m.

HYMN 166.

ALL people that on earth do dwell,
Sing to the Lord with cheerful voice;
Him serve with fear, His praise forth tell,
Come ye before Him and rejoice.

The Lord, ye know, is God indeed:
Without our aid He did us make;
We are His flock, He doth us feed,
And for His sheep He doth us take.

O enter then His gates with praise,
Approach with joy His courts unto;
Praise, laud, and bless His Name always
For it is seemly so to do.

For why? the Lord our God is good;
His mercy is for ever sure;
His truth at all times firmly stood,
And shall from age to age endure.

To Father, Son, and Holy Ghost,
The God whom heaven and earth adore,
From men and from the Angel-host
Be praise and glory evermore.

(First and last verses in Unison.)

LITANY and Two First PRAYERS in Coronation Service.

FIRST LESSON.
Matthew 22, v. 15 to 23.
REV. G. T. D. PIDSLEY.

HYMN 300.

ALL hail the power of Jesu's Name:
Let Angels prostrate fall,
Bring forth the royal diadem,
To crown Him Lord of all.

Crown Him, ye morning stars of light,
Who fixed this floating ball;
Now hail the strength of Israel's might,
And crown Him Lord of all.

Crown Him, ye Martyrs of your God,
Who from His Altar call;
Extol the Stem-of-Jesse's Rod,
And crown Him Lord of all.

Ye seed of Israel's chosen race,
Ye ransomed of the fall,
Hail Him who saves you by His grace,
And crown Him Lord of all.

Hail Him ye heirs of David's line,
Whom David Lord did call,
The God Incarnate, Man Divine,
And crown Him Lord of all.

Sinners, whose love can ne'er forget
The wormwood and the gall,
Go spread your trophies at His feet,
And crown Him Lord of all.

Let every tribe and every tongue,
Before Him prostrate fall,
And shout in universal song
The crowned Lord of all.

(Last line in each verse in Unison.)

SECOND LESSON.
I. Peter, 2 c., v. 11 to end.
REV. B. WOOLFENDEN.

HYMN 165.

O GOD, our help in ages past,
Our hope for years to come,
Our shelter from the stormy blast,
And our eternal home;

Beneath the shadow of Thy throne
Thy saints have dwelt secure;
Sufficient is Thine Arm alone,
And our defence is sure.

Before the hills in order stood,
Or earth received her frame,
From everlasting Thou art God
To endless years the Same.

A thousand ages in Thy sight
Are like an evening gone,
Short as the watch that ends the night
Before the rising sun.

Time, like an ever-rolling stream
Bears all its sons away;
They fly forgotten, as a dream
Dies at the opening day.

O God, our help in ages past,
Our hope for years to come,
Be Thou our guard while troubles last,
And our eternal home.

(First and last verses in Unison.)

SERMON.
REV. J. R. ARMISTEAD.

PROCLAMATION.

HYMN 379.

NOW thank we all our God,
With heart, and hands, and voices,
Who wondrous things hath done,
In whom His world rejoices;
Who from our mother's arms,
Hath blessed us on our way
With countless gifts of love,
And still is ours to-day.

O may this bounteous God
Through all our life be near us,
With ever joyful hearts
And blessed peace to cheer us;
And keep us in His grace,

Coronation Service Sheet

Hassall Hall Coronation Garden Party

They had at their disposal the use of the landau all day with Alfred at the reins. Nellie and Polly with darling little Mary and bonnie baby John had a lovely time. First they were driven for a Coronation Thanksgiving Service at St Mary's Church Sandbach. It was a grand affair attended by many local dignitaries but both Polly and Nellie passed comment that the service for Hassall would have been preferable in Lodley Church, which stood well in a fine setting, but remained strangely and sadly unfinished by the eminent Lowndes Family, who had resided at Hassall Hall before the Yates Family.

However the service at St Mary's Sandbach was very rousing particularly the singing of the hymns:

All People that on Earth do Dwell.
All Hail the Power of Jesu's Name.
O God Our Help in Ages Past.
Now thank We All Our God.

The last hymn was preferred by Nellie, being her favourite and fondly remembered as her school hymn at Rode Heath School and she knew all the words by heart.

The Reverend J R Armistead who resided with high status at Sandbach's impressive vicarage, Tall Chimneys, delivered the sermon. He was a renowned man of the cloth and his words were sensible but heavily biased towards the men, which did not sit comfortably with Nellie. He gave a rallying call to his flock to be loyal and respect the new King. Nellie could not heed his call because she felt sorry for the new Queen Alexandra, formally affectionately known as Princess Alix, who had to publicly deal with the philandering of her unfaithful husband Edward. Probably because of the Queen's acute deafness she learned very little of the truth about his deceiving womanising ways, but wives do not need words to inform them of infidelity; instincts tell them clearly.

For the whole congregation it was a strange sensation to use the word 'King', when they sang the National Anthem, also it was strange to know that they were now in a new Edwardian era, rather than the familiar Victorian one. Changing national habits which had reigned along with Victoria since 1837 would be difficult.

Travelling back to Hassall Hall in the landau in Alfred's capable hands was very pleasant. Nellie looked radiant, her new big summer hat perfectly suiting her ensemble and with Polly's natural help the children behaved and enjoyed themselves. Eating, music, dancing and merriment within the walled garden at Hassall Hall was as warm with fellowship as the welcome crown of the Summer sunshine above.

At one point Polly sat with John firmly on her knee, while

Nellie danced with her darling Mary to the music of the Winterley Brass Band, who played sweetly and added so much to the unique occasion. Pretty little Mary stretched her chubby arms to hold her tall beautiful mother's hands and danced on tiptoe. Nellie felt happiness looking at her little treasure, showing her pretty layered petticoats, dancing with endless energy, chuckling amidst the lady dancers' full length flowing creations. Nellie tried to mimic the size of Mary during one dance and crouched to her knees for a few seconds to appreciate the swirling spectacle of the floating summer gowns from the height of her daughters eyes, causing a fit of giggling between them both.

The pleasant ambience of the day filtered into the evening on their return journey home to Higher Smallwood. Polly and Nellie enjoyed the rare pleasure of travelling home in the open landau, on the verge of twilight, after the roaring red sunset, passing under the huge leafy trees which had trapped pockets of warm air perfumed with wild honeysuckle. Such a special heatwave homeward journey is perfection and gently strokes a country person's soul.

When almost home the children had finally been over taken by slumber and, on arrival, both Nellie's and Polly's arms were beginning to ache from the children's weight. When the fine horse was commanded by Alfred to halt in the farm yard, and he had informed the stable boy to hold the horse firm, George appeared to carry sleeping Mary. He cradled her in his arms and removed her from the carriage. Likewise Alfred lifted bonnie John 'gone to the world' off Polly's knee and carefully followed George into the farmhouse.

Nellie and Polly followed, the men carrying the sleeping children, through the downstairs rooms and as they were all ascending the gracious staircase the heat of the day could be felt, even though Rose had left the windows open to capture a welcoming slight through draft in the upper rooms. Nellie and Polly were still girlishly enjoying themselves sniggering at the confidential knowledge that Polly, when out, kept a reserve of her coins secretly safe on her person and both found further silly amusement in whispering that they were going up the apples and pears.

After they had all entered the nursery and Alfred had attended to his unusual duty he discreetly left the room. The responsibility of motherhood was re-established in Nellie and her decisions flowed naturally. For the first time in their little lives she allowed Mary to be placed in her bed and John into his big cot without being washed, only their chubby hands and around their mouths were lightly sponged and neither of them were undressed. It was decided not to disturb them from their sleep after their 'big little day'. Nellie, Polly and George gently loosened the infants' clothes for their comfort and all three enjoyed the glow of seeing the two little precious ones, lying like angels fast asleep.

CHAPTER 13

A GRAVE VILLAGE ERROR

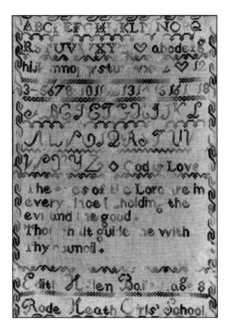

Nellie's School Sampler

It was beyond Nellie to understand why Rose had never courted and married although she was fair of face and trim figured. Nellie was contemporary in age to Rose and could well remember sewing samplers together in their school days at Rode Heath Girls' School and, because they had shared those times, she insisted that Rose could call her Nellie and not Mrs Walker like the rest of the staff. Rose's dedication to Higher Smallwood was appreciated by Nellie, George and Polly who afforded her immense respect, especially in providing Rose with her own bedroom albeit small. On a Sunday Rose could always be trusted to leave the dining table perfectly laid with a cold supper for the Walker family and would take it upon herself to usher, in a kindly manner, the staff of Higher Smallwood Farm to Evensong at All Saints.

It often weighed on Nellie's mind that Rose was too settled and dedicated to Higher Smallwood and on the dark afternoon of the 16th December, whilst sharing duties with Rose cleaning the drawing room for Yuletide, Nellie broached the subject.

'Have you ever considered marrying, Rose, and having your own family? You are very caring towards Mary and Johnny.'

Rose, knowing Nellie well and treasuring their loyalty to each other, did not mind her asking and replied with ease, 'You have made me welcome and secure with a roof over my head here. I am content thank you.'

'Well that's fine for us Walkers and our lives but what about your own life?'

Rose confirmed, 'I really am fine thank you.'

Nellie persisted in her usual gentle way, 'You know what I mean. Have you never considered courting someone?'

Rose knew she could be open and honest, knowing Nellie was not prying but asking out of kindness.

'No, I am content like Miss Polly with my status as a spinster. I have not met someone like you met Mr Walker, who must have turned your head and besides.' Rose stopped at that point, not wishing to burden her with the true reason.

Nellie instinctively detected another reason and eked away.

'Besides what? You have not been abused have you Rose?'

'Oh definitely not! No everyone is genuine here and my mother says that is something to be thankful for and I am.'

'Was your mother abused Rose?' Nellie boldly enquired.

Rose very calmly stopped her work and looked at Nellie.

'I always knew this conversation would one day arise and my mother has sworn me to secrecy but I trust you Nellie. In a way I want you to understand my reasons and perhaps it is time for you to know why I chose to be a spinster.

Nellie nodded in the affirmative and walked to the door and shut it soundly, which indicated to Rose that their conversation would be undisturbed and totally confidential. Rose proceeded with dignity but with nervous shallow breathing.

'My mother has been in Arclid Workhouse and is woefully ashamed that happened to her. She conceived in service immediately prior to moving to Rode Hall. She suffered terrible and after her baby was born the Dowager was very kind to her in her plight and found her a position as a wet nurse for the Shakerley's at Somerford Hall. She suckled one of their young. More kindly, when her milk left her, the Dowager, then the Lady at the Big House, allowed her back to Rode Hall as a laundry maid in service. That pleased her, she much preferred the Wilbrahams. She had an unease about the Shakerleys. Apparently much of their wealth and the building of their extravagant Hall was gained through the slave trade suffering.'

Nellie wanted to hug Rose for being brave but did not do so to allow her to keep her dignity.

'Was the baby a girl or a boy?'

'Oh I don't know that, mother does not speak of it, to blot it from her memory I suppose.'

'You have a good father. Eli is well respected as a wheelwright', Nellie comfortingly stated.

'Oh yes we are fine as a family and as you know I have six grand brothers. But as I am the only girl that is why my mother has guarded me against trusting a man. She said she needed to marry my father for security and a roof. He was getting on in years and wanted to sire. He wed my mother and rebuffed her village shame. However she never wanted more children but you have to, of course, when you are married. You have to lie with your man don't you?'

Rose detected instantly in Nellie's eyes what she had said and immediately put her hand over her mouth.

Nellie remained silent. Rose profusely apologised, 'I'm sorry Nellie. Please accept my apologies. I didn't mean all men. Mr Walker is obviously respectful of you, being there are no more children.'

Nellie didn't want to lie to loyal Rose and took to a seat rather deflated. 'Oh, Rose, you and the staff are not daft. I know in my heart you must have noticed he sometime sleeps in the spare room. To share our bed throughout a month, is a difficult issue in our marriage as I do not want to be with child again.'

As their darting eyes met, Rose began to doubt the trust she shared with Nellie and blurted out, 'Oh Nellie you don't think Mr Walker shares my bed do you? I keep my door well bolted. My mother has convinced me never to lie with a man.'

'No. No of course not', Nellie reassured her.

'Mr Walker does occasionally wander in the night. We do hear him but I assure you, he takes to no maid's bed. He is loyal to you.'

'Yes', Nellie said knowingly. 'Yes and I am loyal to him. I believe strongly in a woman's intuition and I trust you all.'

'Yes, that's right', Rose said with relief, adding quickly, 'Mother says you can always trust your man if you can trust the women around him.'

Rose paused for a while and, thinking she should take the opportunity to confess, gradually proceeded, 'But we older staff do remember that fateful night when you and Mr Walker were shouting and we heard your bedroom door bang very loudly. That was the first time he left your bed wasn't it?'

'Yes', Nellie humbly agreed before asking, 'What do the others think?'

Rose proceeded with utter honesty, 'We, who were here then, worried badly about the situation, we couldn't help it. It is terrible for maids when the lady of the house is not always obliging her husband. It puts everyone in a vulnerable situation. Sometimes some high up ladies prefer their husbands to use a maid instead of themselves. Most masters when they are spurned by their spouses expect a maid to accommodate them on a regular basis for gratification. A few maids have left employment on Boxing Day to try and escape from being carnally abused by a bad master only to move and find themselves in the same boat. Sometimes there is no other way but for maids to suffer constant rape, as their jobs are their roof. Where else do they go? And, if there is a wicked master and such forceful things are happening to a maid, much against her will, there is the constant fear of a babe. If one is conceived in a rape then the maid is doomed to the workhouse. That's how it happened for my mother.'

Nellie was racked with guilt. 'Oh, Rose, you don't think I put you all in danger because I do not give myself constantly to Mr Walker do you?'

'Yes you did', Rose said emphatically.

'Did?', Nellie enquired forlornly puzzled.

'Yes did', Rose continued kindly. 'We said our prayers for you both at that time and Mr Walker is very well respected as he troubles no one in that way. When he was a bachelor he was never troublesome to any maid. You were his first and only woman Nellie. Alfred said he would take to those ways again and keep himself to himself. Yes that's how Alfred assured us it would be.'

'Alfred!', Nellie snapped. 'Does he know?'

'Oh yes.'

Nellie's eyes grew anxiously larger as she asked, 'What about men in the Village, do they know?'

'No I don't think so, Alfred is highly protective of Mr. Walker. He is very proud of Mr Walker's shooting skill and status in the Village. I think the matter is solely kept private to Higher Smallwood and certainly only to a few staff. We keep it from anyone else that there is anything untowards, although it is noticed in Rode that you are not with child again.'

'Oh Rose you must think such ill of me', Nellie uttered despondently.

'That's just it', Rose said promptly. 'I think you are right, although I'm sure I would be in the minority if the Villagers knew.

I think the woman should decide how many children she has. I think she has the capability to be a good wife without always sharing a bed in the middle of the month to risk conceiving, even when married.'

Nellie was dumfounded and stared at Rose, hardly believing that a spinster, who is not troubled by a man, could have such an understanding point of view. Rose in her usual competent way comforted Nellie further by saying, 'There's a lot here important for everyone because we are a happy and loyal team. Mr Walker is an excellent farmer and very well respected at the Big House. You are exceptional at cheese making and are firm and fair to the staff and the Rector is fond of you in a proper way. Because of this we have all got a roof over our heads and good food in our stomachs. Over the other issue Mr Walker has shown immense strength of character and obviously has put everyone else's welfare first and made his own full self gratification a minor issue.'

Nellie was stunned by Rose's full, frank and honest assessment of everyone's life at Higher Smallwood. She regained her tongue and humbly said, 'It is a sorry situation but obviously understood by you and Alfred. I will do my utmost to continue to be part of the 'team' necessary for us all and I did promise George I would be true to my vows.'

'I know', said Rose boldly. 'That is what I overheard that night and I believe you will. That sentence has always given me the belief to continue here at Higher Smallwood. You're a good mother to your children and work hard. I think you have got things right.'

Rose, in an further endeavour to comfort Nellie continued, 'When the Rector takes me on one side and asks about your marriage I always say Mr Walker and you are true to your vows.' Nellie gave a hint of a wry smile at the loyalty of Rose and at the fact that the Rector takes it upon himself to keep a watchful eye on his parishioners' private lives. 'Yes that's what I tell them at church.' Rose reiterated.

Nellie's heart sunk further, although she had always felt

deep down she was discussed at All Saints. 'Am I talked about a lot, Rose?'

'No. No', Rose repeated. 'You are often admired in Rode for your hard work here but, of course, it is noticed that Mr Walker has only fathered two children even though you are from fertile Bailey stock.' Nellie felt emotionally flattened with the reality that her marriage situation was blaringly obvious to many.

She eventually took one of Rose's hands in both of hers and with pronounced sincerity stated, 'Rose you are loyal to us all, particularly to me, but we must not forget you. I want you to know that if you do find a man, which I dearly hope you do, a man you want to share your life with, you will have nothing but encouragement from me. Your life is more important than chores at Higher Smallwood Farm. Never say never.' Rose's warm smile broke naturally before saying, 'Don't worry about me. I really am content here.' With that both ladies continued with the titivation of the drawing room.

Around Michaelmas of the following year a new clerk joined the Land Agent at the office at Rode Hall. He was a tall thin polite man, not as young as his demeanour portrayed, probably around thirty years of age. He was well groomed and seemed suited with his lean strengthless hands for his duty as a clerk. The Rector was most pleased that he was a devout church going man and welcomed him at All Saints. During the early winter it was noticed by the folk of Rode and indeed the staff at Higher Smallwood that Rose had become a firm friend of the new clerk, whose name was Edwin. Rose also confidentially intimated to Nellie that, for the first time in her life, she felt she had met a man she could trust and could not conceal that she was falling in love with him and he with her. Nellie was delighted that Rose was enjoying happiness and was interested to see what the eventual outcome would be.

Another Candlemas passed and on the day of the Spring Equinox, when the rooks and crows were making sport in the strong vernal wind, the clatter of hoofs could be heard loudly, as a fast trotting horse came into the cobbled farm yard at Higher Smallwood. It was the hasty arrival of the Rector in his landau. It was only two o'clock, almost thirty minutes earlier than the Rector's normal time for a visit, however Nellie had changed into her afternoon gown and was ready for visitors in her drawing room.

She could hear the Rector puffing hurriedly down the hall way and a slight frown creased her forehead as she prepared herself for some important news. Rose knocked politely and announced the Rector in her normal way but strangely the Rector stopped just inside the drawing room and did not make his usual sweep across the room with his greeting to Nellie. Instead he stood cautiously until Rose shut the drawing room door on her exit and the Rector then checked that the door was firmly shut, which Nellie thought was odd.

Without pleasantries Nellie immediately enquired, 'Rector what is the matter?' At that point the Rector did make his way to Nellie, kissed her on the cheek and contrary to his usual custom took to a chair without waiting for Nellie to sit first. 'Nellie forgive me for my haste, I have been to see the Dowager this morning. Oh I have made a grave Village error, a very grave error.'

Nellie took to her usual perfectly straight sitting pose and said nothing as it was very evident that she was going to be informed about something important without enquiring.

'I have positively encouraged the situation of Rose and Edwin at church and that has been very wrong of me the Dowager has informed me.'

Nellie was relieved at that point that the important news was not as bad as had seemed and joined the conversation with confidence. 'I think you have encouraged an admirable choice for Rose. It is clear to see they have fallen in love. In fact Rose has intimated this to me and I have given my blessing. George is also pleased to hear of Rose's happiness.'

'No, Nellie, I tell you the whole relationship has got to be suppressed and discouraged. The Dowager has given me a strict talking to this morning and has firmly indicated that is how she wants me to resolve the matter.'

'She cannot do that. What is the matter?'

'I don't know the real reason but, Nellie, be assured there will be one and I must obey her instructions. I must!'

'I totally disagree', Nellie said with firmness. 'The Dowager has no right to interfere with Rose's happiness. I will not allow it.'

'Of course we must', the Rector exclaimed.

'We. We!' Nellie debated, raising her voice. 'Where or why do I come into the situation. Has the Dowager mentioned me?'

'No. Sshh', the Rector continued cautiously. 'I don't want anyone to over hear us, especially Rose.' After a quick glance to the shut door he continued in a brusque low tone, 'No of course not. The Dowager has not mentioned you by name but will be aware that I will mention her wishes to someone who will be influential in dissuading Rose from any notion of persisting in her love for Edwin.'

'Notion! It's no notion Rector', Nellie retorted. 'It is a genuine love between two good people and I certainly support it.'

'That's as maybe, Nellie, but I tell you the Dowager has spoken and we must heed her wishes.'

'You may have to, Rector, but I assure you I don't nor do I intend to.'

'Nellie do not set yourself above your station!'

'What station?'

'Of being a tenant farmer of course. Your roof depends upon the Wilbrahams.'

'How dare you, Rector! The Walkers have been here before the Civil War, well before the Wilbrahams purchased this estate from the Rhodes.'

'Yes but', the Rector treading delicately proceeded, 'you are still tenants to the Wilbrahams. You must follow their instructions, however indirect, and adhere to their wishes.'

'No I disagree. George is an excellent farmer and would be successful anywhere. He happens to be here on the Rode

Estate but make no mistake, Rector, if the Wilbrahams became disagreeable we are not beholden to them, we Walkers would simply move. There are many Estates wanting good competent farmers, especially in the aftermath of the rinderpest', Nellie said with confidence.

The Rector, as usual, felt completely wrong footed by Nellie and proceeded slowly and quietly, 'Oh don't go to extremes. Everyone knows how good George is, but this conversation we are sharing is totally confidential and I know you will not even tell him. All I am asking is that you discourage Rose from any thoughts of marriage with Edwin and hopefully their love will die. Love does die if it is not fuelled. I will discourage it when I see them at All Saints and follow the Dowager's wishes.'

'You can. Do as you please at your church, but I am not kowtowing to the Dowager's wishes. I am certainly not, I refuse to! And I am surprised at you falling into line to ruin Roses's happiness when you don't even know the reason.'

The Rector replied exasperated, 'But that is exactly what I am saying! Because I was summoned by the Dowager this morning and told to take this course of action, there will be a reason and a very good reason, as the Dowager does not interfere lightly. I assure you she has amazing integrity.'

'Oh you are as bad as Polly. She has intense loyalty to the Dowager but times are changing Rector, ordinary village people don't have to dance to the tune of the higher ups. We have our own thoughts and wishes.'

'Nellie, what you say is very credible but I do need your assistance with this predicament.'

'No, Rector, I have helped you on many occasions but this time I am staying out of the situation and allowing it to run it's course, hopefully in the end with a happy marriage between two good folks of Rode.'

They both fell silent, Nellie looked through the window watching the birds being blown off course by the strong wind and the Rector gazed blankly into the flames of the fire. Nellie felt she had been hard on the Rector but just. However, without looking at him, she could sense he was at a loss how to proceed and she would have to search her mind for a solution. She stood and walked to the other window and continued looking into the bright sky, knowing the Rector was half right about something, but what? The Rector remained seated, allowing her to continue her contemplation in silence, hoping she would forgive him his manners in not standing, for he knew in his heart that she was thinking deeply. After quite some minutes in silence Nellie turned quickly, her skirts causing the only noise in the room as she returned briskly to her seat. The Rector thought how piercing her beautiful blue eyes looked and from them he could tell that her thoughts were clearing. Not wishing to interrupt her train of thought he still remained silent.

After her deep deliberation, Nellie, proceeded calmly, 'Perhaps Polly can throw more light on this situation before either of us decide on a course of action. She may know the full details and, if we knew, we could both then make an informed decision.'

'Oh I'm not too sure, Nellie', the Rector stumbled. 'Sometimes it does not do to know everything but just to follow instructions.'

'That's not my way, I assure you. How can anyone understand any situation without knowing all the facts? That's the only way I can properly conduct my life when I know the full truth', she replied firmly.

'That's highly commendable, and please don't think me weak but I am always fully aware of the Wilbraham's power. They pay my stipend. Not only that, sometimes, especially when I am conducting conversations with ladies, I feel as a male, I should not pry too deeply and I simply leave matters where conversations end.'

'Well I don't think that will help us over this situation. Shall I ask for Polly to join us?'

'Do you really think that is wise? Polly is a confidant to the Dowager and would be put in a difficult position perhaps.'

'Excuse me, Rector, I think the difficult position here is the danger of Rose losing her love!'

Their conflicting views held them silent again. Nellie became exasperated and declared, 'We're neither fishing nor mending nets! I am going to ring for Rose to fetch Polly.' With no more glancing at the Rector and to save any further deliberation, Nellie stood and pulled the cord for the bell. Rose politely knocked and opened the drawing room door which made the Rector uneasy. Nellie with total calm enquired of Rose if Miss Polly could be interrupted and asked to join her and the Rector in the drawing room. The Rector was anxious at involving Polly but was helpless to say anything as he did need Nellie's help and also, as he was in Higher Smallwood drawing room and not his own Rectory study, he felt he had to go along with Nellie's idea, although he was at a loss as to how the conversation would unfold.

Polly came into the drawing room and shut the door and as she took a seat she did appear to Nellie to be in a moderately sombre mood for she did not greet the Rector in her usual cheery manner. All three sat in silence and the Rector was aching for Nellie to commence the conversation and thankfully she did.

'Do I detect, Polly, that you know why the Rector is here?'

Polly turned her head completely towards Nellie and pleaded intensely with her eyes that she did not wish to speak in front of the Rector.

'Please say Polly', Nellie continued. 'The Rector has a difficult village dilemma in the fact that he has received instructions from the Dowager to put an end to Rose and Edwins' love.'

The Rector was inwardly shaken at Nellie's forthright manner in which she had plunged into the conversation. However, he was glad that the conversation had started and indeed that the very essence of the position was out in the open and felt he should continue the conversation.

'Well, Nellie, is almost right Polly', he said slightly dithering, attempting to gain control and added, 'I have been given those instructions by the Dowager but I have no dilemma I am going to follow the Dowager's instructions implicitly, particularly when I see Rose or Edwin at church.'

Polly appreciated both Nellie's and the Rector's honesty but knew in her heart Nellie was not of the personality to follow any instructions without a reason and it was time for her to add to the conversation.

'The Rector is right. He is in a difficult position and, to ensure that the Dowager's wishes are fully adhered to, he has had to tell someone in order to achieve this, although I assure you the Dowager will not know you are the one, as she can only trust those who have gained her confidence. I know she trusts few and I also know that the Rector and myself are two of those few she does trust.'

'Oh well that's fine for you two isn't it!', Nellie exclaimed in an unusually impolite way. 'You two know the reason but, seeing that I am too young or untrustworthy for the Dowager, I have got to fall in line with her wishes.'

'Nellie, I know you will think it wrong but I assure you the Rector does not know the true reason either', Polly said in his defence.

'Nor do I wish to know the true reason, Polly', the Rector quickly interjected.

Nellie immediately took control of herself and sat still, upright and silent.

Polly proceeded firmly, 'It does not always do for a terrible village secret to be told to many because of the hurt it can cause but, Nellie, I was told by the Dowager last Friday of her heavy heart over Rose's evident growing love for Edwin and it has troubled me since. I have gone over and over it in my mind and I have decided that if the Rector requested any help from you that I would be honest enough to tell you. And, also I know and love you for the reason that you rarely act without fully understanding all the facts.'

Nellie's eyes grew large with concern but still she kept silent.

'Shall I leave?' the Rector enquired as he sprung to his feet.

Polly looked at Nellie. Nellie could see in her eyes that it was going to be an extremely difficult and confidential conversation. There was a pause as the Rector stood hesitantly. Nellie had the power to give him his instructions.

'Very well', Nellie said with clarity. 'You may go if you wish.'

The Rector relieved that Nellie was providing him with a way out of the situation repeated gratefully, 'I will let myself out ladies, I will let myself out.' Good day', he uttered in politeness as he shut the door behind him.

Nellie was unperturbed by his shambles of a farewell and remained seated keeping her eyes on Polly.

'You have decided wisely', Polly said, her tone returning to the closeness that Nellie treasured.

'Has Rose been abused?', Nellie enquired caringly.

'No not Rose but her mother has, many years ago, and she has been in Arclid Workhouse.'

'But I know that', Nellie confessed.

'Oh well that makes things easier. How much do you know? What has Rose told you?'

'It was in confidence but I do know that the Dowager found her mother employment at the Hall after she had been a wet nurse for the Shakerleys. As far as I am aware Rode knows very little of that and it is certainly no reason now in this new century for Rose not to marry Edwin because of her mother's shame.'

Polly took the conversation with purpose, 'I wish it were that simple and the Dowager does regret deeply ever trying to help those thirty years ago. At that time the Dowager knew of a land agent, whose wife was barren, who worked on the Tabley estate for the Leycesters. Seeing that the Shakerley's were taking on Rose's mother it seemed a good idea at the time to spare the child from an orphanage and so the babe was intercepted at Arclid Workhouse and was allowed go to the agent and his wife. They did very well by this child as obviously he was the only one and they educated him, not above his station, but well enough for him to become a clerk. That child, by a twist of fate and, bearing in mind that this knowledge has always been hidden, even to Rose's mother, has obtained the job of the land agent's clerk here in Rode.'

The colour drained from Nellie's face and she hurriedly concluded, 'It's Edwin isn't it?'

'I'm afraid so. It has been praying on the Dowager's mind ever since he came to Rode Hall and, although she has intimated strongly that he should be moved on, this has not happened and in the interim Rose has fallen in love with him. In short, she doesn't know, but she is in love with her half brother.'

Nellie held her hands over her face and slowly pulled them towards her neck as she felt tears welling up in her eyes.

'Nellie, I can see there is no other way but for you to tell Rose of this lamentable predicament.'

Nellie was profoundly sad and sat in silence.

Polly rose from her seat and knelt lovingly in front of Nellie holding her waist.

Nellie's eyes were despondent and full of tears.

'Nellie, it is right it should come from you, especially as Rose confided in you and you half know the story.'

'Oh, Polly, I am not sure that I will have the strength to do it', Nellie said softly.

'You will', Polly said reassuringly, 'and I also know with your strength of character and knowledge of the true reason, you will be the first to protect Rose against the consequences of such a prejudicial love.'

After an emotional silence and as Nellie was gently wiping away her tears with her snow white handkerchief, she sadly expressed, 'It will be hard Polly, so hard, as she does love Edwin.'

'I know but I also know you always try to do what's right and you will take that course now. You have done right already, it is certainly best for Rose that the Rector does not know the complete story.'

'Yes' affirmed Nellie. 'At least in the future, when the Rector glances at Rose he will do so, half in innocence. Rose will still have some dignity in that the Rector does not know the full details.'

Polly nodded in agreement and added, 'I also feel for Rose's continued happiness here it is best that she does not know that I am aware of her circumstances. I still want to look at her with the respect she deserves and for her to detect nothing between us.'

Yes, of course', Nellie agreed sensitively. 'Yes we must salvage what dignity we can for Rose but I feel even with all our care she will take the news very hard. It will hurt her beyond any hurt you or I have had to suffer.'

'Yes, but the deed must be done, Nellie, perhaps even as soon as tonight.'

Still sitting Nellie hugged Polly tightly in an endeavour to glean some strength from her as she knelt before her. They then rose, linking arms as they made their way sedately out of the drawing room, both consumed with their burden of the care of Rose's feelings.

After tea Nellie drew a deep breath as Rose was clearing the table and asked if she could visit her privately in her bedroom at 9 o'clock. Rose was quite taken aback at such a strange request and without hesitation said that would be perfectly fine to do so.

As the grandfather clock was striking nine Nellie took herself up the backstairs holding her brass candle holder with lighted candle and politely knocked on Rose's door.

'Come in', Rose summoned in a welcoming way.

Nellie opened the door and shut it behind her.

'May I take a seat?', Nellie enquired as she leaned to place her lit candle and holder safely on the side table, where it added extra light to the gloomily lit small room. 'Yes of course you may', replied Rose, indicating to Nellie to sit on the only chair, quite intrigued that she should wish to spend some time in her modest room.

Rose sat on the tidy bed opposite and as she looked at Nellie she felt a sense of foreboding and fell silent.

Bravely Nellie said, 'I have come to you with a heavy heart,

Rose, a very heavy heart.' Rose searched her brain for the purpose of the unusual visit. Surely Nellie was not leaving Higher Smallwood. Although she was not entirely a subservient wife to George, due to their occasional bedroom difficulties, Rose felt that they shared a good marriage and was convinced each were fulfilling their vows. And besides, Mary and John appeared to share an equal love of their mother and father. To leave would be folly was Rose's instant reaction in her mind. 'Is it about you Nellie?', she ventured to ask.

'No, unfortunately not, Rose, it is about your good self.'

Rose sat upright on her bed listening intently.

'You know you confided in me quite some while ago about your mother's time in the Workhouse.'

'You have not told anyone?', Rose demanded.

'No, no, of course, not', Nellie assured her.

'No, but I have grave news about a strange series of events that are a most vital piece of the jigsaw of your life.'

Rose was mystified.

Nellie leaned forward and held one of her hands. 'This is hard for me, Rose, believe me very hard, and I dearly wish I was not the one who is going to turn your world upside down but sometimes we have to do what is right and we do have to learn of what can hurt us deeply.' Nellie breathed heavily, so heavily that the flame on the candle flickered. She summoned courage and continued, 'Do you remember you told me you did not know whether your mother had a boy or a girl in the Workhouse? Well I now know the child was a boy some thirty years ago.'

'Oh well', said Rose quite blandly. I have six brothers, so at least I can stop my yearning for the love of a sister. I had a mind that it was a girl.'

'No Rose the child was a boy and instead of being reared in an orphanage he was fortunate to be passed to a childless couple who reared him with love and provided him with a good education. By a shocking twist of fate that boy, now obviously a man, has come to Rode and been part of our village life.'

Rose began to think clearly and asked, 'Where is that man, my half brother, now? Is he working on a farm or with his education has he a better job?' Her eyes were searching Nellie's eyes and Nellie found it agonisingly difficult to proceed. 'Oh, Rose, I am going to say something that will change your life forever.'

Rose removed her hand from Nellie's and began to recoil on the bed, pulling a cushion to her chest. 'What, Nellie? What!'

'Rose, that man is Edwin.' Rose bowed her head, her hands went an intense white as she pulled them helplessly tight on the cushion, before she rolled her face into the cushion and sobbed.

Nellie dropped to her knees and held Rose in an endeavour to comfort her, although she knew it was in vain as there was nothing that could take away her pain. Rose cried for about three minutes and then peeled herself away from Nellie trying to regain some sort of dignity.

'I'm sorry, Nellie, I'm so sorry.'

'Shh', Nellie implored.

'How do you know that is true. Who has told you?', Rose enquired trying to dry her eyes on her handkerchief. 'Was it the Rector?'

'No, as far as I know, the information is confined to the Dowager. She has alerted the Rector to the danger of your continued love for Edwin but not given him the reason. Really that is very kind of the Dowager.'

'But you do not know the Dowager why should she tell you?', Rose intelligently asked.

Nellie remembered her confidence to Polly. She drew a deep nervous breath before explaining, 'Rose it was deemed proper for me to know the true reason, because I would not fall in with the wish of the Rector's demand, without being sure that the reason was justified. I would have given anything not to know the situation or not to be the bearer of this excruciating news. Can it suffice that I do know? Leaving matters in that way, will not implicate anyone else and will lead to this issue being contained in the confidential way it has always been kept in Rode.'

Rose could see the wisdom of her explanation and nodded in the affirmative with an uncontrolled snivel before asking, 'Does my mother know?'

'No, you are the only one.'

Rose proceeded with bravery, 'I think it best she doesn't. She is elderly, and her shame has faded, especially with her marriage and with us as her family. Us. What have I said?' Rose cast her eyes about in uncontrolled bewilderment before asking, 'Do you think Edwin should know?'

'That is very hard for me to say, Rose. It does seem that he has been well loved by his perceived parents.'

'Yes, you are right, he does speak well of them. How much hurt do we want to cause him in this dreadful plight?'

Nellie winced and blinked slowly, almost in awe of Rose's bravery.

'What will you tell him?', Nellie enquired in almost a whisper.

'I think, I will tell him I have ceased to love him. At least he will be spared all this turmoil. Yes, I think that is what I will do.'

A silence fell as, Nellie, was allowing, Rose, to digest the news and she could see that her mind was racing. Rose bravely proceeded, 'At least I know the babe was a boy and he has been reared well and safely. In fact he has done very well for himself. I have a new half brother and, although he won't know that, I can turn my love into pride for him. I hope we can remain friends. Yes, and perhaps if we do, Nellie, when my mother is dead, I could tell him the true reason and he will look after me in my old age. It will be no trouble for me to remain a spinster and there are several other brothers and sisters living together, in old age to get by, aren't there, Nellie?'

By this time, Nellie, had taken to the chair again and Rose was still on her bed. 'It will be no trouble for me to remain a spinster, you know that, don't you?', Rose repeated in her shock.

'Yes, I do, and I want you to know you will always have a roof here at Higher Smallwood Farm until you wish to retire.'

Nellie reluctantly stood, feeling she should leave whilst Rose still maintained her dignity but lingered and said, 'I'm sorry I had to be the one to tell you, Rose, but as you know, I can never lie to you. I could not have honestly allowed you to continue your courtship with the knowledge of Edwin being your half brother.'

No, of course, not', Rose replied but her voice began to break. Poor Rose could not compose herself any longer and crumbled and lay face down on her bed, sobbing in her pillow.

Nellie gently covered her with her shawl, aware that further words were futile and that only sleep would temporarily take Rose out of her pain. Nellie, gently blew Rose's candle out, knowing her day was totally over. Carrying her own flickering candle in it's holder, she left the cosy bedroom and she walked slowly down the back stairs to George in the drawing room.

Later Nellie could not help thinking how strange life was. George and herself had used their freedom to marry, but shared a good marriage without true love. Rose loved Edwin dearly but, after being informed of the terrible blow of fate, she had no chance of marrying him. Nellie said her prayers that night and thanked the good Lord for giving her the strength to deal with the lamentable day, and gave thanks for the companionship of George, her dear children and for the roof over the entire household at Higher Smallwood Farm.

CHAPTER 14

TO GROW OLD GRACEFULLY

Rode was experiencing a frosty time. Stubborn mounds of receding snow were dotted in the pastures like small icebergs in a pale green sea of poor winter grass. Occasional blobs of old drifted smooth snow could be seen protruding through the stows of the hedgerows, although thankfully the roads were dry and clear.

The fast trotting of the horse in the harness was beating perfect time with George and Mary chanting in a jocund way;

'There's Old Moreton Hall, Ramsdell Hall and
Hall of Alcumlow,
Bowdon Hall, Chance Hall and Rode Hall,
But you should know,
That Bog Hall and Spider Hall are above 'Em all!'

Mary and George finished in unison both laughing. She was quite surprised her father knew the school yard skipping song. After they had gathered their breath and as they were travelling past Ramsdell Hall on their way home, Mary asked in rather a scathing manner, 'Have you seen mother's new hat?'

'Yes I have actually', George replied in an precise tone.

'I don't like it. It is far too big', she stated assertively.

'Your mother suits a big hat', he replied in loyal defence.

'I know she does but this one is like a huge highway man's hat. I don't like it at all, especially as it is in that loud red trimmed with purple.'

'Is there anything wrong in that? She is always up to the minute with her fashion.' 'I feel she has gone too far this time. I like the lovely flowered hats. I think they will be in favour especially for such a society wedding as the Aston Hall occasion.

'Your mother thinks differently for a very good reason. As you know, the wedding is in March and the winds can be askey, her scarlet ensemble will be very smart and warm.'

Mary with ribbons

George smiled, glancing at Mary coping with the cold on the morning of the 5th of February 1910, as she sat beside him. He noticed her sweet pug nose was slightly pink and her long wavy auburn hair was blowing erratically below her bonnet, which prompted him to say, 'The day is fast approaching, Mary, when you will be putting your hair up in combs like your mother and you will be enjoying fine gowns and changing your bonnets for hats.'

'Oh I don't think I will ever be quite like mother', she answered in a positive way and added, 'I have a feeling I will be rather more reserved in my dress sense.'

'Not too much I hope', he said warmly. 'I look forward to you being a lady and I certainly look forward to taking you down the aisle on your wedding day.'

With a smile Mary screwed her little nose in friendly disagreement.

Changing the subject George tried to say in a reprimanding tone, 'Oh talking about you being a lady, a little bird has told me of how fast you are skating on Rode Pool.' Mary cleverly rebuffing him replied, 'Yes, I do thank you for my new skates. I am enjoying my skating, I like to beat some of the lads.'

'Seriously you must take care, Uncle Alec says you give the lads a good race but that is really no way for a young lady to act or for your safety.'

Mary remained silent to imply to her father that she had heard him but was not listening as inwardly she had no intention of curbing her speed. George could detect he was not having success as to the curtailing of Mary's evident enjoyment of fast skating and returned to the subject of clothes.

'It pleases me when your mother buys new clothes and hats. She works very hard and deserves to look nice. You will have more gowns soon when you have stopped growing.'

'I don't think I will be as tall as mother and certainly not as good looking.'

George shook his head with a smile and said proudly,

'We will see.'

Mary always treasured the time when it was just the two of them together and turned the conversation to matters she liked to hear him talk about, gladly enquiring, 'What were you saying earlier about the February light?'

'Ah yes even when the Sun isn't shining you can detect the skies are brighter and the dearth of the Winter is passing. Can you perceive it today?'

Mary cast her eyes heavenwards and tried to understand his wise words.'

'Yes I think I can see what you mean.'

'Oh you most definitely can today. You will learn, as your years roll on, to know exactly which month you are in without a calendar, by receiving the messages the Sun is always sending to you even from behind the clouds.'

Mary, smiling in her desire to learn, implored, 'Tell me again father your little poem about the Sun for me to remember.'

'It isn't really a poem, more a recollection of the sayings the old country folk often recited to help people learn before books, an extension perhaps of the old weather sayings.'

George turned his horse and trap left by Pump House Farm into the long drive of Higher Smallwood. He sensed he was sharing precious time with his dear daughter and slowed the horse down to a walk, and, as Mary had requested, he commenced his familiar words about the quantity and quality of the Sun:

'The Sun is weak in the New Year,
  And rarely cheers cold Janiveer
February Sun changes the sky's light,
Although the rain may be filling the dyke.
Poor March Sun does not know which way to turn,
It hints of Spring but Winter days are often lingering to return.
April Sun Flora and Fauna gently fans.
Phoebe in May our faces tans.
The perfect Sun is ours in June,

Shining for our longest day but alas over too soon.
If the Sun is high in July we fry.
The heat of the dog days hang heavy in the August Sun hazy.
After the mists in September the Sun is welcome but lazy.
The Sun gives us the precision of the two Equinox sight,
When once in Spring and once in Autumn we see equal
day and night.
Waning October Sun can give us an Indian Summer
over the babbling brook,
Known to the old country folk as the 'Little Summer of St Luke'.
In the dark month of November the Sun is hard to spy,
The lovers' or hunters' Moon is more beautiful in the sky.
December's Solstice Sun, for centuries revered for souls
by pagan man,
Gives by the tilt of Earth's axis our shortest day since time began.
And the Sunshine on Christmas Day through the orchard tree,
Foretells of a plentiful fruit harvest for the next year to be.'

Mary had not missed one of his words and did not make a sound, wanting to hold her remarkable feeling of sharing a perfect pocket of time with her father.

George broke the silence, saying with a loving smile, 'You will be a very knowledgeable young lady if you can remember, and more importantly understand, all that. You do know the word 'Phoebe' is the very old country word for the Sun. The men working in the fields often refer to Phoebe.'

'Yes I remembered that from last time.' Mary pedantically answered and added precisely, 'I understand everything you have said and I intend to take with me through life, not only your words about the Sun, but also all the other snippets of country knowledge you share with me.'

George slipped his arm around her shoulder giving her a most affectionate squeeze which Mary reciprocated by holding him tightly with both of her arms about his waist. It was a magical moment for them both. One of those precious interludes when love and contentment makes you feel you are the only ones in the world; something money cannot buy, simply the seamless tie of the Gentle Ribbon.

The following month, in the middle of March 1910, Alfred was sitting smartly at the reins of the shining landau with the hood firmly up. Polly, Nellie and George stepped through the door of the farmhouse, all immaculately dressed for the Aston Hall wedding. Although his master was attending the society wedding in a landau and not a coach, Alfred was determined that it would be the best turnout. His procuring of condition and grooming of the horse, cleaning of the tack and pristine presentation of the carriage was astounding. His attention to detail a credit to his craft of groom. George's first duty was to wink at Alfred to acknowledge that his task had been completed to the highest degree and was much appreciated. Words were superfluous. Alfred's return wink of acceptance to George was their silent language to one another indicating the mutual satisfaction of both master and servant.

Thankfully it was a dry day but the sky was a grey solemn dome, affording no breaks in the thick cloud. There was a north westerly unkind wind that took itself from the cold Irish Sea, blasted over the Bickerton Hills and blew straight across the Cheshire Plain; a bitter, unwelcome askey wind, referred to locally as coming through the 'Gap'.

None of them were in a particularly cheery or chatty mood. The ladies had decided not to wear their hats until arriving at Aston Church. The journey was going to take at least two hours so George dutifully tucked woollen travelling blankets around the knees of Nellie and Polly to make them snug. All three were of the opinion their enjoyment would have been better in attending a lovely Summer wedding at Aston Hall. They knew they were in for a long cold day.

George kept his usual quiet self as he gladly allowed Polly and Nellie to occupy the travelling conversation. Nellie was endeavouring to lift herself out of an irritable mood created by

Mary who had informed her that she definitely disliked her hat, literally minutes before leaving, reinforcing her rudeness by saying it reminded her of a highway man's hat. Polly tried to form a defence for Mary and said her forthright words were due to her age. She was detecting a larger number of the adolescents were becoming very outspoken and impertinent although adding it was a modern luxury. She also stated she would not have dared to criticise either of her parents at any age, with which Nellie promptly agreed quite sternly.

Although not wishing to join in the conversion, George did have his mind stimulated by the ladies' words. He was fully adjusted to Mary's youthful ways and admired her spirit. He earnestly believed Mary had a firm grip on life. She could see her mother wanted to be liked by everyone and was deeply hurt if someone thought ill of her. George knew the reality of life and had taught Mary, in their private moments, to acknowledge that you cannot possibly be liked by everyone, but the trick of life was to accept *faits accomplis* and to live for those who do like you. He was sure Mary already had woven that important sentiment into her personality. Life often takes difficult paths or long tunnels of darkness and George liked Mary's discerning strong nature, which would equip her well to deal with hard times, should, God forbid, any befall her. Even at her tender age George could detect in Mary that she was her own person and felt she had the strength of character to keep going in life and to adjust if need be, despite the hardships.

On a good wide stretch of road Alfred changed the pace of his treasured horse into a canter to allow different muscle action in the majestic animal's stride for it's comfort. Sitting in the landau, jigging along at the strong pace, George's thoughts drifted even deeper as he was thinking about Mary's strong will and he recalled an incident from his own childhood. He vividly remembered an occasion when he was being beaten by his father, in the farmyard of Higher Smallwood, for misbehaving when his grandfather came walking by. Although he was a strict disciplinarian he bid

George's father to ease his hand on George saying 'dunner knock too much out of the lad he mit need it in life.' Because of this profound example he decided he was not going to support the recriminations of either Nellie or Polly as to Mary's definition of the hat. He thought Mary's bold spirit needed to be nurtured so that other worthy traits might unfold into sound facets of her personality.

Much to Nellie's and Polly's relief the wind was much calmer in Staffordshire and the wedding was a classic occasion of fashion, best manners and farmers' fellowship. The lady guests preened particularly with their hats and all the gentlemen were wearing their frockcoats, tall shiners, white gloves and spats. George and Pollys' cousin Clarinda looked beautiful as a bride and was extremely elegant. Her wedding gown was a high collared dream of a creation, cascading in fine tiers of exquisite lace, the height of Edwardian fashion purchased from London Town. Her bouquet was exceptional for the time of year and it was whispered that the delicate perfumed blooms were from the hot house of Shrugborough Hall. No expense had been spared.

The Aston Hall family extended their warm and genuine greetings to all of their guests. Everyone felt welcome. The photographer had been specially commissioned from Stafford and his precision for the group photograph at Aston Hall was almost tedious. Nellie appreciated that herself and George were on the outer parameter of the guests and did not mind standing on one of the forms at the rear. However, George was unhelpful and almost detached in effort towards Nellie's final position. He appeared oblivious to his attitude and Nellie stupidly compounded the situation as she was in no mood to request his help. Thankfully another gentleman was most gracious in assisting her to stand on the form, albeit precariously.

The Stafford Wedding
Nellie and George 5th and 6th from right on rear row
Polly standing 2nd row 2nd lady from left

Polly, of more importance in the pecking order, was standing on the ground in the second row next to the wife of the Rural Dean. She was wearing a floral high crowned hat, with the neatest of brims, tastefully finished with a tuft of pale pink netting at one side. The older ladies sitting on the front row had dressed appropriately for the chill weather. One cousin of the bride, also on the front row, although wearing a fine muslin dress, looked very fetching in a fox fur stole and fox fur muff of the latest fashion, to keep her appropriately warm. The ladies hats were outstanding, the majority being in the style of very high crowned floral masterpieces on pronounced elegant brims.

George's debonair bachelor cousin Edgar had been requested to take his position with an all male section at the rear on the left hand side but because of balancing numbers, the photographer had requested that one male volunteer join the right hand side. Edgar immediately volunteered and stood between a lady guest and George. He leaned at one point behind George and tugged at Nellie's sleeve and teasingly informed her that she had been banished to the rear row because of the size of her hat. She wanted to tick him off but decided not to as he made her smile, more than George in his disinterested mood had done that day. Unfortunately as usual, Edgar took matters one step too far and managed somehow to pat Nellie on her bottom unbeknown to anyone else. When she curtly looked sideways at him, he stared firmly to the front, trying to portray his innocence but she instinctively knew it was him. Just when she had decided to reprimand him the photographer blew his whistle and all the guests immediately paid attention for the group photograph.

In the mid Summer Polly paid her usual Summer visit to her Sister Esme at Stone and always returned to Higher Smallwood much refreshed and eager to relay details of her time spent at The Lodge. On this occasion she returned with something more than memories. The Aston Hall Family had sent the Walker copy of the wedding group photograph to The Lodge for Polly's retention.

In the evening of the day of Polly's return, as expected, George paid a passing glance at Polly's trophy, the photograph, before leaving the farmhouse to train his spaniels. Nellie had the opportunity to take the photograph into the drawing room to study it alone. As she walked across the room there was a beautiful sun set and the Sun's low rays caught the delicate pink lustres on the top of the bureau. Nellie paused for a moment to enjoy the vivid baby rainbows cast on the drawing room walls made by the horizontal sunbeams through the crystal prisms.

She took out the lopers, put down the lid of her bureau, placed the photograph on the lid, drew up a chair, took her large magnifying glass from a compartment of her bureau and proceeded to study the group portrait. She disliked what she saw. George did look old and isolated in his own cocoon, almost suggesting he had no desire to be attending. Nellie's agitation rose and she reflected that he could at least have made an effort to look happy. Most of the Cheshire and Staffordshire farming fraternity would have given their high teeth to have received an invitation to the Aston Hall wedding and there was George, captured on camera, as a guest with a disinterested countenance.

She moved the magnifying glass over the photograph until she could see herself and George very clearly and plunged into deep thoughts. She did not mind being on the back row but she did not like what she saw. Her persona and whole body language towards George was most rude. It looked as though she had purposely shrugged her shoulder as she stood by his side. Was this the attitude she was portraying to the world? She had always tried to hide from relations and friends their lack of true love but in this photograph she was clearly showing a lack of respect towards her husband. She sat back in her chair, all at sea in her thoughts. How could she unknowingly act irresponsibly? Embarrassment consumed her as she imagined in her mind's eye other guests looking at the photograph and interpreting it as showing her and George as having a marriage without love or respect. How foolish she had been to allow her unintended actions to be caught on camera. She could not right the situation. She swiftly gave herself an indignant defensive thought that she cared for George and always fostered respect for him, which was loud in her head as if speaking to herself.

She felt further deflated when she studied her clothes. Mary was right, the hat did resemble a highway man's. It was tasteless and Nellie wished she had not purchased it in the first place. She was perturbed about her self criticism and on further inspection under the magnifying glass the penny dropped that she was also beginning to show her age. She was thirty four years old, yet felt only twenty four years in her mind but at that moment she reluctantly had to accept that even pretty girls and attractive women cannot stem the tide of time.

Studying the photograph, brought home to roost for Nellie, the very gloomy realisation of, an unnatural age gap between her and George as man and wife, her silly hat and the first signs of age in her face. The three torments were pulsing her brain when eventually, in a corner of her mind, she remembered what granny Bailey used to say. She criticised women not dressing to their age as being 'mutton dressed as lamb'. Nellie took another look at her hat and fully decided that was the error. It would have been more suitable for someone younger. She made a mental note to grow old gracefully and dress accordingly.

Another look through the magnifying glass drew her to the scrutinisation of Edgar. How happy and carefree he looked, no worries of married life for him. She remembered, immediately prior to the photograph, his ungentlemanly conduct which had annoyed her at the time. Perhaps that was the reason for the irritation showing in her face but of course not a soul knew of that particular episode. It was the first photograph she disliked of herself. Normally she was very photogenic and she always lived comfortably with the art of the camera.

Polly disturbed Nellie in the drawing room in a kindly way with a supper drink and Nellie took to a more comfortable chair to share time with her. 'Do you like the group photograph Nellie? I think it is very good.'

Nellie immediately put her deep thoughts aside and uncharacteristically replied insincerely, 'Yes. It is very good.'

Feeling immediate guilt, she thought she would take the sentiments of the photograph off on a genuine tangent, by qualifying her words in a gracious manner. 'Unfortunately it portrays that Mary was right as to my hat; not a good choice by me. However, the photograph captures the bliss of the bride in her beautiful gown and the attention to detail her family had generously made towards the memorable occasion. It also shows the great effort the guests had taken regarding their outfits, the ultimate compliment to the bride.'

She could see Polly wanted to talk about the wedding but selfishly Nellie did not and she asked quite out of the blue, 'Tell me about your parents Polly. Did you have a good father and mother?'

Polly took a second or two to digest the unexpected question.

'Yes I suppose they were good parents. Unfortunately father was a natural worrier and therefore curtailed his own happiness. Silly, really, as he was a very competent and well respected in the Rode. He sat as a Village Constable at the Court Leet before Sir Robert Peel formed the National Constabulary.'

After another slight pause Polly continued with a confiding ease, 'And mother? Well mother kept herself to herself. Had no desire to give herself in friendship, although she was dutiful to Astbury church, even though appearing not to glean much fellowship. Strangely she did enjoy Sir Gilbert Scott's contribution in the building and furnishing of All Saints. He designed the Boys School at Sandbach and Lord Crewe's church at Crewe Green.'

Thinking Polly was going off the subject Nellie questioned further, 'Were you close to your parents?'

'Not really. I could never confide in them. Perhaps that is why I treasure our close friendship and my companionship with the Dowager. In fact mother was quite bland in her affection to any of us as her children. I cannot remember any hugs or words of encouragement. I suppose she was good in her own way, we were never neglected and she was always around. She kept this house well and worked hard and was of an even temperament. She recognised she was privileged to live here with father and was satisfied with her lot.

'Were they close as a couple?' Nellie openly asked.

'I've never given that much thought. There were very few disagreements between them, so I suppose something kept them harmonious. I cannot recall any outward sign of affection but they did produce five children. Although he was financially sound he rarely gave mother a gift, but then again, she never wanted for anything. You could say they pulled together within a marriage whereby they had formed their own boundaries of compatibility rather than within a circle of affection.'

'Did they show any irritation towards one another?'

'Not as I noticed. I suppose it is natural for any couple passing through decades together to experience some form of agitation but it is curbed to the outside world by the bonds of love or respect. Perhaps I could say mother and father shared a good marriage based on mutual respect.'

After a small pause Polly, with a little mischievous smile, could not resist adding, 'You ought to hear Esme's interpretation of a man. I think her little saying goes something like this:

In your Twenties you are besotted by your man,
In your Thirties you adore him,
In your Forties you love him,
In your Fifties you know him.

Nellie's warm smile inspired Polly to continue, this time rather thoughtfully, 'On reflection my mother was astute and showed strength of character in the fact she was never subservient to my father. She took her example from the Bible, of course. Woman was made of man. She was not made from a bone of his foot to be his servant nor from his head to be his superior but she was made from his rib to be his companion by his side through life. There's also guidance in Proverbs telling us something like 'many women do great and noble things but to rear a family well is superior.'

Thinking she had talked too much Polly reciprocated the question, 'And what about your parents?' Surprisingly Nellie had not anticipated the question and repeated Polly's request to give her time to gather her thoughts before fully answering. 'They shared a very different lifestyle to your parents in my days at Pack Horse Farm. There were nine of us children, remember, plus two who died. Mother always seemed with child and times were hard. With me being the eldest I was constantly feeding and caring for each sibling whilst my dear mother was bringing another one into the world. However mother without effort made time for us individually and was supportive but it was very evident that her first support was to father. She was regularly praising his hard work and highlighting his kind nature. She seemed to totally disregard her own day as long as she was helping him mentally and physically; he was her prior source of happiness. He drew much strength from her, giving him confidence to tackle life's many problems regardless of his low self esteem. Their love for one another was always shining through. We had many financial worries, particularly over the rent, but both mother and father were very generous to us in other ways, plenty of kisses and love.

Polly forced a laugh in envy before stating, 'Very sad isn't it but I can't remember either of my parents kissing me.'

'But you are tactile Polly especially to myself and Mary.'

'Yes I am. You and your family bring out the best in me. I treasure the fact that our paths have crossed in life.'

Both naturally held a hand out to one another whilst remaining sitting and gently squeezed each other's hand in mutual gratitude. After their hands had parted Polly summed up the conversation outcome with a question, 'We have had different up-bringings haven't we?'

Nellie sighed and lamented, 'Most couples have to worry over money and I feel for them. I wish my parents hadn't had that life long worry.'

'Ah but it plain to see they still enjoy true love to this day. The comfort of money alone can never compare with true love and it's accompanying contentment of the heart. It is evident your parents are blessed with an enduring love.'

Polly once again had naturally comforted Nellie by stopping her thinking about herself and had lifted her spirits. A lovely understanding smile by both sealed the end of their confidential conversation within a slight flutter of the Gentle Ribbon.

CHAPTER 15

IT IS TIME

George and Nellie

Early in the Spring of 1913 village spirits lifted very high with the unexpected royal visit to Old Moreton Hall of the new King George V; a king Nellie respected more than the deceased King Edward VII. Queen Mary was accompanying the King and staying, as they preferred in Cheshire because of the ease of travelling on the royal train, with Lord Crewe at Crewe Hall. The royal couple were making various stops across the County including the Worleston Dairy Institute, where the nationally acclaimed Cheshire Cheeses were made, as well as the quaint Old Moreton Hall.

George V's Automobile at Boarded Barn

At Higher Smallwood Farm George, in his kindness, allowed all of his staff to have time off specifically to stand at Boarded Barn to wave as the King and Queen passed in their automobile entourage. George Nellie, Polly and the children also joined the welcoming crowd, wearing their best clothes. Everyone was delighted to see the King at such close quarters albeit only a fleeting glimpse of him. George had satisfaction at seeing both his family and staff excited and appreciative of being involved in the memorable occasion.

However, during the early days of the beautiful month of June such royal memories had been put to the back of the minds of all the family and staff of Higher Smallwood Farm because of a worry. 'I do take exception to this', Rose declared as she scrubbed the kitchen table with great gusto.

'I know', Nellie replied in a supportive manner, 'but Doctor Latham has visited twice as George's fever is giving him cause for concern.'

'That does not mean our kitchens aren't clean. You could eat your dinner off the floors', Rose expressed forcibly.

'Doctor Latham is only caring for our health in case George's illness is contagious', Nellie debated.

'Do you think George is heading for pneumonia?' Rose ventured to ask.

'Oh I hope not, Rose, I sincerely hope not, but if that is the case the ninth day will be critical.'

Rose softened her tone. 'Don't worry too much Nellie, George is an exceptionally strong man, he will pull through. Although he is not eating fortunately he is taking fluids regularly. You know what they say feed a cold and starve a fever.'

Silence fell upon them as they changed their jobs and started wiping down the housekeeper's cupboard. Ada and Ellen were working competently around them on more cleaning duties. At that moment there was a loud banging on the back door. The ladies looked at one another in surprise at the unusual happening and Ada, without instruction, walked quickly through the maids' kitchen and opened the door. Ambrose, the waggoner, stood there in a dishevelled state. He had obviously been running hard and was puffing. Without any niceties he blurted out, 'Please give Mrs Walker a very important message.'

'I'm here Ambrose, I'm here', Nellie shouted as she ran to the door.

'Oh Mrs Walker, Oh Mrs Walker.'

'Calm yourself, Ambrose. Has a horse bolted? Are you alright?'

'No, Mrs Walker I have terrible news.'

Instinctively all the ladies present guided Ambrose to a kitchen chair at the table and he removed his old felt hat. Rose sat beside him with her arm along his shoulder. Nellie sat opposite him leaning forward holding both of her hands gently on the top of his wrists whilst he was nervously twisting his dusty hat around in his broad palms and he began to cry. 'Please, Ambrose, try to calm yourself and tell us what is the matter, then we can help you', Nellie caringly instructed him.

Ellen hastily put a glass of brandy in front of Nellie, who

nodded her approval, and Rose quickly drew the glass across the table and encouraged Ambrose to sip the brandy slowly. He slightly gathered himself, his puffing subsided and he began. 'Forgive me, Mrs Walker. You know we are hay making in the Willowbeds meadow. Well, when I stopped the horses for a rest, as I sat in the hedgerow at the far side of the meadow to eat my baggin, I spied something strange about five yards away from me. When I went to investigate I could see it was a dead pig.'

'A pig?' Nellie interrupted 'How on earth did a dead pig get there?'

'I swear it is not one of ours Mrs Walker but it is terrible that it is there.'

Nellie looked puzzled but kept silent to allow him to continue.

'You see Mrs Walker.' His tears started to well again in his eyes.

Nellie had a dreadful sense of foreboding and her eyes grew bigger.

'What, Ambrose, what?'

'Oh, Mrs Walker, I am so sorry, so very sorry but I could perceive the rotting carcase was leaching into the top spring.'

Nellie instantly sat up straight.

'The one Mr Walker uses?' she quickly questioned.

'Yes that's right.'

Ambrose began to cry again and said in broken tones, 'He used it Mrs Walker, I saw him. He came over to us in the Willowbeds, on Tuesday, to see how we were getting on. When he was about to leave, he took himself a drink from the top spring.'

Nellie remained silent a while, digesting the gravity of what Ambrose had said and then enquired, 'Have any of the men used that spring?'

'No, Mrs Walker, we tend to use the spring by the gate as we go in or out of the meadow.'

She slowly stood and left the room struggling to suppress her extreme anxiety. In fear she started running and fell into the arms of Polly in the morning room. Without tears, but with her fear in her eyes, she relayed Ambrose's announcement to Polly and Polly started to cry. With Polly in tears, Nellie knew she had to somehow stay strong and positive.

At that moment dear Rose entered the room, her sixth sense telling her she would be needed for instructions. Rose's presence triggered Nellie into action.

'Please, Rose, ask Alfred to fetch Doctor Latham at once.'

Rose disappeared and Ada entered with a tray of strong tea and took her exit without words. Nellie and Polly sat in silence, very agitated whilst drinking their tea. The heavy ticking of the clock constantly punctuated the then slowness of time increasing their woeful worry.

After what appeared to be an age the Doctor was whisked into the room by Rose. Nellie furthered the details of the rotting pig in the spring. He listened intently and nodded. He told them that his original concern was that George had succumbed to a very virulent form of pneumonia and was puzzled why such a strong man as George was being scythed down so profoundly, however, in the light of Ambrose's evidence he wished to see George again urgently.

All three walked briskly along the hall way, up the staircase to George's bedside. It was very evident George was deteriorating rapidly and Doctor Latham asked to be left alone with him. Nellie and Polly returned to the morning room remaining silent and anxious. A slight tap on the door disturbed them and they rose immediately as the Doctor entered. He instructed them to sit. He drew up a chair and proceeded to tell them that his diagnosis was now typhous fever and George and all of them were facing extremely dark days. He offered his support adding that he was very sorry that George was suffering so terribly and the situation was grim. The only comfort he could offer them was his typhous was not contagious and if George was the only one to drink from the spring water the household scrubbing could cease. With that he stood and said he would return after tea and further advised them that Ellen should stay by George's bedside for most of the time, as she was a good home nurse. He then took his leave. Nellie and Polly collapsed into one another's arms and this time Nellie sobbed.

Late into that evening and very early the next morning Nellie sat by George's bedside holding his hand. At mid morning Ellen persuaded Nellie to take a break. Rose, contrary to her usual morning custom, took a tea tray into the drawing room and encouraged Nellie to take the peace of that room which she readily accepted.

After her drink, in her exhaustion, she closed her eyes and lost herself in sleep. When she opened her eyes the Rector was sitting before her.

'Rector! Oh please forgive me I had no idea you were here.'

'Worry not, Nellie, you have managed to sleep for an hour and I have been to George and administered prayers', he answered in a soothing voice.

Nellie was struggling with her tears again as the enormous seriousness of George's illness punched back into her thoughts. She shook her head in hopelessness. 'What are we to do Rector? How can someone as strong as George deteriorate so?'

'God moves in mysterious ways, Nellie. We are not to know everything. I do think it is time to prepare the children.'

Nellie leaned forward and started to cry. The Rector stood by her side, held one of her hands and put his arm around her shoulder. She knew her deepest fears were now founded through his request to tell her children of the impending doom. She turned her head and gazed straight into his eyes. 'Oh Rector we have had our debates, our disagreements but you have a sincerity I trust. Is it really time?'

'I fear so', he sadly replied.

'Mary and Johnny are so young', she pleaded in her bewilderment.

'No Nellie they are 17 and 13. You will be surprised how strong they will be and, believe me, their strength will help you.

I would like to call again this evening after Doctor Latham has made his visit. Please tell Mary and John of their father's condition, we have a duty to prepare them. It is time.'

Nellie stood and clung tightly to the Rector. He held her fondly and patted her shoulders comfortingly. He whispered in her ear, 'You will be given strength by the Good Lord. We all will. You and the children must stay strong, we do not want George to detect there is very little hope.' She pulled herself away from the Rector, nodded and mustered a tight lipped trembling little smile, as if assuring him that she understood all his words.

'Thank you Rector. I will do as you say.' They parted with their customary squeeze of the hands. This time their grasp was tight and almost painful, as though each were trying to gain solace from the other much more than usual.

Although mustering strength from somewhere, Nellie found that late afternoon one of the hardest of her life. Mary was her daddy's angel and John was, of course, the longed for son. To look into their fresh young faces and tell them of their father's impending departure from this earth, was almost more than she could bear. But somehow the Rector was right and after she had told them, even in the terrible darkness of their tunnel of woe, they gleaned strength from one another. They had gathered themselves sufficiently to pray in the bedroom when the Rector revisited in the evening. George despite his heavy fever was aware of their presence and looked pitiful with a cold compress on his head.

Nellie decided she did not want to leave George when it was time for everyone to disperse from the bedroom. She had detected from the Doctor's eyes that time was short and it was very evident from George's shallow breathing that his end was nigh. John was escorted away by Polly but Mary lingered for one final farewell to her father. Without tears she gently kissed him on his deliriously hot cheek and again on the back of his hand and they shared an intensely sad smile before she bravely walked away knowing she would not see him alive again. Witnessing

Mary's tender goodbye to her dear loving father, Nellie felt raw anguish and a deep core of respect for her bravery.

Half an hour later Polly arrived back in the bedroom with a hot drink for Nellie and herself and reported that she had told Ellen that they would attend to the night nursing of George. Nellie gently nodded her head in agreement and felt an immense gratitude that Polly was being brave and felt a huge comfort with her presence. Inwardly Nellie had an acute sense of not being able to cope with a death and she really did not think she was brave enough to stay alone with George to the end, but the presence of Polly erased the necessity of any confession.

As they sat for several hours in the candle light George's breathing became even more shallow with a distinct rattle. Around 2 o'clock in the night hours, he summoned some strength and half reared himself, which quite startled Nellie. He tried desperately to say something but his words were incomprehensible. Polly and Nellie instantly leaned to him and gently assisted him to lie back on his pillow again. He gave one loud strange cry and then his eyes became glazed. Death had taken him. Polly tenderly closed his eyelids to shut away his fatal stare and in trembling high pitched emotion she softly uttered, 'He has gone Nellie. Brave strong George is dead.'

Nellie stood and almost recoiled and could only stand stiffly in disbelief. Polly rose and although gushing with grief herself enfolded Nellie with her arms in an endeavour to comfort her. Nellie took Polly's comfort but she could not reciprocate, her own arms were heavy and remained by her side. She was aware of Polly's arms around her but all she could do was to stare at George's dead body and she was shocked at the realisation of how short his time was on earth, just fifty years, fifty fleeting years.

The whole mood of Higher Smallwood Farm was extremely sombre that June of 1913. Many of the staff were tearful and Alfred particularly was distraught. George lay in his open elm coffin in the drawing room and a stream of disbelieving villagers and friends came to see him and pay their respect to the Walker family. Rode as a village, in a very genuine way, was a sad place at the news of the death of George. He was their tenant squire, a real gentleman and the sense of loss was tangible.

St Mary's Church at Astbury

Because of the evident outpouring of village respect Nellie wanted George to be buried at All Saints at Rode but Polly wished for him to be buried in the Walker family grave at St Mary's Church Astbury and Nellie bowed to her wishes.

Three days later they were on their way to bury him. The funeral cortege was large. The Wilbrahams were in attendance, so formality dictated that their carriage preceded the Walker family behind George's coffin. Two immaculately groomed black plumed horses snorted majestically and pulled the glass hearse containing the coffin. Alfred dutifully took the reins of the landau in which Nellie, Polly and the children travelled behind the Wilbrahams. The three Walker women were heavily veiled and dressed in black from head to toe.

Nellie had insisted that Alfred and Rose were to join the

family mourners in church. George's bearers were his two nephews Cuthbert and Samuel Pointon, Young Alec and three of the workmen Joseph, Peter and Michael. On arrival at Astbury church they proudly carried George high in his coffin, up the steps and along the church path and finally to the altar of St Mary's. Although the Rode Rector did not conduct the funeral service he was allowed to assist the Astbury Rural Dean with a few prayers to the full congregation. Nellie found a slight comfort in hearing his voice but, in the main, the funeral service was a hurtful blur to her and her heavy black veil hid her woeful face.

When outside for the burial she thought how apt the position of his grave was, between the ancient mighty Astbury church spire and the old inn, The Egerton Arms across the road, almost epitomising George's life. He had lead such a worthy life, a centre spire to all his family, always honest and true and ever ready to shoulder his responsibilities throughout the whole of his life. And yet George was a man's man, an excellent respected shot, jovial in the company of men and enjoyed a drink. Yes his resting place was right.

As they gathered by the grave side Nellie managed to hold back her tears but was consumed with disbelief at the torturous job before them on such a beautiful day. She could hear the bird song which was exceptional, as if the birds were aware of the last earthly moments of George and they were bidding him a final farewell. The stormcock was singing exquisitely. George loved all flora and fauna and particularly avifauna. She dartingly hoped that birds sing in Heaven.

Momentarily Nellie closed her eyelids. When she re-opened them it was the dreaded time of the total end of George. She tightly linked her children's arms as his coffin was lowered into the Walker family grave in the church yard. The dear Lord gave all three strength in those terrible moments of final parting, which in turn portrayed their dignity to the onlookers. Her whole being ached in that agonising situation knowing she was now George's relic but strongly feeling she was too young to be a widow. She also intensely felt it was utterly wrong that Mary and John were fatherless when they loved him so dearly. A surge of George came into her mind again; no three score years and ten for him. He was dead, now buried, gone. How could he be no more?

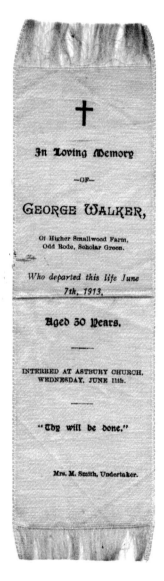

George's death ribbon

CHAPTER 16

AGREE TO DISAGREE

Dutifully Higher Smallwood family and staff mourned in black for several weeks. Nellie to show her respect to widowhood did not attend any village or outer family gatherings for at least three months and continued to wear her black attire for the rest of that year.

Polly grieved deeply for George and was persuaded by Nellie after a month to resume her weekly tea with the Dowager to achieve a change of four walls and to have an opportunity to partake in different conversation. Polly did stop wearing her black gown after some weeks but continued her recognised mourning by wearing a black arm band for months. The children, cocooned in their youthful world, slipped back easier into normal life but appearances hid the deep heartache they felt at their loss of a beloved father, especially for Mary.

In his Last Will and Testament George had settled on both his children an amount of money to be invested and released to them when they each attained the age of twenty one years. In addition he specified that John should inherit his guns and breeding spaniels. Polly had been left the contents of her bedroom and an immediate lump sum by way of a gratitude wage from George, with a specific clause that he hoped she would be prudent with the money as it would assist her in her old age. The rest of his estate, he left to Nellie, which included all the contents of Higher Smallwood farmhouse with a request that such contents of value were to be treasured and handed down to the children on her demise. In a codicil, attached to his will, George expressed a particular wish that John should inherit the oak dresser and Mary the walnut bureau, acknowledging these were his wishes as the bureau was not strictly his to bequeath.

Nellie was unaware that George had even attended to the making of a will, but in the shock of becoming a widow was relieved that the document existed to help her. She felt a comfort that through his will he had taken the responsibility of awkward decisions out of her hands. Indeed the document showed to her once again the natural thoughtful and methodical ways George held in life were still shielding and helping her, in the realms of her genuine grief and confusion caused by his tragic early death.

The loss of George as the business head of Higher Smallwood Farm was very evident. The family and staff worked extremely hard but decisions seemed all at sea. What crops were to be sown? Which animals were ready for market? Who was going to attend to the accounts?

Polly's working commitment waned after George's death. She did not want to take on extra duties but reluctantly agreed to more sewing, particularly the mending of the working clothes and sock darning. This freed Nellie from some of her afternoon sewing, enabling her to undertake the accounts. She found it difficult to adapt to the practicalities of the farm book keeping although she was intelligent and proficient with every aspect of the cheese making enterprise.

The day Nellie was dreading was Lady Day. Was there enough money to pay the rent? Although deep down she knew there would be, as George had always sailed through rent day, it did not stop her from worrying about the matter now that she was officially the tenant of Higher Smallwood Farm. She knew she would be nervous on the day, when she would have to sit alongside the other tenants awaiting her turn in the Tenants Hall before taking her place at the Land Agent's legendary round table to pay rent. Due to her enforced widowhood and subsequent tenant responsibilities she realised that she might be sitting with her own father on that day, a thought that made her most uncomfortable.

Since George's death the Rector had made a few pastoral visits to show his empathy to Nellie but took it upon himself to try to assist in a practical way and paid a visit one afternoon to Higher Smallwood Farm for a particular reason. Nellie was composed and seemed to him even more beautiful and trim waisted as she bid him welcome in the drawing room.

'Rector I am pleased to see you.'

'Thank you, Nellie. How are you coping with matters?'

'As best I can thank you', she replied as he socially kissed her on the cheek.

Nellie indicated that he should sit in his usual chair and took to her seat by the fire in her customary straight backed position.

'Nellie, I hope I haven't over stepped our relationship but by chance yesterday I saw the Land Agent and we talked about what will be a difficult day for you as a widow, namely Lady Day, although it is a couple of months away. He suggested you visit him in his office at the Hall the afternoon prior to Lady Day and you can settle your rent directly with him. I thought it a good idea and on your behalf I said I would inform you of his offer and I further told him that I felt sure you would accept and visit his office with your rent money.

'Oh thank you, Rector. Thank you, I do appreciate your thoughtfulness. I will certainly do as the Agent has suggested.'

'Good', he stated. With a tender smile he asked slowly, 'And how are you managing with the farm?'

'Oh it is impossible not to miss someone as efficient as George. He did so much!'

'Yes he is sadly missed in the village and on the shoot days at the Hall too', the Rector added.

Nellie felt the loss of George acutely again, even after seven months, and looked out of the window for a few moments at the turmoil of the busy Winter sky, feeling it almost mirrored her life.

The Rector kept his silence. She turned her head, looked at him very positively and announced clearly, 'George should not have married me Rector. I was the wrong wife for him.'

'Nonsense he loved you dearly and you bore him his children.'

'No, Rector, I mean what I say. We should not have married. I am only missing him affectionately for his companionship and excellent work, not for any deep love we shared.'

'Nellie, that is a terrible thing to say. What about the lives of John and Mary you both created?'

'Yes I feel very blessed with them and I know I was George's one and only love but I made him unhappy.'

The Rector could talk to Nellie easily and took control of the conversation, 'I will not have any more self recriminations. You are respected for your hard work and you were a loyal wife to George, in the fact you stood firm by your marriage vows.'

'No I wasn't, Rector', she replied very firmly.

He sat back and asked in astonishment, 'Were you ever unfaithful to him?'

'No, no, Rector, on the contrary nothing would move me from my vows but I made him unhappy. I was not a complete wife to him. I did not fully love him. I would not allow him to father more children. I was the wrong woman for him.' The Rector softened his tone, 'Nellie you are punishing yourself too much in your grief. You were a caring and a loyal wife to George.' Raising her voice she continued, 'Yes but I could not lie to him. I never told him I loved him because I didn't. Even with all his admirable qualities I could not bring myself to truly love him and the tragedy was I told him that, Rector. How cruel of me. Why couldn't I have just lied? I feel so ashamed.'

She paused, gained control of herself and continued openly, 'I had no idea I was only going to spend twenty fleeting years with him before he'd be gone. I always presumed we were a couple who would share at least a Ruby anniversary, possibly a Golden. How wrong I was. He did not have one day of total happiness with me. I should have lied.'

They both sat in silence a while thinking deeply before the Rector proceeded, 'Nellie each of us is responsible for our own thoughts and actions and I do believe if we are not true to ourselves we can cause more unhappiness. You married very young. It was a mystery to me why you did not bear children immediately in your marriage and perhaps, on reflection, it would have been better if you had given birth frequently in the early years of your marriage.'

'But I didn't want a lot of children. I was always honest with George in telling him that', Nellie stated in a bewildered manner.

'Yes, but what you are grieving over now started all those years ago. A woman must in marriage always yield herself to her man. It's his right to sire as and when he wants.'

'No you are wrong', Nellie protested.

'No I am right!' the Rector strongly counter debated.

'Look at your mother Emily. She has been subservient to your father and they have had many children. She trusted his judgement about the siring of children.'

Nellie's head was shaking rapidly from side to side and she blurted out, 'But they share a natural and on going love.'

'No, Nellie, your father has always been in charge of his own marriage and created a happy marriage. You did not allow George to be in control and when a man is not in control the woman cannot create the happiness.'

The Rector was gaining the debate as Nellie was struggling to establish some points of her argument, so she took a deep breath and slightly shouted, 'It was because of mother's painful confinements and father's financial worry in rearing a large family that I did not want to be the same.'

'You were wrong! A woman should put up with the pain and George could have adequately funded a large family', the Rector declared with force. Helplessly Nellie replied, 'George asked my parents before me for my hand and they persuaded me it was right to marry George.'

'Persuaded or gave an opinion?' Who actually decided, your parents or you?' he asked in a strong, sharp tone. Nellie rather deflated replied quietly, 'I did, they gave an opinion. They thought I might learn to love George.' 'Exactly, gave an opinion!' the Rector insisted triumphantly before proceeding severely, 'We must all take responsibility for or own actions. We cannot blame anyone else.'

Rather distraught, she continued, 'But they knew I didn't love him. You must have noticed Rector on my wedding day.'

'That is of no consequence, a girl makes her bed in life and she must lie on it', he answered in a high handed manner. Nearing tears in an emotional voice Nellie replied, 'I did, I was always hard working and loyal to George but it was not enough; we had one terrible row about my lack of love for him and from then on our marriage, at times, was difficult in the bedroom.'

The Rector was not moved by her emotion and firmly proceeded, 'Your remorse now stems from a wife having her own marital way. A woman should always give herself to her husband no matter how many conceivements.' 'No! No!' Nellie shouted. 'You are missing my point! Even if George and I had shared a deep love I only wanted a small family.'

'I find that too socially selfish to even comment on', the Rector retorted.

This time the Rector looked at the turbulent Winter sky through the window to create a silence. He knew Nellie was being honest and divulging her intimate thoughts and wisely allowed their heated discussion to calm. In a quieter voice he broke their silence, 'Oh, Nellie, I don't want to be hard on you. I have married several couples who were not in love, particularly monied people. Some fall in love after marriage, some don't. I'm afraid your marriage with George fell into the latter category, but nevertheless other qualities of your married life shone through.'

Nellie smiled weakly, relieved that through their friendship the Rector had given her some middle ground on which to build a bridge. She continued in a softer tone, 'Well perhaps what I am trying to say, Rector, is that potential brides should not be asking what love is, because if they had it they would know and neither should they marry taking a chance love might be found. I am talking from experience and I know, with the best will in the world, it doesn't happen, not real true love. I will constantly guide Mary and John to marry for love, for nothing else. I hope even my grand children and family line for years to come, walk down the aisle with true love in their heart. I sadly know the heartache if they don't.'

Surprisingly the Rector let his guard down and replied quietly, 'Life isn't always that perfect. There are many married couples behind closed doors who don't share love so don't be too harsh on yourself Nellie. Even more sadly, there are couples who were deeply in love at the altar but they have frittered away their love.'

He looked down to his hands and rested them neatly together, looked up and added unexpectedly, in an exacting manner, 'I am sixty four years of age, as you know, and increasingly I feel I am not fitting in with the changing world. I don't like what I see in this new century. It is very difficult for me in my pastoral duties to encourage peace with our brethren when as a country our politicians are always war mongering and meddling in other countries' affairs, causing acute human suffering. No lessons have been learned from the Boer War. I don't like ladies cutting their hair short or raising their hemlines above their ankles and dancing to that appalling new charivari music. Even some ladies of the Royal Family are dabbling in that despicable dirty habit of smoking. Their breath must smell appalling. And, I hold no sympathy with the shinanikins of those dreadful suffragettes. The idea of giving women the vote makes me shudder.'

He paused slightly before continuing with a sigh, 'Yes, I feel the wrong side of the tide of life somehow as my years on earth roll on, particularly with the views of some modern women. I am not over sure, if they do gain new freedoms, that it will be good for family values and I wonder if they will achieve the happiness they desire. Time will tell. Time will tell.'

Nellie managed to warmly smile, thankful that he had opened his heart in words and once more they had gone full circle in their friendship and had reached the stage where they could agree to disagree.

As a softener she underlined their conversation, 'Oh, Rector, you know I want the vote for all women but I promise you I will never cut my hair short, neither will I ever put a horrible cigarette to my mouth. However I sincerely declare that I do want to feel true love in my heart before I die.' With that they both rose, hugged gently and parted with their familiar squeeze of their hands.

CHAPTER 17

I HAVE NO CURB ON

The different light of the brighter skies of February 1914 was subconsciously lifting the spirits of the country folk and it was noticeable that the afternoons were staying lighter longer. Cheshire had suffered a severe bout of weather at the end of January, fulfilling the old prophecy as the New Year gets older the weather gets colder or as the days get longer the weather gets stronger. Mercifully Candlemas was dull not bright, hence Winter did not have another flight and the second week of February had become much milder hastening a thorough thaw. The mildness was continuing with stormy days filling February's dykes.

Nellie was in a positive mood, allowing her mind to churn over work initiatives and she was quietly giving deep thought on how to add to the income of Higher Smallwood or at least to keep it on an even financial keel. She liked January and February as months to enable her to find the time to do this and, the working year was in front of her, which always made her feel optimistic and gave her the opportunity to put any bad markets or poor harvests behind her.

She was attending to her mending sewing on the afternoon of the 22nd February when she happened to glance through the living kitchen window. The sight before her seemed very unusual and gave her cause for concern. John was walking alongside Big Lady, the trap horse, and her brother Alec was holding the other side of Lady's bridle. It led Nellie to wonder, what on earth was Alec doing with John at such a time of the day and why were they both walking? Where was the trap? Nellie immediately left her sewing, grabbed her thick woollen shawl and walked briskly out of the farm house into the farm yard. Her anxiety increased when she saw the dejected state of her dear horse. The facial expressions of John and Alec gave a foreboding of trouble that reduced Nellie to stillness and silence. When eventually they stopped, face to face, Nellie instinctively knew there were complications to be understood.

Alec, without any formal greeting, firmly instructed, 'The mare needs to be taken directly into her stable.' The lamentable state of the horse was clear to see. She had sweated profusely and her breathing was erratic. Nellie held her forehead in a distressed manner before imploring, 'Whatever has happened to her? What calamity has befallen her? Where's the trap?'

John could not look his mother in the eye and, with an excruciating guilty glance to his uncle, pleaded with his eyes for his uncle to further information. Alec answered, 'The trap is safe at Keepers Cottage.' Dismissing the other questions he quickly asked, 'Where's Alfred?' John took to his heels and ran for Alfred.

'I think your mare will be alright, Nellie', Alec said evenly. 'John brought her to me at Keepers Cottage. At least he has had the sense to walk her home since the incident.'

'What incident? Why should John find you Alec? Why didn't he come straight home? What has happened?'

'There's plenty of time for explanation. He's embarrassed by his foolishness. Oh good here's Alfred.'

Alfred walked briskly to the mare and with the most indignant countenance gave a withering look, took control of the mare and led her safely into her stable and shut the bottom door. He immediately began to wipe the animal down with some soft hay to remove the crusty dried sweat and then with the palms of his hands, he checked the mare's withers, and down each hock to her hooves, and gently traced every muscle with his caring hands and finally leaning his ear hard against her flank, checked her heart and lungs. Alec and Nellie stood in silence leaning over the door watching Alfred's competent procedure. John stood slightly behind them watching the action but wishing the ground would open and swallow him up.

Alfred finally nodded after his thorough inspection of the horse and totally ignoring Nellie and John looked to Alec and announced, 'You made the right decision, the mare was fit to return home. I take it she is suffering as a result of his youthful misdemeanour', he firmly stated with an upward nod of the head in the direction of John. Alec drew quite a deep breath and replied in John's defence, 'Yes, but he does bear the burden of remorse and today has taken him well over gorby bridge.' Alfred nodded again knowingly and said vehemently, 'Make no mistake I will not leave this mare's side day or night until she's herself again.'

Nellie could not keep silent any longer and asked curtly, 'John what have you done to Big Lady? How could you mistreat her?' John hung his head with intense shame and remorse. Nellie became impatient and angry. 'John answer me, is her condition your fault?' John managed to raise his head and looked at his mother. 'Yes mother, it's my fault', he replied humbly.

Nellie's rage was increasing. 'We have never treated horses like this at Higher Smallwood. Never! Never!' As Alec was about to speak to calm the situation Nellie sternly declared, 'No. Please, Alec, I will finished.' She launched into a crescendo of strict instructions. 'John you must sleep outside to care for Big Lady. It is not Alfred's duty to put your faults right. You can sleep in the bing next to the stable and the instant you are concerned about her condition you must consult Alfred immediately. And, for every time Alfred has to be disturbed you will personally pay him one crown out of your own pocket.' She concluded by shouting, 'Do you understand?'

John replied reverently, 'Yes mother.'

Alec at last managed to interject, 'Go in now Nellie and make me a cup of tea, you'll be getting cold. I will be along shortly after I have helped Alfred to thatch Big Lady.' Nellie kept silent, gave one last firm stare at John and, forcing herself to follow Alec's instructions, took herself into the farm house.

When Alec joined her in the living kitchen Nellie had calmed somewhat and her usual appreciative manners had returned. After she had handed Alec his cup of tea and he was seated before her at the table she commenced the conversation. 'I am sorry you have been troubled. If George was alive there would be no need to take your important time. No doubt you are going to inform me of all the details.' Alec was his usual friendly self and said with a smile, 'You know it is no trouble. I'm John's godfather and I feel pleased that he knew he could turn to me when he was in mither. Don't be too hard on the lad. It's already hard enough. It's not that bad of an incident, no one has been hurt and thankfully the mare will come round.'

Alec took a drink of his tea and leaned slightly forward and in a more serious tone informed Nellie, 'But, John has got to become accountable for his foolishness because Constable Edge and Sergeant Bowden have become involved.'

'What!' Nellie shouted as her cup involuntarily hit the saucer.

'Oh no. What has he done?' she lamentably asked.

'Like all lads he was enjoying speed.'

'Oh he wasn't racing!'

Realising he had arrived at the point for the full story to be relayed Alec stated in an exacting way, 'I'm afraid so, with his friend Henry Thorley of Clay Lanes Haslington. They were racing their traps and must have had a good gallop along the Weston ridge but then foolishly they started to race through the lanes of Englesea Brook and they were apprehended. They were caught red handed.'

Nellie sat back deflated. 'Oh dear. There's never been a Walker in Court. How will we bear the shame Alec? He won't be imprisoned will he?'

'No you are over worrying. Don't worry on worry. I am almost sure the offence will come before the Magistrate, who may fine him. Thankfully he will be spared from being presented before Judge Yates from Well Bank Bradwall, but if he was, I don't think even Judge Yates would gaol John for a first offence. No, Nellie, in my opinion John and Master Thorley will experience the sharp end of the Magistrate's tongue and possibly a fine, no more.'

A silence ensued for a short while before Nellie said sadly, 'Oh dear. If George had been alive I don't think this would have happened. Am I too lenient with John? Alfred will be very undone that Lady has been raced. How could John have been so thoughtless.'

'Oh come on Nellie. What did old Granny Bailey use to say? Children need a lot of love especially when they least deserve it. Well John's in that boat now.'

Alec finished drinking his tea and proffered, 'All youngsters love speed. Speed and youth has always been an intoxicating mixture. Things could have been much worse. No one has been hurt and the mare is young enough for a full recovery, especially with Alfred's care. He'll keep her from being broken-winded. It'll be a very salutary lesson for John at his age and will show his strength of character as to how he handles the matter. I've already told him we all get things wrong from time to time. The trick of life is how we deal with our wrong and more importantly that we learn from it.'

Nellie felt dejected as a new storm pelted rain on her window pane. Before she had a chance to reply Alec hastily placed his finger on his lips and commanded, 'Sssh. Listen. Yes I thought so, there it is again, thunder, can you hear it?'

Nellie strained her ears and after a pause there was the unmistakable bronte rumble in the distance; it was thunder.

'What do they say?' Alec asked and then immediately answered himself by saying, 'If in February you hear thunder you shall see a Summer wonder.' Even that little gem did not cheer Nellie as she just sighed.

Alec eagerly proceeded, 'You never know Nellie we could be in for a good spell of dry weather in the Summer for haymaking.'

The Summer seemed a million miles away to Nellie and she was well aware she had got to deal with the here and now. She forlornly mustered on, 'You will be caught in this storm, you must stay a while longer.'

'Yes you are right but I will go to Alfred and John to re-check the mare and hopefully build a conversation bridge between them, as I feel John will be suffering with Alfred.'

'No more than he deserves', Nellie added sharply.

As they stood to part Nellie leaned to Alec and gave him a sisterly hug and said softly, 'I do appreciate all your efforts. John is fortunate to share a strong friendship with you.' Alec patted her forearm before his comforting words, 'Come on, Nellie, keep your pecker up. You have dealt with situations far worse than this.'

John did his utmost not be alone with his mother after the horse incident but about four days later they met by chance under the drift house. 'John, please sit on these sacks. You haven't had the good manners to give your reasons for the race. You are very fortunate that Big Lady is responding to stable rest.' Nellie sat on one sack of grain and patted the sack by her side. John sheepishly followed her instructions and when he was seated he stared at the floor. Nellie dished out her advice, to try to obtain his explanation, by stating, 'You are not going to get very far in life if you cannot look people in the eye and explain yourself when you have the chance to do so.'

John lifted his head and looked at his mother properly at long last.

'No, mother, but I believe Uncle Alec explained matters to you.'

'That is not the point. I have not heard your explanation of the race.'

Trying to stand his corner he stated, 'Well, we were responsible at first and attended to an errand for Mr Thorley at Weston. I took my trap because I needed to call in Rode Heath on my homeward journey afterwards and originally we decided to part at Oakhanger.'

Knowing he was going red in the face and embarrassed at the kernel of his confession, he involuntary paused mustering mental strength before proceeding, 'For some stupid reason Henry was goading me for a race and saying Big Lady was useless. I knew she had more spirit than his gelding, so I decided to give her her head and away we went. There was plenty of vision on the Weston ridge and we were planning to return by Crewe Hall but for devilment I swung down the lane to Englesea Brook. Of course he believed he could catch me with his gelding so he turned after me in pursuit. The rest you know.'

Shaking her head in dismay she asked, 'How could you have been so reckless?'

'It was his fault. He kept on and on saying Big Lady was a broken winded mare. I knew she could win a race. He made me start the race', John dared to reply in his defence.

'No he didn't. You had a choice! You knew it was wrong to race', Nellie said severely and continued, 'John you have got to learn life is always choice. You cannot blame anyone else for your decision. You know what is right or wrong. I will never tolerate you or Mary blaming any friends. You are always responsible for your own actions. Do you clearly understand me John? Do you?'

He hung his head in shame and muttered, 'Yes mother.'

'That is not good enough !' Nellie shouted in exasperation. 'Pick your head up and look me in the eyes John, in the eyes and tell me you understand.' To his credit he did what she told him to do and when his eyes were firmly fixed on hers in a clearer tone he said, 'I understand mother. I will never blame any friend again for any of my wrongdoings', sincerely adding, 'I do know right from wrong.'

'Thank you' she said relieved. 'Always search your conscience to know right from wrong and look at people properly. I have a suspicion about people who cannot look me in the eye. Be sure you always present yourself to the world with an open face.'

A profound silence fell before Nellie announced poignantly, 'We will all have to find strength to live through this worry and disgrace you have brought upon us.' After another pause she said, 'Perhaps it's time to continue our work.' With no more words Nellie rose and walked away from John not giving him one glance.

John sat a while watching his mother walking away to the farmhouse. He ached inside that his mother was offering him no warmth, no solace. His dear mother who was normally tactile and caring was cold and bland. He was intensely aware of the wrong he had done and that he alone was responsible for his mother's downcast mood. He could not see how he could make amends to those he had let down and hurt. For the first time in his life he had the realisation that 'sorry' was woefully inadequate.

Although the March edged Winter into welcome early Spring John's racing of the horse and trap brought a cloud of despondency to Higher Smallwood. A good many of the residents of Rode knew of John's foolishness and Nellie distinctly felt extra eyes were on her and her children when they attended the services at All Saints. John would not have blamed his Aunt Poll if she had not have wanted to join him in the Walker family pew but ever loyal she sat firmly by his side. Nellie often pondered whether the incident would have happened if George had been alive.

Up until his presentation before the Magistrate, John felt he was always walking on egg shells at Higher Smallwood. Alfred rarely gave John any eye contact but constantly gave him work instructions which John had the sense to follow implicitly. Alfred was also firm in that he refused John's offer of a crown with great contempt saying that his devotion to his horses was far above receiving such money. This very honourable announcement by Alfred to John did help John's pocket but the embarrassing side to this arrangement was that John knew, that Alfred knew, that Nellie did not know, which obliged John to be even more helpful to Alfred, almost under a form of an unspoken justifiable blackmail.

However in the circumstances John had very little option. He knew Alfred was taking matters very much to heart and that he was on the receiving end of a few verbal jibes in the Village. Alfred felt even more aggrieved because in all his faithful years as groom at Higher Smallwood not once had a horse in his care been mistreated. He could never forgive John that through his one reckless action this proud life time record was gone forever.

To reinforce his mother's disgust on the situation she barred John from riding or driving a trap until further notice and John had to have special permission to visit any friends on foot. His worst restriction of enjoyment was no shooting, not even rough shooting with uncle Alec. John perceived this as being most unfair as he positively ached to be in the company of his uncle. He longed for any time away from Higher Smallwood as a welcome alternative for him to escape from the coolness of both his mother and Alfred. All the clipping of John's wings hurt him in the day time and at night time he was often restless in his bed worrying about the impending court date, but at least after five nights he had been allowed to return to his bed from the yard.

The Court day on the 2nd March came and went, almost as Alec had predicted. For John, being with his friend Henry Thorley reduced his nervousness and fortunately the Magistrate took into account their remorse and issued no imposition of a fine, just costs. The most poignant significance to the matter was the hurt of the inevitable newspaper report. Although the adults of Higher Smallwood had silently dreaded any publication of the Court proceedings, John and Henry prior to their appearance, had not anticipated the gravity of the public written word.

John had never contemplated how exposed and vulnerable he would feel when the Congleton Chronicle was on sale and sadly realised what a two edged sword a local newspaper could be. Normally he enjoyed reading the Chronicle, almost like acquaintance each week with a familiar old friend, but this edition contained the following accurate and damming report:

Alleged Overdriving of Horses - Henry Thorley of Clay Lanes, Haslington and John Walker, Higher Smallwood Farm, Odd Rode were summoned for cruelty to horses on 22nd February by over-driving them. PC Edge of Barthomley stated that at 3.30 p.m. on 22nd inst. he was on duty near Englesea Brook in company with Sergeant Bowden, when he saw the defendants, each driving a horse and trap. The horses were galloping wildly and he noticed that they were exhausted. They were panting for breath and perspiring. The defendants were spoken to about their driving and Walker said 'It's all right; you might look over it this time. I have no curb on.' The other defendant said. 'This horse is broken-winded, and it galloped along after the other, as it had no curb on.' Defendants were told they would be reported. Defendants said they never made it up to race at all. The defendants were ordered to pay the costs and the Chairman remarked 'Don't race again.'

It seemed, whoever John met in Rode after the Chronicle publication, they had read the article and made some sort of condemning remark. Good country folk cared deeply for their horses and took a dim view of a person who was responsible for any mistreatment of one. John thought after the Hearing he would feel better but, because of the Chronicle report, he felt more acutely that he had let his family down badly, particularly the Walker name and he was low in spirit.

It was his sister Mary who came to his rescue and made an effort to lift him from his disgraced melancholy status. She took him on her journeys in the trap pulled by her strong Dartmoor pony, called Little Lady, and even persuaded John to join the church choir so they could have an extra evening away from Higher Smallwood. Mary took the trouble to go out of her way to drop John off at Keepers Cottage to visit Uncle Alec, giving them the secret opportunity to wander a spinney or two, particularly Gehenna at the Hall and chat well away from the rest of the world, before she picked him up again. John felt a deep warmth and respect for his Uncle Alec and always learned something important from him about pheasant rearing, vermin control, dogs and life.

After such visits John desperately tried, in the course of their meal time conversations, not to drop any hint that he had broken the rules of his mother's punishment. Occasionally he could feel his face going red as his mother was inadvertently nearing the truth and he was amazed how Mary skilfully turned the conversation to safe waters without any detection by his mother of a falsehood.

On one of his return journeys from a secret visit to Keeper's Cottage he broached Mary about the truth they were deceptively concealing from their mother. She was causally unperturbed and interpreted her actions as keeping a portion of her life confidential without actually lying. She also added that if her mother ever asked a direct question requiring a direct truthful answer she would tell her the truth and take the consequences. John thought this very brave of Mary and almost foolhardy, especially as he was experiencing a dark portion of his life in which he was swamped with consequences. Mary could read his thoughts and impishly winked at him, an action considered unladylike, and an action which would have received her mother's strong disapproval. With a broad smile she told him not to worry as life was always in phases and, good or bad, phases always passed.

Much to John's pleasant surprise he enjoyed being in Mary's company. He had no idea that she had such depth of character. He had overlooked what a sense of humour she had and she did not seem to mind if he frayed round the social edges when they were with their friends although, occasionally he would feel an emotional tug, when she needed to rein him in slightly. He knew, of course, that she was boss and, not even Mary on a carefree day, was going to be parted from that established sibling platform.

An injustice he knew he had to keep secret was the way she handled her pony and trap at speed. She was extremely competent and had the sense to be in control on the highway but Mary's face lit up with exhilaration when she turned at Pump House Farm and could take some of the early bends on Higher Smallwood drive with her pony at full canter. Whilst doing so she and John shared fits of laughter as they leant far out sideways to keep the trap on it's wheels. Always at a certain point on the mile long drive she slowed her pony to a walk for the last bends and the drive rise. Mary had a wicked twinkle in her eye as they entered the farmyard sedately.

What panache John thought Mary held to achieve her own excitement of speed, cocooned within the veneer of acting at the appropriate times, that she always drove slowly and sensibly. John wanted to perfect Mary's art, living her own day in her own way.

CHAPTER 18

THE PAGEANT

A welcome diversion descended on the village of Rode. The news was quickly rippling that Sir Philip and Lady Wilbraham were heavily involved in a forthcoming pageant, being overseen by the Lord Bishop of Derby and Mrs Abraham, to take place at Old Moreton Hall. The Pageant was the re-enactment of the alleged mediaeval visit of Queen Elizabeth I and her Court reputedly in the year of 1589. This local folk tale appeared to the educated as being rooted in fable rather than fact. However the Bishop was pressing on with the popular story and he and Sir Philip had secured a huge patronage commencing with His Imperial Highness The Grand Duke Michael of Russia and the Countess Torby.

Bishop Abraham, as he was referred to locally, preached from time to time in the private chapel at Old Moreton Hall. Many locals knew of him but few knew him well. He was the custodian owner of the Tudor timber framed Old Moreton Hall, or Moreton Old Hall as it was sometimes referred to. The Bishop's home was in Derbyshire so consequently the rallying of the local troops, to encourage people to take part in the vast production of the Pageant, fell mainly to Sir Philip and Lady Wilbraham. They were a splendid choice of ambassadors, took control and very competently recruited a magnificent list of Cheshire patrons.

The hive of activity surrounding the Pageant was a tonic Polly enjoyed, for she was commandeered by the Dowager to be in the group of special sewing ladies who were to attend to the important duty of producing trimmings for the collars and cuffs of the vast array of costumes. Polly loved her little slot and effortlessly attended to her meticulously neat crochet and shared confidential gossip about the Pageant with the Dowager. Nellie only made a commitment of once a week, usually on a Tuesday afternoon with the lesser important sewing ladies. She could not muster the same enthusiasm as Polly and felt her duty lay more towards the farm and keeping herself within the bounds of her mantle of widowhood.

There was hardly an able soul in Rode, particularly of the tenant fraternity, who was not taking part in some way and in the main the frenzy of activity was surrounded with enjoyment. Rode Hall, All Saints Church, Rode Heath Girls School and the Boys School at Lunt's Moss were the pivot and Mary thought it most amusing that she and John, because John had recently joined the church choir, were to be in the pageant choir and in the dancing group. John felt quite aggrieved that his unwitting choir membership had lead to him being press-ganged into the pageant dancing troupe with bells to boot.

When his Aunt Poll put on his knave-like costume for his first dress rehearsal he positively squirmed, for Mary, standing conveniently behind their favourite Aunt, was sniggering. He also knew he was heading for ridicule from his contemporaries. However his burden was modified by the fact his fellow choristers were included in the same fate and similar hapless costumes. Dancing practice eventually did yield a bit of fun with the pleasure of twirling the girls around and, after several weeks of singing and dancing as a choir and dance group, they felt at least they were spared from learning endless lines unlike the poor fellow villagers who had been given acting parts. Yes, the assembling of the pageant was unfolding and Mary and John felt on the whole they were perhaps at the tolerable end of the proceedings.

To mark the grand importance of the forthcoming Pageant some form of memento was required. It was believed the potters

Wedgwood, Royal Doulton, Cauldon and Moorcroft vied for the honour. Royal Doulton won the commission to fire and produce all manner of commemorative ware from tiny trinket dishes and plates to large jugs and vases. The hope was to produce affordable items to suit people's pockets accordingly, from a shilling to a few pounds. These items were on sale well before the Pageant day and Royal Doulton, with their confident use of unusual colours, gave great satisfaction in creating a whole range of wares that captured the spirit of the Tudor Period. This was an astute marketing ploy because such designs and particularly the colouring had not graced any home high or low before, thus the items were much sort after. The success of the idea enticed many people from a wide area to treat themselves to a commemorative piece of pottery. Mary was swept along on the wave and purchased a small dish and a plate for herself to remember the occasion of the Pageant. Nellie purchased a pleasing large jug with extra relish as she was convinced her giant of a man cousin, John Cuthbert Bailey, had secured the commission for Royal Doulton.

Nellie made Mary's costume and enjoyed the task. She created a cream taffeta gown with a rouched bodice, knowing the sensible ankle length creation would give Mary the confidence to dance with safety. The garment had long leg of mutton sleeves made from bright fern green taffeta with cream taffeta cuffs and inset to each side of the bodice was a panel of the green taffeta. Matching green piping was around the boat neck line and also around the hem and the two side panels of the gathered skirt. Mary snatched the time to create for herself two bunches of red satin roses which she was required to hold when she with the other choir members had to walk in procession over the moat bridge at Old Moreton Hall on the pageant day

At the practices, after processing over the bridge, the choir stood on forms in the garden area to perform their dual role; first they sang facing the courtyard and then, after performing a delicate about-turn on the forms, they co-ordinated their singing with the important moment of the cast's arrival over the moat bridge.

Mary could feel a diligence in those involved in the production and was looking forward with excitement to the whole procedure being drawn together on the Day.

Prior to enactment at Old Moreton Hall there was going to be a pageant procession starting at The Broughton Arms, locally known as the Gap at Rode Heath. The route was past Rode Pool, All Saints, along to Scholar Green taking a left turn, along Boarded Barn and over the brow to Old Moreton Hall. John was elated that Alfred was allowing him to ride the shire horse Prince in the procession. Prince, although not the best looking horse at Higher Smallwood Farm, had all the attributes of being a calm faultless horse who would easily cope with being involved in an extraordinary day of noise, flag waving and pageantry.

Nellie & Mary
Mary in pageant gown
Nellie wearing her treasured brooch from George

Mary & John
Both in pageant costumes

John on faithful shire horse
at Broughton Arms Rode Heath

Weeks of commitment to voluntary practices provided village happiness and there was much enjoyment to be gleaned from taking part and pulling together. The task of co-ordinating the talents of the writers, acting participants, singers, dancers, costume designers, seamstresses and the large number of ancillary workers making props, painting and co-ordinating the procession from the Broughton with the horses and carts down to the boat pageant on the moat, with the eventual arrival of 'Queen Elizabeth I', was a huge undertaking.

Mr. Dale, the farmer at Old Moreton was allowing his fields to be used for the massing of the arriving Pageant and to accommodate the fete, the watching public and the parking of their various means of transport; of horse drawn traps, gigs, landaus, coaches and charabancs, fandangled automobiles and penny farthings, bicycles and tricycles.

Locals who were not directly involved in the Pageant on the day would be involved in manning the stalls and sideshows of the large fete. Nellie thought it best to keep a low profile and simply volunteered to help with the bran tub when the fete would be in full swing. However, even with the humble bran tub job, she knew she would find delight in watching the younger children running their lovely chubby hands through the saw dust and, on finding a preferred shape of prize to keep, their eyes would light up bringing infectious smiles to their faces.

Old Moreton Hall

Souvenir Programme

At last in the May of 1914 the Pageant Day arrived. On the grass outside the moat at Old Moreton Hall the Rode Silver Band, proudly conducted by Mr Pierpoint, commenced playing their faultless majestic music at two o'clock in the afternoon, putting people in the mood for this extra special occasion. To have such notable patrons in their midst was exciting and most of the crowd were quite aghast as they presumed to know one distinguished guest after another. Mary particularly was glad that she was in the choir sitting very close to these eminent people. She felt their jewels and fine clothes were bedazzling and the whole spectacle was a joy to behold.

However, the privileged choir position in witnessing the memorable event was wasted on John. He had much preferred riding his shire horse in the procession beforehand but was glad the first slot of dancing around the huge bedecked Maypole, had run smoothly before 'Queen Elizabeth and her Court' as he found the procedure embarrassing. Fortunately the practices had been of benefit. He had not put a foot wrong but such competence was reinforced by Mary being his partner. Any contribution to life by Mary was always at a high standard and this personal demand of herself left John with no leeway for error.

Timing was of the essence as the programme was performed with strict interludes. The interludes allowed John and Mary to join their friends and enjoy the merriment of the fete but they had to manage their time carefully between fete activities and their duties as singers and dancers, for the Pageant flowed from the afternoon well into the evening. There was a huge crowd from the surrounding villages of Mow Cop, Scholar Green, Kent Green, Lawton, Rode Heath, Thurlwood, Betchton, Hassall, Arclid, Brownlow, Wall Hill, Brereton, Smallwood, Somerford, Swettenham, Hulme Walfield, Radnor, Astbury and Newbold, also many people from Alsager, Radway, Oakhanger, Barthomley, Sandbach, Congleton, Cloud, Timbersbrook, Knypersley, Biddulph and the Potteries. The whole occasion was a triumphant success and an immense tribute to fine organisation, crowned with fair weather.

Nellie returned to Higher Smallwood Farm with Alfred shortly before sunset, being the Higher Smallwood volunteers to shut the hens and ducks up around dusk before sly Reynold trigged about on his nightly check, in the hope of catching an easy supper. All the maids and the yard lad had been given a much appreciated extended curfew for them to enjoy the evening activities at Old Moreton Hall. Through their selfless dedication to hen and duck duty Nellie and Alfred had foregone the final Farewell Gathering, when all of the Performers in the courtyard at Old Moreton Hall were to process to the gates while singing 'O God Our Help In Ages Past'. Mary and John, being involved in the finale, were trusted to take care of themselves under the overseeing eye of their Uncle Alec, and bring themselves home sensibly.

After a welcome cup of tea at home at the living room table Nellie did not like the thought of Polly staying the night with a village friend and was stealing herself not to err on the side of self pity at being alone. She forced her mind to ponder on the remarkable day and confessed to herself she had enjoyed the occasion more than she had imagined and had felt proud watching Mary and John singing and dancing. Thankfully, in a lighter vein, she was drawn to reading the souvenir programme and was quite astounded by long list of patrons.

She was very intrigued to read the eminent names of the Cheshire elite and those of neighbouring Counties. The Duke and Duchess of Sutherland, Katherine Duchess of Westminster, The Marquess and Marchioness of Cholmondley, Lord and Lady Hugh Grosvenor, The Earl and Countess of Dartmouth, The Earl of Haddington and Lady Ruth Baillie Hamilton, The Countess of Stamford, Lord and Lady Hatherton, Lord Hampton, Lord and Lady Roger Newton, Lord Kenyon, The High Sheriff of Cheshire and Mrs Phillips Brocklehurst and The High Sheriff of Stafford and Mrs John Royds amongst them.

Nellie felt a warmth when she read the remarkable number

of villagers' names in the souvenir, including Mary and John, and held an inner gratitude towards whoever had put together the grand keepsake. She read every name and word in the publication and was amazed how the interest had consumed at least an hour of her time.

When she had finished her reading it left her with the feeling of being lonely as she dearly wished George had been alive to have shared the day. She knew he would have revelled in the memorable occasion and thought how proud he would have been of the children. In her mind's eye she could imagine him enjoying his fellow farmers' company in his own inimitable way.

She walked into the drawing room and, in her melancholy mood, placed the souvenir in her walnut bureau. Her thoughts clearly recalled the very moment George gave her the bureau for a wedding present and she could distinctly hear his words 'for your personal use Nellie.' She felt acute sadness as it seemed like only yesterday that he had spoken these words yet now he was dead. She was woeful at the swiftness of anyone's years on earth and the finality of death and she involuntary shuddered, as though someone was walking over her own grave, which the old ones used to say about such a shudder.

Whilst drifting through more memories of George with a fixed stare, she was distracted by the noise of approaching hooves. She briskly walked to the living kitchen window and in the twilight she could thankfully discern it was the children returning in the trap. As she further watched, when they came to a halt in the farmyard, she could see it was John at the reins. She took a deep breath, knowing she had not given him her permission to drive again. But something told her to take stock and say nothing. The children had made her proud that day and were coping without their father. Intuition told her that Mary would have instigated the reinstatement of John's driving. Maybe Mary was right, perhaps it was time to draw a line under the issue.

Nellie stepped through the back door and after her grown children had put the horse and trap away, they walked towards her with smiling faces. Nellie had a deep sense of gratitude in acknowledging that Mary had skilfully steered the family rudder well through recent difficult waters and Mary was silently requesting with John's driving, to allow bygones be bygones. Nellie outstretched her arms, Mary snuggled into the embrace of her right arm and John her left. All three shared a simultaneous squeeze and mercifully there it was for each of them, the Gentle Ribbon.

CHAPTER 19

REMEMBER MY WISHES

In the Autumn of 1914 it was not just the dark cloud of War that was causing uneasiness in Rode, unfortunately concern was increasing about the deteriorating health of Sir Philip Wilbraham. At Rode Hall on the 28th September, a mellow afternoon when the robins were singing sweet territorial recitals, Sir Philip asked to be carried in his chair beyond the ice-house to the crest of the drive to see one of his favourite views, the folly of Mow Cop castle. He had become increasingly irritated with female attention in the form of family members and nurses, so Lady Wilbraham had put Old Alec in charge of her husband's request.

At two o'clock Old Alec had summoned the Head Gardener, the Head Groom and Young Alec to assist him and they carried Sir Philip well wrapped, gently but purposely to his desired spot and rested his chair firmly on the gravel of the drive facing towards Mow. Sir Philip tried to make the odd comment but emotion caused tears to well in his eyes and he kept on shaking his head in embarrassment. Old Alec pressed his forearm and assured him his emotion was of no consequence, what really mattered was that he was following his desire. Sir Philip appreciated the ease Alec brought to the situation and from thereon he remained silent, deep in his thoughts, able to control his tears.

After a good twenty minutes Old Alec nodded to the others and they reversed the procedure, carrying him back to Rode Hall. Whilst resting in his chair at the entrance Sir Philip gained strength and dignity and issued stern orders.

'Take me to the west side Alec, I wish to look over the Pool.'

The waiting nurses were about to announce their anxiety at such a demand when Old Alec stepped forward, took charge and, with no eye contact to the nurses, said, 'Certainly Sir. Steady lads, lift the chair, away we go.'

'Put me close up to a garden seat Alec so you can sit at the side of me and talk.'

Old Alec had no need to repeat the instruction as the men followed Sir Philip's request. The three carriers then wandered to the north side of the house, out of ear-shot of a conversation but close enough for a firm command.

Old Alec sat on the garden seat and as both men sat side by side their eyes were drawn to the beautiful view of the Pool, the gentle ripples twinkling in the delicate Autumn sunshine. After enjoying the view for some time Sir Philip stated, 'That ash tree wants taking out Alec. It offends my eye. It's been struck twice by lightening hasn't it?'

'Aye Sir. It's still living at the bottom though and the birds like to use the high dead branches as a vantage point. That's where you hear the tawny owl hooting or the little owl screeching their evening curfew. However, I will tell the woodman. It will be gone within the week Sir.'

'So will I Alec.'

'Aye Sir', Alec acknowledged sadly and truthfully. It hurt him to see his proud master fading.

'Are you ready to leave the world Sir?'

'Yes I am Alec. My days are only an existence.'

'I understand Sir. I would wish the same for me-self.'

'I knew you would understand Alec. Family and nurses do not allow me to talk like this but we know, don't we Alec? We see the end in animals, we do know.'

'Aye Sir.'

'You have been a loyal and trusted servant to me Alec.'

'It's been no trouble to me Sir. Rode Hall has been my life and

I feel well contented with my days here, although my advancing years are telling. My spirit is willing but my body sometimes weak. I'm glad to have young Alec around.'

'He is a fine shot', Sir Philip said in admiration and added in further praise, 'he is becoming a knowledgeable Keeper, you are teaching him well. Since you have no sons of your own, your nephew was a good choice to follow in your footsteps. I have already instructed Randle that on your retirement Young Alec is to be appointed Keeper and on no account must he be rabbled in this bloody War.'

'Thank you, Sir. I value that confidential knowledge.'

After a slight pause for thought Sir Philip said, 'I hope my son Randle will be competent in dealing with all this.'

'Be assured he will, Sir. The young-uns with any nouse do rise to their responsibility in life. It has ever been thus. All this will be here well after we've gone. It will go on the same Sir.'

'I'm not too sure, times are a changing. I often wonder if my eldest Grandson will survey Rode Estate in it's entirety.'

'Remember nought two Sir. We didn't think King Teddy had it in him to be competent after our good Queen but the wheels of our Nation are still turning.'

After a lingering gaze on the languid scene of all before him, the Pool and spinneys bathed in an almost mystical light, that only the September sun can romantically provide, Sir Philip announced with deep sincerity, 'I've had a fine life Alec and enjoyed the Hall and my family and staff. You especially have made my shooting days good. The bag was always there, you never let me down. I've had immense pride providing reciprocal visits for the Duke of Westminster, Lord Derby, the Tollmaches, Shackerleys, Davenports and the Egertons. You added much to the richness of those glorious days. You know my land and spinneys better than me.'

'Thank you, Sir.'

'But the end has to come to us all.'

'Aye just like the old Ash.'

Both men paused and glanced once more at the old Ash tree.

Alec ventured a dog's chance for the tree.

'But even the humble Ash has a proud record. It's the Viking tree, Sir, revered for healing and connected with Norse mythology. It is reputed to have it's roots in mythical hell and it's branches in mythical heaven and the god Odin has a connection with it.' He then added with his dry sense of humour, 'No wonder it cops the lightening.'

Sir Philip gave a wry smile.

'I'm the educated man Alec and I did not know that. How do you know?'

'Oh just passed down through country knowledge I suppose', he answered modestly. It was second nature for Alec to hide his light under a bushel.

Sir Philip gave a long stare at the tree and said positively, 'You've changed my mind about the old Ash. Leave it be for the birds and, after I have gone, when you think it is unsafe deal with it then.'

'Very well, Sir, but I will pass your instruction on to Young Alec because I feel the old tree will out live you and me both.'

A natural chuckle was shared between the two men, after which Sir Philip said in a relaxed manner, 'You've many years in you yet, you old trout.'

'Oh I don't know Sir. You know what they say, 'the young may go but the old must'.

Sir Philip drew a breath and requested efficiently, 'There is something I need to ask of you. Will you be my chief bearer?'

In a broad Cheshire dialect Alec replied, 'Nwew Sir, I'm too eowed, that's a young-uns job.' But after purposely changing his tone announced, 'I will, with your permission, organise your chosen bearers. I'll see to it that they carry you high with pride. Also I'd like to attend to your Purdeys, Sir, for one last time and put them by your coffin.'

'Very well', Sir Philip agreed and after a short pause for

thought added, 'Yes please do it that way. I will inform my family. There is something else. Will you attend to my Vigil? My Bible chapters are ready.'

'That will be an honour, Sir. I assure you on the hour I will see to your request.'

Sir Philip gave a grateful sad smile and an easy silence fell as both men, lost in their individual thoughts, gazed once more at the consuming beauty of the vast Pool and surrounding trees. Sir Philip broke the silence with a friendly request.

'There is another little thing you can help me with.'

'Yes, Sir.'

'I'm told by my nurse there is a Blue Moon tonight. I don't want to show my ignorance. It's slipped my knowledge, refresh me. What is a Blue Moon?'

'It's the second full moon in one calendar month, Sir. Apparently it happens several times in our lives. They say about every three years or so. Remember there are thirteen lunar cycles in a year.'

'Ah yes. That information does seem familiar to me. Thank you.'

After a short pause Alec stated, 'Cocoa Island looks tidy, Sir.'

'Yes. Amazing how it was built. All those Irish men fleeing the potato famine. They took endless loads of soil on to the ice one severe Winter, when the thaw came there was an instant island. A simple idea but after that hard work by cheap labour, you would have thought my family could have given it a better name. I'm not sure where cocoa came from.'

'I am, Sir. I was always told by my grandfather that the Kitchens here took pity on the wretched workers and supplied them with hot cocoa through that bitter weather.'

'Hmm. I never knew that. You have a knack of adding to my knowledge.'

Another pause ensued while both men watched a heron take off from the heronry and fly towards Alcumlow.

'They do cover some distance in their effortless flight.' Sir Philip commented and then added quite unrelatedly, 'Did you know Alcumlow is the smallest parish in Cheshire?'

'No I didn't, Sir. I think Gawsworth is the largest but I do know we have a few too many rabbits particularly in Withybeds. I've put the purse-nets down.'

'Good. Make sure the groom gets one when you are successful. He likes a rabbit pie.'

'Yes Sir.'

Sir Philip took a deep melancholy breath. 'All incidentals now Alec. All incidentals.' His emotion was welling as he announced, 'I've pondered many times on how to achieve this solitude with you out of doors and thankfully this opportunity has worked. We will not talk again. Time is short for me. I'll soon be snuffed out.'

'Aye, I know, Sir', Alec answered slowly in excruciating honesty, looking straight ahead to keep his manly guard, ensuring that Sir Philip did not detect the smear of a tear in his eye.

'As men I'm glad our paths have crossed.'

'So am I, Sir. So am I', Alec managed to say quite strongly, hoping his normal voice would hold, to suppress his aching heart.

'My body's weak, Alec but at least I've kept this', Sir Philip bravely stated, pointing to his temple.

'Aye, Sir, it is a rich blessing to keep your sanity to the end.'

Sir Philip held out his feeble right hand and Alec leaned forward, turned slightly and shook his hand in a most poignant way. A simple handshake by two men on very different rungs of life's financial ladder, looking one another in the eye, their handshake sealing their mutual respect and individual contentment with the many years they had shared together on life's journey.

Sir Philip lowered his eyes and released his hand. He raised his head and surveyed all before him once more. Old Alec decided enough was enough. He stood and gave his shrill sharp whistle. Sir Philip's countenance was intensely sorrowful knowing his final moments outside his beloved Hall were over and he desperately struggled to hold back his tears. With tight emotional lips he nodded slightly in agreement with Alec's whistled decision.

Young Alec, the Head Gardener and the Head Groom heard the familiar whistle and made their way back to Sir Philip and Old Alec. Without any more words they gently carried their ailing master in his chair back to the entrance of the Hall to be met by two agitated nurses.

As the men were about to move away back to their work Old Alec commanded, 'One moment gentlemen. A handshake for Sir Philip please.' The three formed an orderly line and in turn shook Sir Philip's weak hand. Sir Philip nodded with hidden pride, summoning deep inner strength to maintain his dignity and not to cry. With immense gratitude he said, 'Thank you, Alec. Remember my wishes.'

'I will, Sir.'

'Goodbye.'

'Goodbye, Sir.'

Old Alec almost stood to attention as the nurses took control. He watched as they put Sir Philip into his bathchair, turned him, pushed him into the large entrance hall and shut the doors. As Old Alec wandered sadly back to Keepers Cottage mulling over all Sir Philip's words, the penny dropped that they had never said 'goodbye' before in all the years they had known one another. Good morning, good afternoon, good evening or good night but never goodbye. Two days later Sir Philip died in his sleep. Old Alec in his prayers thanked the good Lord that his master's end had been relatively swift. He wished that for himself.

On the eve of the Vigil at one quarter to the hour of seven Old Alec, immaculately dressed in his full game keeper regalia, stood in line at the church porch with the chosen Readers from the Tenants. Holding their hats they bowed their heads whilst the sealed oak coffin containing the deceased Sir Philip was carried high and sombrely into All Saints church by the proud bearers and placed in the chancel. The immediate Wilbraham family members, the Rector and the undertakers Williams & Lowe departed. The bearers, one of which was Young Alec, stayed in church to double as readers. Old Alec carrying Sir Philip's beloved Purdey guns in a highly polished rose wood case went inside the church with the other readers and shut the stout door behind them. The candles were lit. As the church clock struck the hour of seven, Old Alec walked to the wooden lectern and commenced reading Sir Philip's first chosen Bible lesson. The all night Vigil had begun.

The hourly readings until midnight ran smoothly and with reverence. After Old Alec had distributed the contents of the large food basket sent from Rode Hall kitchens, including a flagon of cider, the hours thereafter began to veer into friendly debates, jovial recitals from the pulpit of Shakespeare and poetry, graduating to entertaining odes. But true to Sir Philip's wishes, Old Alec drew the readers to heel on the hour and each in turn read a designated lesson.

As the pre-dawn hours were approaching a few of the men who had performed their duty as reader nodded off to sleep, some even stretching horizontal on a pew in full sleep. The waiting readers, Old Alec and those who had read but wished to remain awake, spiralled into deep reminiscences of Sir Philip. Laughter, pride, raucous shooting tales and good banter flowed through their stories, against the backdrop of the coffin. Each man found the opportunity to talk openly and warmly about most aspects of their shooting life, with their dead master in their midst, most uplifting and it eased their grief and realisation that those times were to be no more. The episode was a once in a lifetime interlude perfectly interpreted as a men only gathering could encapsulate. There was an unsaid pride that they were sharing the last few earthly hours with the deceased Sir Philip and that they were the inner circle of the vigil, within the hallowed walls of All Saints church.

When Old Alec thought it appropriate and there was a lull in conversation, he proudly opened the classic gun case and allowed the men to handle the pair of Purdeys. They did so almost in awe of such a privilege and one or two put a gun to their shoulder pretending to fire, looking down those magnificent straight barrels. Many had known the guns for years but it was the first time they had been given the amazing opportunity to hold one of their deceased master's treasures. A dignified length of time ensued before Old Alec collected the guns and with the oiled cloth from a small compartment within the case, gave them his usual thorough cleaning. After this enjoyable but sad last cleaning of the guns of the deceased Sir Philip, he replaced them fondly into the wooden case, shut the lid and put the case alongside the coffin.

Old Alec then fumbled in the inside breast pocket of his smart jacket and took out the smallest of leather pouches, seemingly half full of something important. He walked to the foot end of Sir Philip's coffin and tied the small pouch by its thin leather draw strings to a handle on the right hand side. When questioned about his action by one or two, Alec simply informed them that he was making sure that a little bit of Sir Philip's soil from his beloved Rode Hall spinneys would be resting with him in his grave.

At the correct time Old Alec shouted rousingly, 'Gentlemen, your respectful attention please!'

The sleeping men awoke and took to their feet, gathering their senses. When everyone was standing Old Alec, on the stroke of seven in the morning, walked to the lectern for the last time and read with dignity, loudly and clearly, the final lesson from the large Bible.

With a strong sense of a loyal mission accomplished he stepped down from the lectern, gave instructions for the door to be opened and for the weary candles to be snuffed, with the exception of the two large ones flickering either side of the coffin. He stretched his right arm in silence, reverently indicating to the men it was time to leave the church and prepare for the day ahead; the day of burying their master. Old Alec gave one last faithful pat on the lid of the coffin before following his neighbours out of the church. The vigil was over.

CHAPTER 20

You'll Understand

In 1915, one November Sunday evening, ragged clouds were racing in a high wind across an uneasy haloed waxing moon. Polly and Nellie were reading in a relaxed manner by the roaring fire in the drawing room. Nellie was most enthralled with the correspondence from her second cousin Amy Dalby who was an actress living in London. Amy was believed to be an illegitimate child who was reared in a dwelling facing the ancient Crosses on the market square in Sandbach. Now through her success in London she had moved to a ground floor home at No 12 New End, Hamstead and she had sent to Nellie a natty little sketch depicting her new abode opposite to the Duke of Hamilton a public house. Amy had secured an acting part in Lady Precious Stream as Madam Wang and the production was in the prestigious West End. Her excitement at securing such an important step on her career ladder was indicated in amusing terms in her letter, causing Nellie to chuckle.

Polly and Nellie heard the dogs barking but, knowing it was time for the return of the staff from church, they continued reading. Suddenly they both glanced in alarm at one another as they heard a most eerie noise. The noise became louder and as the back door burst open it was apparent, even in the drawing room, that the noise was the loud wailing of a woman.

Nellie immediately rose to her feet and said she would go though to the kitchens to see what the noise was about. As

Nellie entered the back kitchen Rose was disappearing from sight up the maids' stairs in a terrible state of sobbing and howling, and she ran to her room in the darkness without taking a candle. Nellie was taken aback and asked the other maids why Rose was so distressed. Ada told Nellie that Rose had been in that state for most of the way home in the gig and was totally inconsolable. Nellie quickly issued instructions for everyone to carry on without Rose and to have their supper. After taking control Nellie lit a candle in a tin holder and took herself up the backstairs to Rose's bedroom.

Holding the candle in the darkness on reaching Rose's door, she could see no light coming from underneath her door, so she gently knocked and enquired, 'Rose, are you ill; are you in pain?'

There was no reply other than the noise of Rose crying loudly.

'May I come in Rose?' Still there was no reply.

'Rose let me comfort you. Whatever has upset you in this manner? You need some brandy.'

Nellie gently tapped again on the door.

'Please, Rose, let me come in there must be some way I can help you.'

Nellie waited to no avail and after several minutes she walked slowly down the backstairs, through the house and rejoined Polly in the drawing room.

Polly was sitting alone and was concerned at the incident and even more concerned when Nellie told her that it was about Rose. It was most unlike Rose to act in that manner and take to her room with such an emotional outburst. She normally controlled her feelings. Nellie walked to her bureau and on putting down the lid on the lopers she began to write an important concise letter to Rose.

'Dearest Rose,
Please don't worry about your duties in the morning or the next day if need be.

The only knock you will hear on your door will be from Polly. She will come to your room regularly tomorrow with drinks and meals for you. You are obviously acutely distressed about something. Only rejoin the others when you feel the strength enough to do so.

Please call me at any time in the night should you need me or the Doctor.

With my concerned love,
Yours Nellie'

Once again Nellie walked with her flickering candle to Rose's room and this time, without knocking, pushed her folded letter carefully under the door. It hurt Nellie deeply to walk away hearing Rose sobbing.

The following morning Nellie met Polly, who regrettably informed her that the tray outside Rose's room had not been touched, but added that she would keep taking food and drink to Rose's room for as long as necessary.

Nellie asked that Ada should join her in the breakfast room which Ada dutifully did. 'What exactly happened at church last night, Ada? Please think clearly and tell me all the details', Nellie instructed her. Ada stood very straight holding her hands neatly over her starched white apron and began.

'Everything was normal at church, Mrs Walker, perfectly normal, but it was after we had shaken hands with the Rector that Mr Alec Bailey, your brother, took Rose's arm and they moved well away from the rest of us to the side of the church and talked for quite a while.'

'Was Rose upset then?' Nellie asked.

'Not at first, although she had the most pitiful of stunned looks as she rejoined us in the lamp light of the porch.'

'What did she say Ada?'

'Nothing. She has not spoken since that time. She rejoined us and remained silent. Alfred helped her into the gig because he could see there was something amiss. As we were riding home, about half way up the drive, she started howling Mrs Walker, not just crying, she was howling in her tears. Try as any of us might we could not console her and then you dealt with the situation on our return.'

'Do you think Mr Bailey upset her Ada?'

'Well Mr Bailey does not upset anybody does he? But he must have said something amiss for Rose to take on so.'

'Are you sure there's nothing else Ada? Was Rose clutching her stomach, was she in pain?'

'No, Mrs Walker, it all seemed to stem from her talking to Mr. Bailey.'

'Thank you, Ada, you may return to your duties.'

Ada did an unnecessary little bob, more out of nerves than politeness, and left the room. Polly put her head round the door and enquired, 'How is Rose? Any news?'

'No', Nellie replied shaking her head, 'I am no further forward as to the cause. Ada assures me she does not think Rose has any physical pain.'

'Rose is very proud and stubborn sometimes, perhaps she is hiding something. Shall I asked Alfred to go and fetch the Doctor?' Polly asked in a sympathetic way.

Nellie's mind was beginning to race.

'No. I don't think we will trouble the Doctor at this stage but you can ask Alfred if he will please take me to my brother Alec in the trap', she said firmly.

'Whatever for?'

'I need to Polly, I need to speak to Alec, I think he can throw some light on Rose's situation.'

Polly tried to stop Nellie's proposed course of action by stating, 'Alec is a busy man. He will be feeding his pheasants in the spinneys. There is no telling where he will be.'

'Please, Polly, do as I ask, I will find Alec I am sure I will.'

Polly knew there was nothing to be said when Nellie had set her head.

'Very well', she puffed, stating blandly 'I will instruct Alfred for you', before disappearing.

Nellie made haste. She removed her working apron and gave instructions for the work to be carried on as normal particularly the cheese making duties. She pulled on her stout walking boots, using her silver button hook to fasten them on her feet and put on her very warm top coat. She chose to wear her bonnet in preference to her hat, as she thought it would tie on tightly and be of more use to her in the strong wind. As she hurriedly pulled on her long leather gloves she was pleased to hear the timely sound of Alfred with the horse and trap, trotting to the back door to collect her for her spontaneous journey.

Alfred had the common sense not to speak as he could see Nellie was on a determined mission and instinctively felt it was about Rose. Nellie asked him not to go down the Rode Hall driveway but to wait around the church.

'I feel I am going to be quite a while, so if you wish to visit your sister to keep warm and take refreshment, please do so Alfred. I will knock on her cottage door on my return', Nellie informed him.

Alfred nodded in the affirmative as he gave his arm for Nellie to alight from the trap. Before he sought the welcome refuge of his sister's home he watched Nellie, walking with much haste, down the Hall drive and thought what a strong caring lady she was, even in her widow-hood, going to all this trouble just for a member of staff.

Nellie was tousled by the turbulent November day but felt warm enough in her outdoor clothes. In fact, even in her anxiety to find her brother, she took in the late beauty of the oak trees. The other trees had lost their leaves but the mighty oaks had still kept theirs and they looked quite outstanding with their thick ginger coloured tresses. This eye catching finale mantle of the oaks was accentuated by a shaft of languid sunlight in the foreground, illuminating them most strikingly against the dark November sky.

On the brow of the Hall driveway, after she had passed

Gehenna Spinney, she could see to her left in the Nettlehole what she thought were some men engaged in activity. She walked briskly down the rise and across the pasture to the spinney and yes, she could then see it was Alec in his distinctive plus-fours with his two helpers.

'Alec! Alec!' she shouted, as she took to a running pace in her relief that she had found him.

Alec stood watching this female figure coming towards him and eventually he could see it was Nellie. As he strode quickly towards her he loudly enquired, 'What on earth are you doing here at this time?'

When their extended hands joined they politely squeezed one another.

'I had to come Alec. I had to come and find you.'

Before she could say any more Alec interrupted, 'Just a minute Nellie.'

He turned to his men and in a loud clear voice gave instructions for them to make their way to Horse Coppice to feed more pheasants which they promptly did.

'Now we can talk. Come here, Nellie, and sit out of the wind.'

He inadvertently took her arm roughly and they walked about ten yards and sat on an old tree trunk and he was right, it was well out of the wind.

'Do you know why I am here?' Nellie asked in a puffed manner.

'Yes I think so. It's about Rose isn't it?'

'Yes, what did you discuss with her after church Alec?'

Alec looked at Nellie, then looked down to the decayed leaves on the ground and after a pause gazed straight into Nellie's eyes and positively announced, 'I have decided not to tell you Nellie.'

'What! You can't do that Alec. How can I help Rose?'

'I don't think any of us can help Rose now. I dearly wish I had not spoken to her last night. I had no idea how stunned she would be with the dreadful news.'

'Dreadful news! What dreadful news?'

'No, I am not going to tell you. I should not have told Rose, I should have kept it to myself.'

'It's too late now Alec, Rose is beside herself with distress. She will be ill if someone does not help her. She is not eating or even drinking. She wont speak to anyone. It is almost as if she has been struck dumb.'

'I'm sorry, I really am sorry for causing Rose such hurt, I had no idea it would have such a profound effect on her. Sometimes the less who know about a terrible situation the less people suffer.'

'That won't do Alec, it's all too late, I have to know for Rose to go forward.'

Alec started to twirl a small stick between his legs realising that perhaps Nellie had to be informed. He paused and continued firmly,

'Nellie I mean this, if I tell you, you must promise to tell no one. Not Polly, the Rector, no-one. Do I have your word?' he said almost savagely.

Nellie always knew she had the strength to handle anything so she nodded in the affirmative and as a extra reinforcement of trust said, 'You have my word Alec, only Rose'

'No, especially Rose!' he said in anger.'

'How can I help her if I can't discuss it with her?' Nellie replied curtly.

'You'll understand', he reiterated, 'you'll understand and when I have told you, I grant you that you will never want to utter it again to another soul.'

Nellie sat upright as she waited for Alec to proceed. He stood and sat down again on another tree trunk almost opposite, as though he wanted to see every flicker of her facial emotion, in the sure knowledge and to give reassurance to himself, that she would never repeat the story.

He commenced, 'Saturday afternoon I happened to meet the Agent walking home, after he had finished his week's work in the estate office at the Big House. He looked very tired and drawn and I passed comment that his work must be hard, as indeed is mine, with many men in the trenches at war and I also said it must be hard without Edwin. He was a good clerk you know Nellie.'

Nellie's heart sunk as she quickly exclaimed, 'Was! Is he dead?' Alec paused and sighed, 'Yes he's gone. The Agent told me this and I offered my condolences but the Agent seemed very bitter and angry. I told him not to take on so. The slaughter is everywhere. The loss of men is terrible. Look at the Accrington Pals. I mentioned to date the dead and injured in Rode. In fact no village or town in the land has been spared from loss of life and grief. And the higher-ups have been scythed down as well. Huge numbers of officers have been killed, finishing the family line of a few Halls. But he just kept on shaking his head in disbelief. And then in even more anger he told me Nellie.' Alec paused, and with bitterness slowly stated, 'He told me Edwin had been executed. He met his death by the firing squad.'

Nellie took a sharp intake of breath and held her gloved hands over her face. Alec pulled one of her hands down and demanded severely, 'I trust you will never utter that to anyone.'

He continued grimly, 'The Agent also sorely laments the fact that Edwin's distraught parents have not had the dignity of burying their only much loved son at Tabley. Edwin's body was thrown in a crude grave with a few other bodies and scattered with quick lime. It's beyond all comprehension.'

Nellie could not speak. Alec proceeded with further explanation, 'This is what I told Rose last night and now you understand. I thought I was being honest and loyal to Rose. A few years back I thought Rose was in love with Edwin but I was mistaken as for some time they do seem to have shared a very strong platonic friendship, which is right to see between two good people in a village. I honestly thought I should tell her the truth in case she heard it from someone else but now I realise my judgement was woefully wrong. I doubt if Rose even knows Edwin's parents and I do believe I caught the Agent at a very low ebb and he will not repeat it again. So I do feel guilty about telling Rose as she could have been spared her anguish but she did take it very badly.'

Nellie had nothing to add. How could she say anything, even to her own brother dear Alec? She could not tell him that Edwin was Rose's half brother. Nellie felt immense turmoil in her mind and for the first time realised what a tight rope the Dowager and Polly sometimes have to walk concerning confidential village issues.

Alec broke the silence with a lamenting passionate voice, 'This War is bloody heinous Nellie. An utter waste of good lads, lives. And poor Edwin can you imagine his fear. He was not strong of arm. I doubt if he ever fired his gun without pain. And what training did he have? We know how to shoot from knee high and yet we are not allowed to go, those of us who can shoot. We are told to stay on the land and feed people. It's the wrong way round Nellie.' Thumping his fist on his knee he exclaimed, 'I should be the soldier! I'm going to enlist. There's no stopping me. I must help the lads at the Front!'

After a deep breath and in a forced calm he continued 'Edwin should have tended pheasants and cultivated the land. He was a brave older volunteer unsuited to being a soldier. He had no chance. How he survived as long as he did was a miracle. He's been eight times to the front in the trenches. The Agent said the last time Edwin went over the top he had two hundred and thirty six comrades. Apparently only twenty nine returned including Edwin, which had a most dire effect on him according to his last letter. The Politicians are het up achieving nothing thus the Generals give senseless orders. Apparently when Edwin was called to go over the top again he was seized with fear and refused orders. The following day, after swift court proceedings, he was marched away and put in front of the firing squad. In the General's eyes he died in disgrace but in my book he's one of the bravest men I have ever known. What fear and terror must have run through his veins. Imagine helplessly waiting for your end blindfolded with a target patch pinned over your heart.'

By a strange twist of Nature's fate a moorhen, locally known as a waterhen or 'waggie', chirruped it's startled mono tone alarm which took the attention of both Nellie and Alec. The bird strutted slowly but purposefully away showing it's distinctive rear end, a black bird with an orangish red coloured beak but poignant at that moment were it's white rear end feathers, only seen when the bird is retreating. The conscientious objectors of the War were referred to, all over the Country, as 'white feathers'; an insolent term derived from the white feathers showing on the retreating moorhen, meaning the men were cowards for turning away from their Country's need, or through refusing orders in battle were open to execution. Alec shook his head in disgust watching the humble waterhen twitching it's white feathers wending it's way out of sight. He felt through the disparagement of the bird, many men like Edwin were woefully misunderstood. The coincidence of seeing the waterhen whilst talking about Edwin's cruel death was hurtful to Alec.

In a more controlled way Alec continued the conversation, 'I am sorry the story is so grave but try not to be too worried about Rose, perhaps she will be different when you return to Higher Smallwood. She didn't know him that well and in one way she has only lost an acquaintance.' Nellie, hoping that Alec could not detect any deceit in her face, rose to her feet in an endeavour to escape from his piercing gaze. He stood quickly and again demanded, 'You will never repeat the tragedy of Edwin will you Nellie?'

'No I have given my word and I assure you I wont. I think you are right. The less anyone in Rode knows the better. You don't think the Agent will tell them at the Big House or the Dowager do you?'

'No', Alec stated with certainty. 'No, he was very fond of Edwin and he told me he wants to hold good his memory and purposely wants it known in Rode and, especially at All Saints, that he died in action. I mistakenly thought it was right for Rose to know the truth.'

Nellie held the pause with a heavy sigh before saying reassuringly, 'On reflection I am sure you were right to tell Rose last night. I would have done the same to protect her from a futile search one day for Edwin's grave. I will take your advice and leave the matter as it is to ensure a dignity for the memory of Edwin. I will comfort Rose on the basis Edwin died in action.'

'How have you got here?' Alec enquired turning to practicalities.

'Oh don't bother about me. I know you are busy. I will leave you now. Alfred is waiting for me with the trap at his sister's. I've only to walk to the church cottages.' The two hugged, although with little solace, but none the less the embrace was warm and meaningful.

Nellie strode off at a pace towards the drive looking at Rode Hall nestling low to her left and, as she walked up the drive rise, she shuddered at the thought of how many suffering soldiers were convalescing there. Most of the Hall's chimneys billowed the whitish-grey smoke from the fires, lit in an endeavour to keep the inmates warm. The high wind bashed the busy smoke away making it unimportant in an instant, almost mirroring the dashed lives of the once proud soldiers within. She turned when about fifty yards away from Alec and stretched her arm and holding her snow white handkerchief with her gloved hand gave a farewell wave, which he reciprocated by plainly hoisting his right arm high and slightly waving his strong cupped hand.

As Nellie walked along the Hall drive the peeping sun cast shafts of sunbeams on to All Saints Church, making it look majestic against the dark purple tinted sky. She was consumed with her thoughts, and selfishly was quite relieved that Alec had informed Rose of the terrible way in which Edwin had lost his life, as it had spared her the duty of telling Rose. In her brisk small stepping gait, towards the latter end of the drive, within full view of the church, she made a darting prayer for brave Edwin's soul to find eternal rest.

She tapped on the Church Cottage door and was rejoined by Alfred and they were soon in the trap and home at Higher Smallwood Farm. As Nellie was taking off her bonnet and coat in the morning room ever caring Polly joined her in a hurried manner.

'Has Alec thrown any light on Rose's distress?'

Nellie sat and calmly stated, 'Yes, we must be strong for dear Rose, Edwin has died in the War. Alec told her last night at church.'

Polly winced in sympathy for Rose and sadly remarked, 'Oh dear, it is very evident it must be something extremely serious. Alec was right to tell her but he is not aware that Rose and Edwin are half brother and sister, is he?'

'No, no, of course, he isn't and I assure you Polly I have not enlightened him.'

After a slight pause Polly softly enquired, 'How did Edwin die?' Nellie dug deep for an inner strength and announced with a blatant lie, 'On his eighth time over the top.' Polly slightly bowed her head in respect and on raising her head uncharacteristically snarled, 'This War is sickening. All the needless loss of life of valiant young soldiers.'

'Yes', Nellie emphasised, 'extremely brave soldiers.'

Polly leaned forward and squeezed Nellie's arm and affirmed, 'We will assist Rose through her grief.' The following moment she disappeared from the room.

Nellie took herself to the window and could see the farmyard activity. So normal, seemingly a million miles away from the hell of War in France and Belgium, even feeling miles from the soldiers at Rode Hall suffering from the loss of limbs or sight or both. Now she fully understood how Polly and the Dowager had to decide what delicate Rode matters had to be concealed forever. She pondered on the times she had been highly critical of the Rector and Polly and thought hard on how she had strongly debated and even argued, many times with Polly, that all facts should be known.

Now she knew different. She, the virtuous Nellie, who had always striven for true values, had just lied to Polly for the very first time. Lied, not to deceive, but to protect Rose's true feelings of her grief and to hold Edwin's memory dear. Nellie also knew she would never divulge to Rose that she knew the real circumstances of Edwin's death, the death of a brave soldier at the end of his tether and his plea for help brutally ignored. Alec was right to demand confidentiality about the issue but her concealment of the full truth about the relationship between Rose and Edwin from Alec was another lie, albeit a silent one.

The burden of steadying life and dealing with the right course of action was hanging heavy in Nellie's heart. She was weary of always seeming to be involved in some serious crisis, even though she knew it is a lot and a burden that many people have to bear on this earth. Nellie's strength flagged at that moment. It did not sit easy with her conscience to live with a cobweb of necessary deceit and her welling tears began to roll gently down her cheeks, as she forlornly looked out of the window.

CHAPTER 21

THERE IS A UNIFORM AWAITING

Although having to accept it was well over due for her dearest friend and sister in law to have a life of her own, Nellie hid her shock that Polly had left Higher Smallwood Farm. Sadly Nellie had to acknowledge that even though Polly was slim and agile, she was a good ten years older than George, hence she had reached the age of retirement. However, Polly had kindly given an afternoon of her time to visit and help Nellie to darn socks. They had made themselves comfortable in the large living room and the hand knitted wool socks with the holes were neatly laid in pairs on the large table. The ladies sat to the table in the rushed seated wooden arm chairs to attend to their stitching, stretching one sock at a time in the vicinity of the offending hole, over smooth hand held wooden mushrooms for easier and skilful darning.

They were quite happy and diligent with their chore and their conversation had become rather deep. Nellie trying to be knowledgeable remarked, 'You did warn us didn't you? You have been most concerned about Lord Haldane being our Cabinet War Minister, in the light of him being on intimate terms with the Kaiser. Again, as you warned, he was even able after his visits to Germany to blur the senses of Mr Asquith.'

Polly answered with intensity, 'He has been a grave misleader of Great Britain. Although he saw first hand the build up of the huge German fleet and army he always believed through his strong friendship with the Kaiser that he could achieve some sort of appeasement, whereby England would remain neutral or subservient if a European War erupted. Lord Haldane speaks German fluently and has received many gifts from Kaiser Wilhelm. Apparently when he entertained the Kaiser at his London home in Queen Anne's Gate, immediately prior to the War, there were blue corn flowers adorning the dining table.'

Nellie felt she was unable to give a intelligent answer as she did not know the significance of the corn flowers.

Polly perceived this lack in Nellie's knowledge and added accordingly,

'It is the national flower of Germany.'

Nellie decided to simply nod and keep silent realising she was the learning listener and Polly was the learned speaker.

Polly continued eagerly, aware that Nellie was interested in her conversation. 'The German Emperor, Kaiser Bill, has always been a most disagreeable and undesirable visitor, particularly to Cheshire, as I have said on the few occasions he has visited the Tolmaches at Peckforton Castle. It is reputed that as a child he was most churlish and a demanding member of the House of Hohenzollern.'

Nellie attentively nodded again before Polly continued in a zestful way. 'Oh yes. With the hoodwinking of Haldane we were very unprepared for War. It was reported in several London presses, the Daily Telegraph, Westminster Gazette, The Spectator and the Pall Mall Gazette to my knowledge, that Lord Haldane even announced that he had a belief in unreadiness. The British to him were never ready but they fought the better the less ready they were, and they used to astonish the world by the way they fought.'

Nellie was quite wide mouthed at Polly's last statement and remarked emphatically, 'The audacity of the man and he a Lord as well.'

'Also', Polly included whilst she was on a roll, 'it is reported in the Daily Telegraph that it is Count Zeppelin's birthday and even in his old age he still superintends his airships. A telegraph from Berlin states that the German public confidently expect

Count Zepplin's birthday will be celebrated by some daring raids on British towns.'

Nellie stopped her sewing and placed the fingers of her left hand over her mouth in astonishment.

Polly realised she had run her course on politics and brought matters around to their immediate worry. 'What is it your wish for Mary?'

'Oh yes', Nellie replied. 'I know she will volunteer for something soon, she seems slightly within herself of late. She often talks of her respect for her former school friends who are nursing the injured soldiers at the Red Cross Hospital in Congleton. Thankfully she is not qualified as a nurse but you know how headstrong she is, she may help at an auxiliary level. I don't want her exposed to such intimate nursing of young soldiers. Am I wrong Polly?'

Polly stated with firm assurance, 'No you only have protective thoughts for Mary and so do I. Perhaps I can be of some help as the Dowager has already stated that the Congleton Hospital is short on catering staff and has said that some of the girls in Rode would be competent. Leave matters with me, maybe Mary could be safely steered in that direction without any knowledge of interference on our part.'

'That would be greatly appreciated Polly but I can hardly believe that we are having to discuss such details and that this War is biting into everyone's family life in some way.'

'It is very sad but we must all buckle down and try to do our extra duties with a gracious spirit.' Polly contributed in a philosophical tone.

Nellie proceeded with slight fervour, 'With the John Bull spirit.'

The ladies ceased their conversation abruptly on the sudden entrance of John who had a beaming smile for his favourite aunt and he leaned to kiss her on her cheek as she sat.

'Good to see you Aunt Poll. Are you well?'

'Yes, thank you, John.' she answered slowly. 'I can see you

are well. My how tall you are getting. Much taller than your father. They say sons always grow taller than their mothers but you have well surpassed your father's height. He would have been proud to see you now. It is a great pity he was taken, we all lost when he died.'

Even Polly's sad lamenting for his father did not dampen John's spirits and he quipped, 'I remember father being much taller than mother.' However, being unable to discern as to what his aunt was implying by her height statement he added quite unrelatedly, 'Rose says you are staying for tea. It will be good to share a meal with you. Oh, by the way, she says it's ready.'

At that moment Mary entered the room in her youthful way and almost mirrored John's welcome, expressing happiness at the presence of her favourite aunt. After their pleasantries they soon made their way into the dining room, all genuinely grateful that they were sharing time together. After a delicious tea perfectly prepared by Rose, in light hearted conversation John asked, 'Have you seen the Congleton Chronicle Aunt Poll? There's an article and photograph of my pet gander, Jack, with Pip.'

'I'm sorry John I don't seem to have had time to read the Chronicle this week.'

'Aunt Polly has been busy reading many national publications to keep abreast with the War news.' Nellie interrupted in her defence.

Gander Jack with dog Pip

Mary, Nellie & John
with Polly sitting

John was not interested at that moment about the War and proceeded, 'Yes, Uncle Alec was talking to the Chronicle Reporter, Mr Boon, about my tame Canadian gander and he was interested and came with photographic equipment and took a picture here in the yard and it has been published.'

Thinking about the whereabouts of the Chronicle John stood, hastily ran into the living kitchen and back again with the publication. The ladies had moved the tea dishes away from Polly's place at the table and John proudly placed the article before her. Polly put on her glasses and read aloud with importance:

'News Attachment.

Mr John Walker, son of the late George Walker, of Higher Smallwood Farm Cheshire keeps a tame Canadian gander which has formed an extraordinary affection with the terrier dog which

Mr Walker keeps chained to his kennel in the farmyard. The gander (a domesticated wild one) who is named Jack lives entirely with the dog; they sleep together and eat together in the most affectionate manner possible. If a stranger enters the yard the dog begins to bark furiously; the gander at the same times does his best to prevent the stranger going near the dog. Mr Walker assured the writer that the gander never leaves the dog, except for a few minutes while he adjourns to an adjacent grass plat and pecks a few mouthfuls of grass, then he trots contentedly back to his chum.'

She looked up at John smiled and said, 'That is very good John. Very good.'

'Yes, and he also gave me my own postcard sized copy of the photograph he took of Jack and Pip', which John thrust under his aunt's gaze like a proud trophy.

After they had retired to the drawing room Nellie decided it was time to balance the sibling occupying of Polly's time and announced, 'Mary, of all people, has penned a poem Polly. Would you like to hear it?' Mary was most startled by the announcement and request which led her into a frown of unwillingness. 'Oh it isn't worthy of listening to Aunt Poll. I'm not in any shape or form a poet.'

'No she isn't', John rudely reiterated.

Polly was unperturbed and gently asked, 'There must have been a good reason Mary for you to string some words together?'

'Oh yes, there was', Mary replied unwittingly unfolding to Polly.

'I was jiggered up after haymaking one heatwave evening, reminiscent of 1911.'

'Mary!' Nellie exclaimed which was an instant command to Mary to correct her grammar.

'I beg your pardon, mother', Mary said in a subservient way and proceeded to rectify her words. 'I'm sorry Aunt Poll. I was tired and weary after a day of heat and it was midsummer so the twilight lingered well after ten o'clock. The men were drawing some their loads of hay under the drift house and others into the stack yard. I had journeyed home from the fields on top of a load, sitting travelling with a birds eye view of the beautiful surrounding countryside and bending occasionally into the load as we passed under the full summer foliage of a leafy tree. There is something very rewarding and satisfy about journeying home on top of a waggon full of hay you have helped to load, at the plodding pace of the horse.'

Drawing breath she continued, 'Alfred had assisted me to shimmy down from the load and I took the dogs and a drink of ginger beer beyond the garden and sat on the wooden seat in the croft by the old duck pond. I felt particularly pleased with the hard work of the day. It had been a perfect sunny day, a good farming day. Plans had come to fruition and I was well contented with bringing the hay home. Remember it is my responsibility now.'

Polly was already fascinated by Mary's reason and could see a lot of George in her perceptive thoughts and words. Eager for Mary to continue Polly asked, 'Was that the source of your inspiration?'

'Not really', Mary admitted and furthered truthfully, 'It was perhaps the fact that my ignorance was highlighted as I sat there having my drink, tracing the sky after a roaring red sunset. I had finished my day and mistakenly thought Mother Nature had too but as I sat the old duck pond unfolded to my ignorant mind a haven of activity. The fish were feeding and the pond skaters were darting about. Although it was on the edge of darkness my eyes became accustomed to the light, enabling me to see creatures like the bats flying and Mrs Hedgehog at the side of me foraging for her supper. I was almost like a sponge soaking up the twilight activities of Mother Nature crowned with Her twinkling stars. It was easy to string my words together because all I was doing was simply chronicling the happenings around me.'

Polly was quite besotted with Mary's introductory explanation and begged, 'Oh please, Mary, please read your words. I would dearly like to hear them.'

Mary still held a thread of reluctance in her eyes and looked at her mother for guidance. Nellie with a tender affirmative nod said, 'Yes, I am sure you should read for us Mary. Your words are safe in my bureau in the top drawer on the left hand side.'

As Mary walked to the bureau to collect her words Nellie expertly gave a firm parental prodding look to John for him not to interrupt in any way. John clearly understood his mother's unspoken message and indicated such by sitting up straight and placing his hands together.

Thankfully Polly had not perceived Nellie's controlling instruction, as she was pre-occupied by slightly raising herself to straighten her skirts and make herself more comfortable. Her excited eyes followed Mary back to her seat in anticipation of the poem.

Even sitting with the paper in her hand Mary was still trying to make prior excuses in case her words were not liked. She reiterated it was not really a poem, more perhaps a chronicling of what was happening around her at the time. She looked up once more to see her mother's beautiful encouraging smile and decided deliberating was over. She took a nervous deep breath and, after summoning the inner strength to do her best, she began her words with clarity and feeling:

Twilight Charms of a Heatwave

To see and feel my dear England in her finest cloak,
Beyond the garden by the pond I sit on the old wooden seat
With my loyal stout friends the tall Lime, proud Beech, strong Oak,
To enjoy the cool stillness of twilight after the day of heat.

The balmy silence is broken by the lapping of my dogs as they drink.
I cast my eyes heavenwards to the mellow oranges, yellows and greys

Tracing the sky after the roaring red sunset as Pheobe sinks,
Taking with Her yet another of our precious God given days.

As the dusk hovers the water before me yields many clues
Of it's residents: the feeding fish safe from the heron's sight,
The pond skaters scurry the surface in their tiniest of shoes,
And the drinking bats enchant me with their spectacular flight.

I love these rare moments of true Mid Summer upon me,
To count my blessings and be awash with such calm,
Glancing at the silhouette of the huge leafy tree,
All the hustle and noise pleasantly gone from the farm.

Who is roaming beside me? It's Mamma hedgehog,
Scavenging the grass leaving her footprints in the dew.
She may roll to prickle my inquisitive dog.
In the stackyard she'll sleep when tomorrow is new.

Curfew for the tired birds I've heard announced by the owl.
The podgy badgers will check soon on the wasps' nest nearby.
Sly trigging foxes abound but roosting safe are my fowl,
And the darker it filters pure twinkling stars jewel the sky.

Time for me to rest, I feel contented with Nature's late charms.
I rise, the sweeping garden looks beautiful even in the gloom.
The open-windowed farmhouse welcomes me with familiar safe arms.
I will sleep soundly tonight under one sheet in my warm room.

Mary raised her eyes from her paper to see two big tears of pride in her Aunt Poll's eyes. Silence reigned for quite a few moments. Her tears of emotion reinforced to Polly her conviction of how proud George would have been of his darling daughter composing such words to encapsulate a pulse of Mother Nature. It was well known to all that George was always attuned to the messages of

Nature and Mary had inherited his perceptive country mind.

Mary was unaware of Polly's intense feelings and looked further to all three in a modest way, in a manner to accept constructive criticism. No words came. The silence spoke volumes as to the resounding welcome of her words from her mother, aunt and brother but still Mary was unaware of the deep privilege they felt having listened to her.

'Well?' Mary questioned.

Her request brought Polly through her silent state.

'Your words were truly lovely. I am so thrilled I persuaded you to share them with us.'

'What shall I change?' Mary asked, indicating she did not mind any alteration of her poem.

'Nothing at all. Not one word', Polly replied in a genuine manner.

Mary glanced at her mother whose face was lit by a huge beaming smile of pride and contentment. At that moment she realised perhaps Aunt Poll was right. Her poem was to be left unaltered.

To reinforce her liking of the words Polly enquired, 'May I take your poem to the Dowager please Mary? I would like to read it to her.'

Although thinking her words were not worthy of being read out to the Dowager Mary decided to answer, 'Yes, of course, if you wish.' She folded her paper and passed it to her aunt.

John could not remain silent any longer. 'Would the Dowager like to read the newspaper cutting about my gander?'

Not meaning to rebuff him but, nevertheless, doing so, Polly stated, 'Oh I am sure she will have already have read it John.' However, seeing slight disappointment in his face she graciously added, 'May I take your postcard photograph? I am sure she will be interested in having a look at that.' This appeased John, who gladly passed the photograph over to Polly's waiting hands.

As Mary lay on her pillow that night recalling the reading

of the poem about the old duck pond at which she had gleaned enjoyment, a parallel thought made her cry. She could see in her mind's eye the other pond, the old dew pond, that had recently taken her close friend's life. Secretly and alone Mary was suffering frequent waves of deep sadness. The futility of her friend's death haunted Mary.

Rode was coping well with the tragic loss of one of it's lovely girls, Mary's deceased friend, under the guise of losing her life to insecure footing around a pond, leading to the Coroner's verdict of 'death by accidental drowning'. Mary knew the truth but loyalty kept her mute, even to her own mother. Before her death her friend had confided to Mary that she was with child. The poor girl was demented with the fear that she had conceived out of wedlock and was consumed with distress because of the shame it would cast on her family. Her sweetheart was also beside himself with the same fears. He dearly loved her and begged her to elope as somehow he felt they would manage, their love would see them through their dark tunnel.

Mary's friend had been unconsolable. She had the intense fear that her father would thrash her, thrash her mother and throw her into the workhouse in disgrace, even though they were a family of standing. Try as Mary could in their confidential conversations she could not remove this fear.

Mary had offered to tell her dear friend's parents and to shield her from their wroth had even offered for her to stay at Higher Smallwood for her confinement until perhaps she and the father of the child could think of a positive way through the situation. All to no avail as her close friend was seized with extreme anguish when her figure was altering and the babe was beginning to show. At the end she was overtaken by sheer terror that her terrible plight was about to be discovered and she constantly sobbed in Mary's company.

As Mary lay gently crying on her pillow she winced at the intense bravery her dear friend must have mustered to have entered those dark waters of the pond to end her life. Mary also knew she must bear her own grief totally alone. Out of loyalty to her friend and family the truth had never to surface. If Mary ever uttered that her friend had been with child the inhabitants of Rode would instantly know that her death was suicide and the recriminations would be far reaching.

Scorn would have fallen on the deceased young lady's family as attempted suicide carried the punishment of imprisonment and even with the knowledge of a successful suicide, if it was known to be such, brought the matter of burial into question. People who had taken their own life were deemed to have insulted the core of life and were subject to the persecution of God. It was totally at the discretion of any vicar as to whether such deceased persons were buried in the paupers section or even within the churchyard. Bodies of suicide victims were often buried without a coffin and sprinkled with quicklime to ensure rapid decay.

As Mary lay in her bed she at least had the small comfort that Rode, The Coroner and her close friend's family had accepted the false story of an accident. Also the grief of her friend's family was genuine grief and they were able to bury their loved one with dignity within the church yard. Mary knew she could also personally draw consolation from her friend's grave for she could take flowers as and when she felt inclined to do so, without anyone knowing that she was aware that the death was no accident. As she turned over in bed Mary's heart ached at the senseless loss of a very dear friend. Heavy with the deep confidential dark secret Mary found it very difficult to put many hours of sleep together that night.

As the weeks went on Mary's hurt was intensified when she occasionally met her friend's lover as she could see the desolation in his eyes at the loss of his beloved. It was obvious to Mary he was solely and silently bearing the responsibility of her death acutely. All Mary could do to console him discreetly was to convey with her eyes that she would never betray him or his deceased sweetheart. Their secret was safe.

Mary often asked herself how could the pleasure of true love result in an appalling ending of a young lady's life, in the bloom of youth, taking with it an unborn child? Why was society so rigid and shallow and would not accept the occasional normal happening to decent people within a loving relationship?

A few days later, through Polly's conniving, it came about that Mary received a letter from Commandant, M D Antrobus, of the Congleton Red Cross Hospital requesting her to volunteer her services to help with the cooking. There was a uniform awaiting her and her duty rota was for two shifts of morning cooking from 6 o'clock until 2 o'clock in the afternoon namely on a Tuesday and Sunday of each week. She was to be in the position of assistant cook but had no duties of purchasing as this was totally in the hands of the quartermaster. She would be assistant cook for one fortnight and chief cook for the following fortnight alternating between assistant and chief cook each fortnight accordingly. It was necessary to report for duty at 9 o'clock in the evening prior and she would be made as comfortable as the premises allowed but naturally the accommodation was not large because the 17 extra beds for patients had made it necessary to open five wards.

Mary was relieved she had received the summonsing letter, as she was ready to have her thoughts and actions put to a more positive use after her friend's tragic hidden suicide. She read the letter aloud at breakfast time, with a certain pleasure, feeling it was high time she volunteered for war time duties, although her preference would have been to serve in some capacity at Rode Hall. Nellie was relieved that the letter requested Mary to volunteer her cooking skills but along with Mary would have preferred the proximity of Rode Hall. She felt sad that Mary would be losing her Monday and Saturday nights but assured her that Alfred would attend to her journeys in the trap to and from Congleton which Mary had to confess was a comforting contribution.

Mary worked extremely hard on the farm and never once shirked her Congleton Hospital cooking rota and neither did she ever complain about her time almost being taken up with work. She fitted in extremely well with her Congleton colleagues and was a cheery member of staff.

Unbeknown to her family, Mary befriended the nurses and volunteered to help with the patients who were being made comfortable for the night. The Commandant noticed her natural enthusiasm and decided to harness it by suggesting that Mary take her First Aid nursing Red Cross examination which she did and passed. Mary decided to keep her success totally to herself and pressed on for her full nursing certificate. She was an eager student of nursing and was blessed with exceptionally competent Congleton nurses around her who were a positive incentive for her to qualify as a nurse.

The British Red Cross standards were high and stringent and Mary was very proud when she passed her full Nursing Certificate, although her written examination had been hidden from her mother under the necessity of a white lie of volunteering for extra cooking rotas.

Mary's Red Cross First Aid Certificate

Mary's Red Cross Nursing Certificate

A few weeks later, when she was wondering when to tell her mother and John of her nursing qualification, fate played a hand. A letter arrived from Katherine M Ffoulkes the Commandant of the Red Cross Hospital at Rode Hall. Mary read the letter and, as she had anticipated, it was requesting her to volunteer for a nursing position at Rode Hall. She simply left the letter on her mother's pile of post for her to read alone.

When Nellie eventually read the letter, stating that Mary had qualified as a Red Cross nurse, she was initially shocked that her daughter who was only eighteen years old, was pushing herself into a line of duty that would be harrowing and difficult. Nellie pondered for a while over the implications of the letter and came to the realisation it was typical of Mary. She was not a difficult daughter, in fact she had many qualities to admire of leadership and competence, but Mary was more distant from Nellie than Nellie was at that age to her own mother Emily. Perhaps it was not Mary's fault. To a degree, although Nellie's teenage years were hard financially, at Pack Horse Farm she was in a secure cocoon of a complete large family with William and Emily at the helm. All family members worked on the farm, albeit with no monetary reward; food, clothing and a roof had to suffice. Mary had been reared in a more financially favourable way at Higher Smallwood Farm but had suffered the dreadful loss of a close father and did not have the benefit of many siblings, particularly a sister. Also the War had forced Mary, like many others, to adapt to another world and work alongside other people.

Nellie was forcing herself to make allowances for Mary and she was aware of her own sense of guilt in not allowing George to father more children. Mary was more mature as a consequence of her rearing particularly with the responsibility of the farm and subsequent decisions and dealt with life's circumstances sooner rather than later. Nellie inwardly admitted to herself that she did not like change and took much longer to adjust. Mary could face need and change better but did keep things to herself in an endeavour to achieve her own way and, of course, the letter before Nellie reinforced her opinion of her daughter's strong independent personality.

When Mary walked to the dinner table at noon she knew she would have to fight her corner. Nellie coldly opened the conversation.

'Thank you for allowing me to read your letter.'

Mary remained silent. John sat back feeling he was going to be privy to something important and private.

'I did not know you were studying to be a nurse', Nellie said evenly. 'Congratulations, you must have worked very hard to qualify, but I would have preferred to have known.'

'What!' John exclaimed. 'Mary a nurse. I wouldn't want her near me.'

'Be quiet!' Nellie instructed firmly, without moving her gaze from Mary.

Mary realised she had to speak. 'I'm sorry, mother, but I have qualified out of necessity. I was not fully aware of the graveness of the War and the severity of the soldiers' injuries until I went to Congleton Hospital. I feel deeply for their plight and felt I had to do something much more positive to assist. I think you would have done the same at my age in the darkness of war.'

Nellie felt helpless and humble but still fragile. 'That's as maybe, Mary but I think this is the first time I have been excluded from your plans and it has hurt me.'

'She'd deliberately hurt if she had to nurse me!' John blurted out.

'John please do as I ask and be quiet', Nellie instructed sternly.

Mary thought she needed to continue the conversation to ease the tension. 'Mother, you have always said to believe and follow your inner feelings. That is why we have them. Something told me if I divulged my desire to nurse you would confide in Aunt Poll and then I would be doomed. Aunt Poll would probably have had a word with the Dowager and wheels would have been put into motion to block my intentions. I had to do it my way.'

Continuing with pure gratitude but stating blunt facts Mary declared, 'There is no disputing Aunt Poll's love for me and John but occasionally, only occasionally, a loving aunt, and you as a loving mother, can be formidable because you both do what you think is best for me and not what I really want.'

John stood. 'Can I say something please?' Both Nellie and Mary looked at him slightly irritated but allowed him to speak.

'This is getting a bit beyond me; can I go to feed my ferrets?'

Both women raised their eyebrows but appreciated that John had lightened the atmosphere a little.

'Very well', Nellie replied, relieved he was leaving them in peace.

Uncharacteristically John leaned to Mary, gave her a slight peck on her cheek and said in a meaningful way, 'Well done, Mary. You'll make a good nurse but I still hope you never have to deal with me.'

Mary smiled, knowing that was the nearest she would get to a decent compliment from John.

When he had left the room Nellie was aware of her guilt of colluding with Polly to spoil Mary's desire to nurse, and therefore mellowed her voice.

'Perhaps you have a valid point about Aunty Polly and me but it is only because we care deeply. You are very young to be exposed to the working parts of a man's body.'

'Oh, mother, you are being naive and ignorant. It simply isn't like that when you are nursing. The soldiers' injuries are horrific and the utmost care has to be taken to keep their wounds clean and free from infection. Septicaemia and gangrene are the killers but do you really know what is also injured to an indescribable depth?'

Nellie had to confess, 'No, I'm afraid I don't, what?'

'Their minds, mother', Mary answered with passion.

'When they first arrive at the hospital they are often dumb, some unable to come to terms with the stark fact that their lives will never be the same. They have suffered the horror of the trenches; the earsplitting noise and peril of the battle field with many of their pals and comrades killed at their side, the desperation of the field hospital and then a new hospital in an area they don't know. They are bewildered and afraid and are of such tender years to be facing life with a mutilated body. I've heard their stifled sobbing in their pillows in the middle of the night. I've seen it all at Congleton but I have also seen, through the wonderful care of the nurses, the soldiers' wounds heal; they begin to speak but most of all the nurses put a belief in them to go forward in life with whatever injuries they have and put that belief firmly into their minds. It is vital work the nurses do, absolutely vital. I need to do it, mother. I really do.'

Nellie felt deflated and saddened that she had over looked what a courageous daughter she had and, as always, when Mary had a problem or came across a stumbling block, Mary alone contrived her own way through or around a situation, precisely why she had become a nurse in her own way.

After a brief silence Nellie stood. She recognised that Mary was not as tactile as herself and, although she wanted to hug Mary, she knew it was not the time so she stretched out her hand and Mary held it lightly in hers and thankfully both could feel a tiny tug of the Gentle Ribbon, which was a comfort to each of them.

When their hands parted after such a poignant moment, Nellie leaned on the table supported by her clenched fists and said pragmatically, 'Well if we have a nurse at the farm John must be instructed to undertake more farming duties. He is old enough.'

Mary was relieved her mother had understood her side of the situation and warmly smiled before answering, 'Thank you mother. But he'll still have time for a bit of shooting. I'm only a qualified volunteer nurse, remember, on part time duties. I do not intend to neglect the farm.'

CHAPTER 22

PARTING OF THE WAYS

On a damp and windy afternoon early in the May of 1916, the Rector made a cordial visit to Higher Smallwood Farm. He was greeted fondly by Nellie and they sat together in the drawing room with the usual tea tray. The customary topic of conversation, the weather, this day unkindly battering the beautiful new green leaves on the trees, was surprisingly condoned by Nellie. True she disliked windy weather but took into account the time of year, quoting the age old country saying that a wet and windy May filled the farmers barns with corn and hay and therefore was to be accepted as a blessing.

After their initial 'how are you' chat the Rector stated in a serious tone, 'I want to tell you of a personal decision I have made before you hear it announced in church. I have been in contact with the Bishop about my retirement and we have come to an agreement that Harvest Festival Evensong will be my last service at All Saints.

Nellie warmly smiled and replied, 'You have made a bold decision, Rector, and I feel the right one. It is time you thought of yourself and spent more time with your wife. You deserve a long and happy retirement.'

'Thank you, Nellie, I do feel weary. Although Rode is a lovely village in which to live, unfortunately, like any corner of God's world, it has had it's share of tragedy and crisis.'

'You have handled it all excellently', Nellie replied with a beautiful sincere smile.

'You are most gracious. I have felt sometimes our debates have been perhaps too forthright.'

'On the contrary Rector, I feel you have perceived my nature well and I have always appreciated your opinion and guidance.'

As they sat together Nellie was slightly amused and said chuckling, 'Oh, shall I be visiting you in your retirement, perhaps for tea? We will be like Polly and the Dowager.' There followed an unexpected silence prompting Nellie to proceed on another tangent. 'Which residence have the Wilbrahams offered you when you vacate the Rectory?'

'Well, the issue is, my wife wishes to return to her family roots in Malvern and we have decided to purchase a dwelling there.'

Nellie's smiling face suddenly changed to one of anxiety.

'Oh dear no! I will not see you again.'

'I'm afraid that is the situation Nellie. All good things come to an end my dear.'

'Will Autumn bring the end to our good friendship?' she sadly enquired.

'No, of course not. We will no doubt communicate by letter.'

'No, it will not work that way for us. Oddly I feel we will not', Nellie announced with certainty and slightly lamenting continued, 'What is happening? All is changing. I've lost George, Polly and now you.'

'Not quite', the Rector replied, thinking Nellie was being a touch dramatic.

'Although you bare the loss of George, Polly lives in one of Church Cottages here in Rode, you still see her.'

'It's not the same, Higher Smallwood is all wrong without George and with Polly gone, the very rooms here and the atmosphere of the farm is sadly different and now you are leaving.'

'Oh, Nellie you pay me too high a regard. I am not part of Higher Smallwood.'

Nellie forcibly butted in, 'You are, Rector! You are! I have always valued your visits.'

'Yes but on a few occasions my visits have led to heartache.'

Nellie leaned over to him and took his hand. 'Please, Rector. I want you to know I really do treasure our friendship and you have been exceptionally kind to me.' He slightly leaned to her and put his hand on the top of her hand and answered emotionally, 'Yes, I too feel we share a very deep friendship. Sometimes in our heated debates possibly the worst of friendships but we have always been open and true and that is rare between a rector and a parishioner. I have, over the years, been more honest and open with you that any other person in Rode, knowing our actions and time together has been treated in the strictest confidence and shared in the correct spirit. We have been strange bedfellows within the parameters of genuine friendship and you are one of my few trusted companions.'

As he was speaking and looking into her beautiful blue eyes he could see her sadness. She appreciatively replied, 'I have leaned on you too much I know but I have a deep fondness for you.'

The Rector momentarily placed one of his fingers on her lips as if to guard her from any confession she might regret.

'Please don't', she quietly said. 'I want to tell you what you mean to me, I really do.'

She took a deep breath before commencing with deliberation 'I do have feelings for you. Not improper but a strong affection. An affection a woman can rightly share with a dear male friend. I will miss you there is no denying, I know I will. I think you will have a little place in my heart for the rest of my days.'

With a swelling of emotion and with deep sincerity the Rector replied, 'That is extremely kind of you to tell me your inner feelings as I too share a similar sentiment in my heart. It is rare between a man and a woman on two very different paths of life to share such a true friendship as ours with profound understanding. We are very fortunate.'

'Thank you', Nellie acknowledged with a sigh and a warm slow smile.

Slightly brighter, as they uncoupled their hands the Rector announced, 'I am not indispensable. The churchyard is full of people who thought they were. No one is indispensable. After the interregnum, no doubt, Rode will take kindly to a new rector. You will cope.'

She purposely replied quite loudly, 'Of course I will cope. I am Nellie. Everyone seems to think I can always cope. There is no allowance in this world for me not to cope.'

Thinking she had shown too much self pity she took check of herself and in a quieter manner enquired, 'Is the news of your leaving confidential Rector?'

'Yes for a few days. I am proposing to make my announcement at Rogationtide although they already know at the Hall.'

Nellie in a more understanding tone continued, 'Very well. I have appreciated our open chat, it has been long over due for us to share our hidden sentiments. Why do people only talk like this when they know there is a parting of the ways?' He shook his head slightly and commented, 'I don't know. Call it human nature but the deep tragedy of life is, when there is a sudden death, and much is left unsaid. There is never the chance to talk like we have just done. I feel the real grief of the world is the unspoken word.'

'Well we have a double reason to feel fortunate', Nellie replied with ease. 'At least we can share another season together before we finally say farewell.'

After enjoying his a cup of tea the Rector took his leave. He held Nellie's hands and shook them slightly with gratitude for their special friendship and gave her a tender kiss on her cheek. As he did so she closed her eyes, suppressed her sadness and made a mental note to treasure the short time she still had to share with him.

The passing of the Summer was slow and yet strangely fleeting at one and the same time. The occasional thunder storms had been a two edged sword. Although, in small parts, the growing corn had been flattened by the heavy rain the thunder and lightening had wove it's mystical country thread and served to ripen the grain. Mercifully apart from the occasional storm the weather had been predominantly sunny, thus the heads of swaying corn adorned the fields with the purest golden blaze. The clement season yielded a bountiful and gratifying harvest, and the bushel weight of the grain was good.

On the Sunday of Harvest Festival the 16th of September All Saint's looked magnificent in its decorated splendour. An abundance of fruit and vegetables overflowed from the altar to the church porch. The recent spell of dry weather had put a polished shine on the fruit and a healthy hue on the vegetables. Cascades of lovely yellow, orange, red and russet flowers punctuated the harvest bounty in a profusion of colour only gifted to Autumn.

Shining bright golden sheaves of wheat from the farms, stood as thankful sentinels at each pew end and under the pulpit. Numerous small clusters of oats on small stems dangled prettily from the candle chandeliers, over the door arch and even dangled from the lych gate arch, another indication of the farmers' gratitude for a good corn harvest. The perfect oats had gained their muted light golden colour through standing in the fields bathed in sunshine, their sheaves thereafter stooked together for the three weekly peals of the church bells, before being carted to the farms for storage in the ricks.

How fitting Nellie thought the whole ambience of the church was for the leaving of the Rector, as she took her seat that evening in the Walker pew. He deserved to see All Saints at it's best as a reward for the dutiful years he had dedicated to the parish. Many parishioners gathered in the congregation for various reasons; those who wanted to give thanks for a successful harvest and loved that particular service, those who felt it was their duty to attend and be seen in their paid pews and those who wanted to say farewell to the Rector.

The pecking order of the congregation was in evidence. The Wilbrahams in their special seats in the chantry and the Walkers in their pew, three pews down the nave by the main aisle, where

Nellie sat with Mary and John and Polly joined them as usual. Nellie had already fondly nodded to her parents, William and Emily, who were sitting about ten pews back on the other side of the aisle.

Nellie was sad but prepared for the Rector's last service. She glanced at her grown children sitting unperturbed by her side. To them it was only a Rector leaving. She could feel their nonchalance and quite envied the attitude of youth for having a better acceptance of the inevitable. Nevertheless her dear close friend was leaving, another profound change in her life.

Harvest was usually the service where the rural men sang loudly and proudly and that gathering was no exception. To be involved in the unique singing of the old faithful harvest hymns with loved ones, friends and good neighbours, made the tiny hairs on many necks stand on end.

The congregation was deeply united within the bond of gratitude for the harvest. All true country people feel proud of their occupation at Harvest Festival but this year seemed extra poignant because they were feeding the Nation in the throes of war.

The Rector interpreted the seasonal Thanksgiving well, made profound prayers for spiritual succour during the darkness of war, and rose to the occasion of his farewell service. He knew the individual reasons for his congregation's attendance and hoped there was a crossing of the several sentiments in some way on that particular evening.

After the service the Rector stood well inside the church at the rear to shake hands with every member of the congregation as they filed slowly to the door. Nellie deliberately held back in the Walker slot. She allowed Polly and the children to precede her for his handshake, believing she could snatch an extra second or two to make her farewell to the Rector meaningful. She put her hand out at the appropriate time and as the Rector shook her hand there was no warmth just an automatic grip and, more upsetting to her, his smile was false. As Nellie's turn in the queue came and went she received no closer recognition with him than any other in his congregation.

Shuffling along to the church door she could hear behind her the comments of 'thank you Rector', 'a splendid sermon Rector', 'a perfect farewell service Rector'. She glanced back at him in the candle light as he was continuing his handshakes with his nodding head and fixed smile. She felt bewildered. It was not how she had imagined their parting would be. She could not remember her final words to him, his handshake was so brief. He was not looking her way as though he gave her no more thought. How she longed for the familiar squeeze of their hands and their social lingering kiss on the cheek.

She turned and continued forward through the church door with the swelling numbers down the lamplit pathway. There was a crescendo of noise as people were catching up on friendly fellowship conversation or politely bidding one another good night, whilst they ambled along.

In the throng she felt very sad and almost prostituted. She was saying goodnight to the right people, she could hear herself doing so, but her mind was racing. How could the Rector's final adieu be so meaningless? Had their time together counted for anything? Had she deluded herself? Had their friendship been deep? Were the fond feelings she felt for him really justified? During the previous weeks she had often imagined their final goodbye and mentally rehearsed a meaningful farewell, but such thoughts had not come to fruition.

She had gone into the church in the evening light and as always nearing the Equinox it was dark after the harvest service. The darkness seemed to underline that their special friendship was over. The intimate light had gone out. The Rector's parting of the ways was bland and hurtful to Nellie.

CHAPTER 23

THE POSTCARDS

'Mary what on earth are you are wearing?' Nellie wearily questioned when Mary joined her for breakfast in the morning room.

'A pair of John's old breeches mother. I am going with the men to glean the Shoulder of Mutton and I have made a decision that I will wear breeches in the meadows and fields. They are comfortable and practical for such work.'

'That's dreadful Mary. Ladies do not wear breeches.' 'Some do and I have decided to be one of them. They are much more functional.'

Nellie nodded her head in mild despair as she sat pouring out Mary's cup of tea.

'Whatever is happening to life. Ladies never had to wear such clothing, neither did they have to do mens work.'

'I am always telling you, mother, life is changing fast. The War has hastened change and you know very well we cannot afford a lot of men, nor are they around, so I have to assist with the field work. We have already discussed this many times.'

Nellie counter debated, 'I worked hard at your age but I always wore a skirt. But then,'.

Mary stopped eating and gave her mother her full attention awaiting the sentence to be finished.

'But what?' she had to impatiently ask.

'Oh I suppose you are right. I did not do much field work as a matter of course only at harvest or busy seasonal times. My brothers, in the main, worked alongside your Grandfather Bailey at Packhorse.'

'Well, you protect John too much. He could give me more help but where is he again today?' Mary asked even handedly.

Nellie dropped her gaze and agreed, 'Yes perhaps you are right but a man needs to be a good gun. Your Uncle Alec is bringing John on splendidly with his shooting and he seems to have the natural eye of your father. He has gone rough shooting over the stubble fields at the Home Farm. We will be eating rabbit or pigeon tomorrow.'

Mary raised her eyes and smiled in friendly acceptance, also knowing in turn that her mother had to accept that she would be wearing breeches when necessary for farm work.

Changing the subject Nellie said, 'Look I have received a postcard from your Aunty Polly saying she will see me this afternoon at 2 o'clock and she requests me to remain in my morning working attire.'

'It seems as though we are both going to have a busy day', Mary replied.

'Your Aunty Polly is unaware of the present routine. Gone are the days of me changing after mid day, in fact, I am lucky if I manage to be changed for tea time.'

'Exactly, mother, that's what I mean. Your days have altered as well as mine', Mary stated harping back to her decision to occasionally wear breeches.

'How strange of her to send a postcard though. Polly knows she is welcome here at any time', Nellie said pensively.

'She says on the card, doesn't she? She has informed you that she wants you in your working clothes. She is probably coming to give you a hand with the brushing of the apple room.'

'That has been done and it is half full of apples already.'

'Well perhaps she is coming to give you a hand in removing hibernating flies from the far attics', Mary suggested cheerily as she quickly finished her breakfast before leaving her mother with an encouraging pat on her shoulders and adding, 'Tell Aunt Poll

I am looking forward to having tea with her.'

In the afternoon, on the chime of two by the grandfather clock, Polly came in sight. She was never a minute early nor a minute late. Nellie had spotted her through the living kitchen window as she arrived in the farmyard on her new tricycle and ran out to greet her. They both laughed as Polly came to a perfect halt with her back peddle brake.

'Fancy you taking to tricycle riding, Polly, do you like it?' asked Nellie as they kissed warmly on the cheek.

Puffing she answered, 'Oh yes, Nellie, you must get one. It is much better than bothering with a pony and trap. Well it is for me journeying around Rode. Yes, I most definitely like it, although I do need more practice on the rise of the drive here. Did you receive my postcard?'

'Yes I did but there is no need for you ever to make an appointment, you know you are always welcome at whatever time.'

Gathering her breath Polly proceeded, 'Yes, of course, I do. I really wanted you to remain in your working clothes and I can see that you have, good.'

Nellie decided not to explain that the daily routine of the lady of the house at Higher Smallwood had deteriorated and she would have been in her working skirt and apron anyway and asked, 'Did you have a particular job in mind?'

'Yes, I want us to take some stout baskets and collect the conkers like the children in Rode are doing', Polly replied cheerily.

'Oh yes, I have heard of such a collection. John was telling me about it the other day but I am sure the children of the village are quite capable of doing that. We can find much better jobs to do. Shall we help with the damson picking in the croft or wander the hedgerows to collect the sloes off the blackthorn for the winter gin?'

'No', Polly replied firmly. 'We must find some conkers, they are quite early this year. The Queen has requested in a national newspaper that we should do so. It is our duty to gather them.'

Nellie was puzzled and stood motionless. Polly chivied her on.

'Please do as I say. I intend to come here twice next week to gather more if you can find the time to assist me.'

'Where are we to put the conkers when we have gathered them?' Nellie asked in almost an elementary way.

'We must ask Alfred to take them in the pony and trap, either to the boys school at Lunts Moss, or direct to the station at Mow Cop and the gatherings will be taken by train to Queen Mary.'

Nellie remarked, 'I thought you do not over care for this Queen.'

'I grant you I could not take lightly to her reputed self inflicted neck wound nor her betrothal engagement to the first and then the second Prince. She really must have wanted the throne obsessively to go to such lengths, but.'

Nellie rudely burst into the conversation. 'They say the deceased Prince was ..'

'No!!' Polly thundered, instantly knowing what Nellie was about to say and commanded severely, 'That was coarse malicious gossip. We must credit ourselves as being ladies and never utter such words from our lips.' Nellie immediately felt like a naughty girl and fell subserviently silent.

Polly realised she had spoiled the opportunity to spend a pleasant afternoon with Nellie and felt obliged to qualify her command so adopted a lighter tone to make amends. 'You know 'they say' is usually half a lie and the bedrock of gossip. We should let the rumours concerning the deceased Prince be. However, you rightly spotlight my reluctance to accept the present Queen but I do feel history will portray her in a fair way, especially regarding this War. The troops are very fond of Her Majesty and particularly treasure the Christmas gilt tins she sends directly to them, even in the trenches. I believe she is anxious to produce a book of comfort specifically for the soldiers and sailors who have lost limbs.'

With no more deliberation Nellie was walking with Polly,

carrying between them three large baskets, across the barn pasture to the ridge of land with the seam of fox bench. There five proud chestnut trees stood near to Chance Hall Farm. Polly was quite elated to be walking her old haunts again and being in the company of Nellie on such a lovely Autumn day. Finally they reached the trees and started collecting the conkers, the fruit of the horse chestnut tree, half hidden in the grass under the spread of the trees.

Polly started conversation. 'The War is dreadful Nellie much worst than ever anticipated.'

Nellie nodded and replied, 'The injuries of some of the wounded soldiers at the Big House are horrific. I don't know how Mary copes nursing them. She does wonders especially as she works very hard on the farm and then finds time for her nursing shift. She never complains, she fits it all in. But time is the least we can give in comparison to the generosity of the Wilbrahams, who have opened their home as a hospital.'

Polly continued in a lamenting tone, 'The Wilbrahams spend a good deal of their time in their London home and the casualty crisis is so grave they had little option of allowing the Hall to be a hospital before it would have been commandeered in the War Effort. The Dowager wished it had been allowed to be a school to spare the premises from the obvious harsh treatment it is receiving. She does worry about the eventual condition of the Hall when the War is over. The beautiful iron gates have gone to be melted down already.'

Suddenly changing her tone Polly eagerly announced, 'I have some confidential information about King George and Queen Mary. It is known by the higher ups that they are seriously considering changing the Royal Family name from Wettin to the House of Windsor.'

'Why?'

'To sever ties with the House of Saxe-Coburg Gotha.'

'Isn't that a snub to the deceased Victoria?'

'Yes, that rudeness is acknowledged. However there needs

to be a disassociation from the Saxon Arms as matters have gone beyond that now with this dreadful War. The national hate for the Germans is intense and it would be prudent for the Royals to portray themselves as English.'

Nellie stopped bending, straightened herself and pondered before saying, 'House of Windsor, perhaps that wont be strange to accept, I can't recall saying Wettin anyway.' Polly also stood and emphasised, 'Well, we will have to get used to it to protect the Royals from any national backlash, especially as Prince Albert was German.'

Nellie decided to bring the conversation back to the conkers as she felt there was more to be divulged. 'Why are we collecting these Polly?'

'I've told you. Queen Mary wants them.'

'For what exactly?'

'We don't need to know, we should simply do as we are asked.'

'There's more to it, isn't there, Polly. You are hiding something.'

'Nellie don't push me into a corner', Polly firmly replied.

'You know more', Nellie pressed her. Polly usually smiled slightly when Nellie was getting close to the kernel of a situation and that was normally an indicator to Nellie to give one last push of inquisitiveness, to extract some sort of confidential truth out of Polly. However, this time Polly's eyes gave way to fear and alarm.

She took a slight step forward to Nellie and grasped her forearm.

'Please don't ask anymore. It is a secret.'

'Oh you and the Dowager and your secrets', Nellie said dismissively, trying to brighten Polly's countenance.

'No, Nellie, it's true it is beyond a confidence between myself and the Dowager. It is a State Secret!'

'A State Secret!' Nellie exclaimed rather loudly.

Polly shook her arm with a prolonged 'Sshhh', as though they could be overheard.

'I'm sorry', Nellie said in a quieter subservient tone.

Polly continued softly but forceful in an endeavour to harness Nellie's open nature. 'Please don't tell a soul why the conker gathering is imperative. They are needed for the war effort. I mean it, Nellie. We must not say a word.'

Nellie was taken aback at Polly's words and was visibly shocked. She nodded affirmatively, biting her lip with a sincere indication to Polly that she totally understood.

A silence fell for a while and they both continued filling the baskets with the conkers in a good brisk working spirit. When they were nearing the end of their task Nellie enquired, 'Do you like your cottage Polly? Have you settled?'

'Oh yes, very much. I have learned the meaning of words like tranquil and contentment. I admit it broke my heart leaving Higher Smallwood Farm but all good things have to come to an end. I feel immensely fortunate to have lived here for all those years and experienced the life and ambience of such a beautiful big Cheshire farmhouse as my home.'

Pausing with a lovely reflective countenance Polly commented at length, 'They were in the main happy days and I have many fond memories of the working seasons, the entertaining, Queen Victoria's Jubilee, your wedding, the christenings, the turn of the century activities with the staff, the Coronation and, of course, the happy precious Christmas festivities. Can you remember how each of us had a family birthday tea on the Sunday nearest to our birthdays? Yes every good get together is tucked firmly in my heart.' Nellie was warmly smiling at Polly's vivid recalling of fond memories of her farm life yet detected in her eyes the evident liking of her new cottage life.

Polly added brightly, 'Yes, I am pleasantly surprised how I have settled into Church Cottage and my smaller lifestyle. I do appreciate less work, less cleaning. I enjoy being in the centre of Rode. It has many advantages, especially the ease of travelling on my tricycle. I don't need a large outbuilding for a stable. I am physically independent and able to visit the elderly and do little jobs for them and I especially visit the Dowager more frequently. She is becoming quite frail, and very appreciative of any time I can spare her as a companion. Looking back I simply do not know how I coped with the work rate of a busy farmhouse day but we all do, when we have to.'

After a short pause she continued, raising her shoulders slightly in her excitement. 'Yes all in all I am very content with my little cottage by All Saints, I can walk to church and I am trying to foster what my grandfather used to say, some of the warmest welcomes come from the smallest hearths.' Nellie leaned and hugged Polly and gave her a gentle kiss on the cheek and as their embrace ended Nellie stated, 'I have certainly missed you living here, Polly, but I am very pleased that life has unfolded nicely for you. You deserve it.'

They reciprocated loving smiles and Nellie was pleased to detect the old definition of happiness in Polly. It was clear to see her eyes and heart were level.

After placing the last few conkers on the laden baskets the two ladies carried a basket each and one basket between them in the customary country way to share the weight. They made their way back to the farmhouse for tea busily chatting, primarily about Mary and John, and enjoying the easy tug of the Gentle Ribbon.

One week later Nellie was busy attending to the bedding of new straw in the hen cote and thought of how well her hens had laid but also thinking that it was time to make a decision as to which ones needed to be killed for the pot. During her task she recalled clearly her days at Packhorse Farm when, her mother Emily, occasionally announced 'William there is a crowing hen!' This was an immediate instruction for her father to kill the offending hen for the pot. Country folks were reared to believe a whistling woman and a crowing hen would bring the devil out of his den, implying to keep the crowing hen would bring the devil and bad luck to a farm.

The penny dropped at that moment to Nellie that neither

herself, her mother nor her sisters Lily and Lucy, were allowed to whistle when they lived at Packhorse Farm; probably a throw back to the old curse of the devil. However Nellie felt it was much easier to follow other people's instructions as to the killing of old hens. She was fond of her hens and found it difficult to rise to the necessary job of culling and wished a few of her old hens would crow to lighten her decision, instead of contentedly clucking.

When she reached the farmhouse she washed her hands in the maids' kitchen and walked through to the morning room in haste. John and Mary were already eating their breakfasts and were rather irritated that she had undertaken an outside job before her own breakfast. They didn't need to say anything; Nellie could read their thoughts.

'I was only trying to catch up on a hen job or two', Nellie offered in her defence as she drew up her chair to the table to join them.

'Mother, we do not want you working like this, especially before breakfast and outside', Mary retorted.

'I have very little option. We have lived through another busy harvest without your father and little jobs get neglected. All I am doing is catching up with a few.'

Trying to be diplomatic and ease the tension between mother and daughter, John said, 'Mary has got a point. You are excellent at the cheese making and that is a big job and a responsibility in itself, plenty to occupy you and it certainly is the earning venture at the moment. The price of grain is down with the plentiful harvest so we do depend on your skill with the cheese for the necessary income.'

Nellie gave one of her rare despondent answers, 'I can well remember when the cheese was just for extra income and did not have to subsidise the farm. What is happening to farm prices? We are at the mercy of the Manchester dairies who are suppressing and distorting the milk price, although demand is reasonable. Also Uncle Leonard had a dreadful day at Congleton market with his beef cattle and is worrying about when to advise me to sell our steers.'

John in his youthful jest commented, 'I hope he didn't let his belly know he'd had a bad market.'

'Stop it', Mary said sternly glaring at John. 'Mother is right, farm incomes are serious at the moment. It is no time for joking, although I sometimes feel that Uncle Leonard is one of life's pessimists; perhaps in a couple of weeks the market might be better. If it isn't we will have to winter the steers ourselves.'

'At what cost, Mary? We only have enough fodder for the dairy herd. We cannot afford to buy in', Nellie realistically stated.

'I am not giving stock away, mother, to a poor price, I refuse to.'

'You may have to, my dear. Sometimes the first loss is the best loss.'

An uneasy silence fell as they continued eating their breakfast. Nellie trying to be slightly re-assuring remarked, 'Perhaps this war might help. I know it is a dreadful thing to say but farm incomes always fair better when there is a war on.' The rest of breakfast continued in silence.

After finishing their food Mary announced, 'I've something else serious to say, there is blight in the potatoes.'

'I've not noticed any blight', John quickly said trying to be in authority.

'I know blight when I see it and I tell you we have blight', Mary firmly declared.

'Oh no', Nellie sighed in despair and held her head as she uncharacteristically put her elbows on the table. 'Now the whole crop will be worthless.'

'Well, I'm sorry to say, we have', Mary confirmed positively.

A worrying silence reigned for a while before John changed the subject to the unopened post at the side of their table. 'Do you want to open your post, mother?'

'Not really it will only be bills to be paid.'

'How are we doing with them?' Mary questioned.

'Oh I am up to date as I can be but, of course, that leaves little for Lady Day and I know from old that rent day soon comes round and if you are financially down then it obviously takes you down even further.'

Mary could see fear and sorrow in her mother's eyes and let the farming conversation lie.

John unaware of the severe mood, lightly announced, 'Here's a postcard from Uncle Edgar.' On cheekily reading it he continued, 'He says, he hopes your spirits have lifted sufficiently since father passed away, as he wishes to take another portrait of you mother. He is intending to visit on the second Wednesday of October and will travel here on the afternoon train. He says he has checked and there is no train running in the aforenoon so could he possibly put on your good nature and make use of your guest room over night. If he hears nothing to the contrary he will see you as written.'

'Oh no!' Nellie exclaimed. 'That's all we need to hold us up from our work', she declared with an extended sigh.

Mary thought for a moment or two, watching her mother take the post card from John to read the words for herself, before she proceeded with caution. 'Perhaps that would do you good. He is a lovely jovial man and would certainly lighten Higher Smallwood at the moment.'

'No, Mary. What do I want another portrait for? I only really had the others done to please your father. Besides they are expensive. We have no money for such frivolities. No, I think it is a bad idea and why should I want a photographic portrait now, of all times, in my widowhood? I shall write back with the excuse it is too soon after your father's death.'

'Please don't', John interrupted. 'I like Uncle Edgar, he will lift all our spirits. He is good with dogs and I would love a portrait of myself with my best spaniel.'

Nellie looked at her children and saw in their faces a chance for a smidgen of pleasure and decided she could not rob them of that, so after a long pause she nodded in the affirmative.

'Perhaps you are right', she said and added, 'I will have to take better care of my hands or hide them on any photograph.'

Mary slightly smiled and used the opportunity to say, 'You can start by staying indoors with your work and leave the outside to us', giving a prodding glance to John to buck his working ideas up. He took note of Mary's glance and as they all parted after breakfast he had a gangly spring in his step.

How Nellie lamented that Rose had left Higher Smallwood. She had to attend to the cleaning of the spare room personally and the freshening of the bed linen. Whist dutifully doing so, her thoughts drifted to Rose and the times they had worked competently together. Nellie found it ironic that through concern for Rose's delicate health, due to her growing nervous disposition, Polly had taken it upon herself to reveal Rose's plight to the Dowager. Alfred's sister had sadly died so through Polly's information to the Dowager, the Wilbrahams in their kindness, offered Rose Church Cottage next door to Polly. Nellie further pondered on how strange fate was. Little did Polly or Rose know when they resided together at Higher Smallwood, on different levels of life, that in their later life they would be spinster neighbours in their adjoining tied cottages, and able to continue their genuine help to one another.

Edgar

Edgar timed his Autumn visit to weather perfection. St Luke's Little Summer, sometimes known as an Indian Summer, was glowing and highlighted the intense beauty of the time of the year punctuated by the blazing seasonal colour of the leaves on the trees. The warmth was most welcome and the hint of a zephyr breeze stirred the sunny haze with Autumn's ever familiar damp scent of Flora's decay. As he alighted from the train at Mow Cop he was astonished to see Nellie by the station master's office on the platform, waiting to greet him personally.

When they were a few yards apart, he removed his trendy brown bowler hat and almost bowed to his waist. Nellie could not help smiling at his overdone gesture on meeting and hurriedly made the short distance between them disappear, to kiss him on the cheek to avoid anyone noticing his flamboyant arrival. He held her shoulder to slow down such an endearing moment for him and returned her sudden kiss with his own kiss on her cheek at a much gentler pace. He tried desperately to put forward his caring family side but, in reality, he could feel that her very presence had made his heart skip a beat.

He thought she looked radiant on that halcyon afternoon. Although she had suffered the dreadful death of George; her hair was shining, immaculately pinned high under her boater hat, showing her long attractive neck and her big blue eyes were bright. Her waist appeared trimmer than ever and her smile was as alluring as he had remembered it through all the time of absence.

On arrival at Higher Smallwood Farm, Mary and John made a dash across the farmyard, as their Uncle Edgar alighted from the landau and they boisterously hugged him simultaneously. He was surprised to see how grown up they both were and that John had grown much taller than Mary. Nellie was pleased to see her childrens' first real spontaneous demonstration of happiness since the sad loss of their father.

Edgar brought a variety of light relief to Higher Smallwood. The change of conversation was a tonic for Nellie, Mary and John and he had the good sense to share his time between them during the rest of afternoon and fitted in extremely well.

Just before the evening meal he took Nellie by the arm, placed it over his and they walked from the back door to the garden side of the farmhouse. The hanging warmth of the day had been pressed to the ground by the heavy chill air of the Autumn twilight, filling the undulating meadows with thick folds of white mist, a rare magical sight to behold.

He stood behind her holding her shoulders and raised his right hand in front of her face, pointing to the zenith of the exquisite orange full moon rising over Mow Cop. It was huge and as perfect as any sphere could be in the heavens. To see the full moon sandwiched perfectly between the pure white mist and the early twinkling stars was, without doubt, amazing. A precious chance, to a receptive soul, of witnessing a fleeting togetherness of Mother Nature's time and place. Nellie was well aware the minutes were gems to treasure; the heavens and the mist would move on.

Edgar told Nellie that some people were confused about the Harvest moon. Many thought it to be the September moon but true country folk always took the full October moon to be the real Harvest moon, the one they were looking at. Nellie loved to learn something new and, for a split second, missed George's country knowledge. She remembered George had told her the November moon was referred to by men as the Hunter's moon even though country ladies claimed it for the Lover's moon.

As they were returning to the farmhouse she had an impulse to hold his hand, and followed her desire with ease. Her immodest instigation was a welcome surprise for Edgar. For her to hold his hand rather than link his arm was a step closer to intimacy, so he purposely tightened his grip, indicating to her his pleasant acceptance. He kept looking forward unable to believe it was happening. Nellie did not turn her head either as she kept walking, and the evening gloom masked his Cheshire Cat smile, whilst their hands entwined. Nellie was naturally tactile and she did lament that the cacoon of widow hood kept her away from small actions of human touch. She was quite intrigued with herself that she was enjoying the clasping of their hands, although very conscious to attend to immediate cessation, on entering the farmhouse.

During the meal in the dining room Nellie was surprised by Edgar's sound grasp of political knowledge. He even stated that it was time all women had the vote, which pleased her. Edgar worried that there were more intricate forebodings for Europe, particularly in Russia, appertaining to the Tzar. He felt strongly that the Tzar was not listening to the will of his people and warned that it was a very dangerous game for any monarch to play. Nellie inwardly noted she had never had the opportunity of listening deeply to Edgar before. She liked sharing time with a man with a good brain and was pleasantly stimulated by his discerning mind.

Thankfully Edgar had the sense to include in his conversation, many lighter points about life in general and it was good to hear laughter once more around the dining table. He cleverly turned the conversation to cheese making asking many questions, the answers to which made Nellie and her family sound knowledgeable and proficient. Tongue in cheek, Edgar commented that bad cheese needed butter and good cheese deserved butter, which brought a chuckle from Mary. Whilst he was on a roll, he decided to give John some manly advice, stating that apple pie without cheese was like a kiss without a squeeze. As John was laughing loudly, obviously understanding the adult connotations of the little ditty, Edgar glanced at Nellie hoping to see a flicker of a signal in her eyes. Nellie was astute and, although she could feel his gaze, she purposely kept her eyes away from his, not rising to his bait.

After their meal, the long over due use of the drawing room with it's focal point of the roaring fire, was cosy. Quite late in the evening the children took their leave for bed and kissed their mother good night and their Uncle Edgar. When they were alone, Edgar thought Nellie had relaxed enough in his company, so he ventured to mention the portrait. Nellie intimated that she did not think it was the correct time in her early widowhood but he persuaded her that they would try and accomplish the photograph in the morning light of the drawing room the following day.

Nellie was slightly nervous when changing her clothes on the morrow, in the mid morning, after she had finished her jobs. Apart from church and a few family occasions, it was the first time she had worn one of her lovely gowns for another man. She kept thinking of Edgar, as though she was dressing solely for him. He had kept an upright youthful figure, no middle age paunch for him. She liked his full head of grey wavy hair and thought his new brushed back style looked fetching. His grey green eyes were very unusual and beguiling. In her welling anxiousness, she inadvertently dabbed her ear lobes twice with her lavender water.

She was even more nervous when she entered the drawing room at eleven o'clock, perfectly groomed and adorned with much of George's jewellery. Edgar was busy setting up his photographic equipment and when he turned around as Nellie entered the room, he was stunned and entranced by her beauty. However, he instinctively knew it was all to no avail. He did not want to capture Nellie with a nervous smile. She was right; the timing was totally wrong.

She stood before him and immediately said, 'Edgar I'm sorry.'

He walked swiftly across the room and hugged her, and as his face was near to hers, he commented, 'Don't worry, my dear. You are right, I am wrong. Say no more we will forget the whole idea.'

The relief he felt in Nellie as he held her was apparent. She pulled herself away and said softly, 'Thank you for understanding me. I feel as though I have wasted your time.'

In a kind tone he stated, 'Think no more of it, my dear, please. I will go into the garden and make John happy by photographing him with his dog. Yes, that is what I will do.'

Nellie was grateful for his consideration and stepped back, as he collected his equipment and took it efficiently away for his outdoor photography. She watched from the window at John's proud stance with his best dog, holding his father's gun, while the photographs were taken on the front lawn. Edgar also persuaded Mary to change into a nice velvet dress and he took a lovely portrait of her and her favourite cade lamb Thumber. How like George he thought Mary was and she was not going to be as tall a lady as her mother. A lovely girl but could not hold a candle to her mother's beautiful looks and he pondered on how often Nature does that; it seldom follows that the daughters of a beautiful mother can capture their mother's perfect countenance.

Mary with Thumber the cade lamb

Nellie, in her embarrassed state, thought the least she could do was to extend Edgar's stay in the guest room for a further night, to which he agreed and thankfully the happiness they all shared the second evening seemed even more pleasant than that of the previous evening.

After the children had repeated their goodnight and Nellie and Edgar were alone sitting by the fireside, he ventured to speak from his heart. 'Nellie I really did believe I wanted to see you to take your portrait once more and, don't worry, it matters not that it has not come to fruition. I think I have captured some important photographs to record the children's activities, which I am sure they will appreciate in due course. But I have not been honest with myself or, worst of all, with you. The plain fact is you are the last person I think about when I go to sleep at night and the first when I awake. I have always had a fond regard for you, you know that, even when George was alive and, he too was very aware of it, although he knew it was always within the bounds of correct affection. But since his death the feeling is increasing in me. I have never married but I do want to spend the rest of my days with you. I am not, on this visit, going to ask for your hand in marriage but would I be wrong to let my deep affection for you cross easily over the line to having a love for you?'

Nellie rose sharply to her feet and elegantly paced the room, in an endeavour to take control. To watch her slowing walking heightened Edgar's desire, her gown enhancing the lovely contours of her body, like the perfect silhouette of a single lily tilting serenely with perpetual beauty from it's stem. After a few seconds she stopped and, looking at him confidently, stated, 'But you are George's cousin and of his age.'

He immediately interrupted, 'Only ten years your senior Nellie, only ten years.' 'Yes, I know', she said assertively and added, 'but you have never been married and I have thought, together with many other family members, of you as a ladies' man. You adore their company in general and often flatter ladies, you cannot deny. You also bear the scar of being responsible for a broken engagement thus being legally sued for Breach of Promise.'

'Yes that is true but I have never really loved. I have sown my wild oats but never found a woman, in the many I have known, who has truly taken my heart. But you have, Nellie. Now I have that feeling.'

With utter openness Nellie instructed, 'Well please don't. I have never thought of loving you, as pleasing as your company has always been to me. I do not think I could trust you, even if fate put us together in love.'

'Oh, Nellie, that is a cruel thing to say.'

Nellie would not be put off course and pressed on. 'The purpose of any adult conversation between two good friends, and I do consider we are good friends, is to be honest. I would not knowingly lead you to believe that you are free to love me.'

'No, Nellie, you are wrong. When we are at our time of life, decisions can be taken with clearer minds. It would be easy for us to live together in a marriage with or without love, a deep affection would be sufficient and, I could also offer you financial security, much sought after by many women, particularly widows.'

'No!' Nellie declared, raising her voice and continued firmly, 'It is because I care for you and for my own feelings, I will not consider any remarriage just for security. Love will come first, second and third! Selfishly, I will not have it any other way for myself.'

Even though she was verbally tearing a strip off him, he was heady with the intoxicating delight of being alone with Nellie and talking intimately with her. He did not want to waste the contrived opportunity of enjoying her beauty, company and conversation so he quietened his tone and declared, 'It is too soon, Nellie. I should have bided my time, before I gave you an understanding of my feelings. I am sorry, you are right. I will leave in the morning sharing, I hope, the same friendship we had before the death of George. I have misjudged your lingering love for George.'

Much to his surprise Nellie replied rather coldly, ' On the contrary I know it was evident to many, from a few of the staff here to family members at wedding gatherings, particularly at Aston Hall, that George and I did not share a close love but we did have a devoted marriage. I will not lie to you. I sadly don't think I ever truly loved George. You have no dying love to conquer. All I am saying is before any thoughts of remarriage love will come first and a marriage thereafter. Marriage for security will never enter my mind.'

He thought what a proud, honest and beautiful woman Nellie was before him. She had conducted herself with aplomb, the only thing wrong was his timing. He must be patient he kept telling himself.

'Very well', he said in a caring tone, 'I think we can credit ourselves for being direct and who knows what the future may bring.'

With that he said good night, kissed her politely on the cheek, although he longed to linger, and took to his bed like a gentleman.

The following morning passed without any tension between Nellie and Edgar. His debonair ease won the day, so much so that in the afternoon Nellie escorted him to the railway station in the landau, with Alfred at the reins.

On the small platform they parted the best of friends, with a social kiss that was extremely warm. As the majestic train steamed out of Mow Cop Station, Nellie waved her snow white handkerchief, by way of a fond farewell. He leaned out of the window of the railway carriage and blew a meaningful goodbye kiss from his hand. The intertwining of smoke and steam, swirling in the draft, as the carriages went out of vision, held Nellie's thoughts deeply. She could not correctly pigeon hole her feelings for Edgar, nor in her blurred stare could she decipher which was reality or fantasy, the smoke or the steam?

When she turned to leave the station she paused to gather her thoughts properly. She was surprised how she had enjoyed his visit, although she had been unaware of his deep feelings for her. However, his declaration had stirred her into thinking that she could not deny the time was lighter in having a man around for herself. In his company he had made her feel special and she had enjoyed being touched and held, simple physical actions which she missed through being a widow. She felt good to be in fine gowns again and to be in tune with her inner feelings as a woman.

CHAPTER 24

THROUGH THE VEIL OF FAMILIARITY

On the 16th December around eleven o'clock in the morning, on an unusually mild day, John burst open the kitchen door in anxious delight. 'Quickly mother! Come Quickly! Come on!' 'What is it John? What is the matter?' Nellie hastily asked as she wiped her hands on her working apron and grabbed her thick woollen shawl.

'I can hear something, please come quickly', John replied as he disappeared out of the door way to the farmyard. Nellie ran after him light heartedly pondering what could have stirred John suddenly. When she was in the farmyard she could see him near to the drive, so she ran further to join him.

'Ssshh! Listen!' he instructed her. As they both listened they could hear the honking of a horn. 'I think it's an automobile coming up the drive!' he shouted in exhilaration. 'Who could be coming here in an automobile? Do you think it is the Wilbrahams?' he asked, jumping uncontrollably on the spot. Nellie stood by his side looking down the long drive and put her hand on his shoulder to try and calm him and stated, 'No, of course not, the Wilbrahams won't be coming here unannounced making such a noisy arrival. No it certainly will not be the Wilbrahams.'

'Who do we know with an automobile?' John persisted in his excitement. 'It definitely is one, listen it is getting closer!'

John and Nellie watched almost spell bound that an automobile was making a first visit to Higher Smallwood. The intermittent happy honking of the horn had attracted the attention of Alfred and Ada who were making their way into the yard and Mary was running to join her mother and John.

'What is the commotion about? Is it an automobile?' Mary asked in wonder.

'Yes it most certainly is!' John pronounced and he and Mary ran spontaneously down the rise of the drive. Nellie stood her ground watching her children running at speed, Mary's loose long auburn hair flowing, as the machine appeared around the corner near to Green Lane. Yes it was an automobile!

The horn was almost incessant when the vehicle was in view and Nellie could perceive a man, wearing a baggy peaked hat and goggles, solo at the wheel. Who on earth could it be? In the distance the children met the gleaming, cream, tub-like automobile and ran excitedly alongside as it took the rise of the drive. Nellie stood to one side as the vehicle with large chrome headlights trundled past her and she instantly recognised the huge smile of Edgar. Gushing with smiles and carried away by the momentous occasion herself, she quickened her pace to the centre of the farmyard, where he brought the automobile to a triumphant halt.

Alfred, Ada and the children were almost mobbing Edgar as he pulled back the huge handbrake and stood on the running board waiting to climb down. Before doing so he stood, looked in the direction of Nellie and raised his arms in the air stretching them wide as possible, as if in acknowledgement that his journey had been worthwhile and he had received the welcoming acclamation he somehow knew he would. She thought, of course only Edgar could have made such an incorrigible arrival. Hardly before she knew it he was down from the vehicle and holding her tight. She was trying to be sensible but she reciprocated with a wonderful embrace and allowed him to kiss her fondly on the lips as he twirled her around. Nobody observed their welcome for each other. John had hurled himself into the driving seat of the automobile holding the steering wheel and Mary had quickly positioned herself in the passenger seat. Alfred and Ada were in awe of such a vehicle and touching and admiring almost every part of the exterior.

When Nellie came to her senses and peeled herself from his loving embrace she worried about the automobile, particularly the children sitting in the shining brown leather seats and her slightly anxious glance relayed her thoughts to Edgar.

'Don't worry, Nellie, let them enjoy themselves. Do you like it?'

'Of course I do! but what about you, are you cold? Are you hungry?'

'I'm not cold, I have deliberately chosen my day for the journey, that is why I come rudely unannounced but yes refreshment would be most welcome.'

Nellie took his hand, pulling him in the friendliest, almost girlish of ways and personally made him a cup of tea in the kitchen and added a dash of whiskey. Their privacy and his rest did not last long before John and Mary ran into the farmhouse requesting a ride. Nellie allowed her children, well wrapped, to disappear out of sight with Edgar for their first journey in an automobile to the church and back. John sat in the front passenger seat and Mary easily squeezed into the small dickie seat at the rear. They arrived back very excited and elated and confessed that they had persuaded Uncle Edgar to extend their journey along Boarded Barn before they returned to Higher Smallwood via Chance Hall Farm. Although Nellie shook her head slowly at the fact they had put on Edgar's good nature, she knew it had been a pleasure to him, so she did not reprimand them for over stepping the mark. By that time Ada had resumed her duties and produced a delicious hot lobby for Edgar, Nellie, Mary and John and they dined in the large living kitchen with a roaring fire.

After the meal, which was very lively due to the childrens' bombardment of questions regarding the automobile, Nellie enquired, 'Do you require overnight accommodation Edgar?'

'No! No! circumstances are different with an automobile. Although petroleum is limited, I have a very good friend who has helped me around that situation and I have sufficient to take me home this afternoon but it must be sooner rather than later as I would prefer to be home before it is completely dark.'

The children were visibly disappointed but Edgar proceeded, 'I will, of course, take you a ride, Nellie, before I leave.'

Knowing the light was pressing Nellie declined.

'No, Edgar, you have been very kind to Mary and John, I do appreciate that. I will not take you up on your offer but I certainly will go for a ride in the automobile with you in the Spring when the light is better, if you care to visit us again?'

Edgar was delighted and relieved that such an invitation had been extended by Nellie in a natural way. He was aware that he had achieved two visits to Higher Smallwood by his conniving and felt, out of courtesy and, not wishing to show his desperation to see her, that he would need a direct invitation from Nellie next time. To his joy she had just extended that invitation. He tried to keep a calm even voice and stated, 'I think you are prudent and thoughtful about the light and yes I would very much like to revisit in the better weather and take you for an excursion then.'

He paused slightly and changed his tone of voice, 'I will give you the photographs, the purpose of my journey today, and take my leave within about half an hour.' He stood and reached for his large leather pouch and produced his photographs. They were a charming capture of John's pride in his dog and gun and Mary's love for her darling cade lamb Thumber and were very well received. After Nellie and the children had studied them with evident gratitude Nellie enquired, 'How much do I owe you Edgar?'

'Please, Nellie, it is a pleasure for me to provide the photographs, I do not require payment.'

Nellie could see the question of money was slightly embarrassing to him but she did want to keep financially straight with him.

'Very well, I insist, when you do revisit you must stay overnight and use the guest room again. It is the least I can offer for your kindness, as I know the process of photography is expensive.'

His heart skipped a beat that she had so graciously extended her invitation to him.

'Thank you', he said, trying once more to subdue his inner elation and suppressing over exuberant words he simply said, 'I would like to stay at Higher Smallwood once more.'

Smiles overtook the need for any further words on that matter but the quizzing questions of the children regarding the automobile soon ate away the remaining half a hour. When Edgar was re-garbed and about to climb into his vehicle in the farmyard, by way of a farewell he tried to kiss Nellie again on her lips. She was more in control and he had misjudged that fact. Two hours earlier he had shared with her a divine kiss to treasure but that was two hours ago. He thought he had gone through the veil of the familiarity of the cheek to the lips but Nellie expertly extended her cheek and he fell into line once more and had to content himself with a tender kiss planted on her cheek, although he did his utmost to linger close to her. She pulled back with dignity and encouraged the children to forward their familiar hugs and kisses to him.

They all watched as Alfred bemusingly turned the starting handle. The engine initially ticked then roared and they waved the contraption away down the drive rise. After Edgar and his strange new vehicle disappeared from view they could hear the occasional honking of the horn as he was travelling down the long twisting drive, which made them all smile.

It was difficult for the occupants at Higher Smallwood to settle to work after the visit of the automobile. Nellie tried to chivy along the yuletide work of plucking and dressing of the chickens and geese but the work was harder without George. Things were not the same, could not be, and another Christmas seemed to highlight his passing and created a cloud of melancholy.

Among the cards and letters from the postman Nellie could recognise the handwriting on the envelope of one as being from

George's sister Esme at Aston Lodge, Staffordshire. As she carefully opened the envelope and unfolded the yuletide card a letter fell out. Nellie always liked reading Esme's correspondence, so took the time to digest her written words. Apart from asking if all were well and hoping Nellie had coped with the poultry dressing, Esme informed her that she had heard she was receiving visitors and perhaps adjusting to the loss of George, which she sincerely hoped was true. If that was the case, Esme suggested that in the early Spring it might do Nellie good to have a few days away from Higher Smallwood and she would like to extend an invitation to her to visit Aston Lodge.

Nellie re-read her letter and pondered for a moment and had to admit to herself that such a visit would be most welcome and something to look forward to. Later, when she had tea with Mary and John she mentioned their Aunt Esme's letter and the children instantly thought it was a good idea.

When the first sign of Spring appeared Mary and John had not forgotten Aunt Esme's invitation to their mother and persuaded her to press forward with arrangements for an April visit. This would accommodate Nellie's return home to attend to the intense cheese making work involved with the flush of good milk, produced when the cows would be put out to grass day and night, normally around the 12th May.

On the 17th April after issuing endless instructions as regards the smooth running of Higher Smallwood during her absence, Nellie was sitting beside Alfred in the trap with her travel bag to visit Aston Lodge and looking forward to her four nights stay.

Much refreshed and in what seemed no time at all she returned to Higher Smallwood where the children greeted her with beaming smiles in the farmyard. Later, at tea time, she relayed almost every detail of her very pleasant time with Esme.

'Who is the most handsome, Cuthbert or Samuel?' John enquired in an impish way.

Nellie played into his hands, thinking she had caught a thread of his tantalising teasing of Mary, and replied, 'Oh I think

Cuthbert. Yes Cuthbert.'

'Oh good, can we marry him off to Mary?' John predictably asked.

'Stop it!' Mary exclaimed, 'I am not going to marry a cousin and besides he is a decade older than me', she said firmly.

'That's not bad', John said, continuing his sibling mischief making. 'Father was only about that age older than you, wasn't he?'

Nellie slightly frowned, wishing that she hadn't allowed John so much freedom of speech, before answering, 'Yes but an age difference is no detriment if it is a good marriage.'

'Well, you and father were happy weren't you? We could marry Mary off to Cuthbert.'

Nellie could see Mary's irritation at John's playful persistence and decided to defuse the situation.

'Yes, of course your father and I were happy but that does not mean Mary should marry Cuthbert, or Samuel, for that matter, they are older than her and her cousins and she has already told you she is not marrying any cousin, so we should heed Mary's wishes, not yours, John.'

John changed his tact and started to agree. 'Oh yes, I agree, I am not going to marry a cousin, Uncle Alec says we shouldn't. He doesn't like cousins marrying. He's not keen on two brothers from one family marrying two sisters from a different family either. He says there's plenty of local pretty girls around.'

Nellie took the conversation, trying to keep a maternal balance. 'Some cousins are happily married, particularly second cousins. I know a few.'

'Well, I'm going to take Uncle Alec's advice', John said with certainty.

'I am definitely going to take his advice!' Mary forcibly announced. 'In fact I don't think I will ever visit Aston Lodge, as nice as Aunt Esme is. I don't want either of her sons to get the wrong idea or for her to palm me off with one.'

Nellie gave a little smile and was grateful that their family conversation from division had returned to a general agreement.

After Rogation Service at All Saints Nellie decided she was mentally strong enough to entertain in the usual Higher Smallwood way and have many family members back for supper. She did find catering for over twenty people quite time consuming and, of course, she had to attend to many of the detailed chores that otherwise would have been undertaken by Rose and Polly, when they resided at the farmhouse. Mary pulled out all the stops, helping with cleaning and food preparation and even chivied John into tidying the garden, which looked quite respectable on that chill dry May Sunday evening, when the guests arrived after Evensong.

The get together was thoroughly enjoyed in many ways. Emily and William were pleased to see their daughter, Nellie, looking much better and coping with life as a widow. Polly was pleased to revisit Higher Smallwood and appreciated that things were going along without her assistance, and as always John managed to sneak away with Uncle Alec to the yard, this time to proudly show him his new spaniel pups in a loose box, before they joined the happy family gathering for supper. The fact that the new Rector had not bothered with Rogation tide beating of the bounds, as he thought it was out dated and a superfluous activity, was commented upon. However, there was a consensus of opinion at the supper table in the big living kitchen that his sermon that evening at All Saints was very appropriate for country folk. He had preached well.

After the appreciative guests had taken their leave and Nellie, Mary and John had attended to their fond farewells, it was well after nine o'clock. As it was now his responsibility, John went to check the stock in the fields, feeling thankful and lighter in heart for the long May twilight. Nellie and Mary decided, as Ada was absent, they should clear away all the food to the pantry and put the room back to normal, for they would have no time for such work on the following morning.

While they were attending to this task Mary decided she would broach with her mother a subject she had been thinking about for some time. 'I've been giving serious thought to the farm and the tumbling income.' Nellie paused and decided to sit, as she too thought some things had got to alter but she was not quite sure what. 'Yes, I too have been worrying but I am at a loss to find a solution.'

'Well, I think I have one. Please listen', Mary said as she sat on a dining chair. Nellie inwardly ached with her awareness of wishing that there was no need for any such discussion but accepting the reality of the situation, she nodded at Mary to continue.

The time was nigh for Mary. Her mental sentences she had often rehearsed over the farm finances, were now going to be uttered, so she took a deep breath before stating, 'Through no fault of anyone, just the times harsh financial times we are having to live through, we are having to let staff go and I have particularly been giving thought to Alfred.'

Nellie quickly lamented, 'No, I couldn't possibly ask Alfred to leave, Mary, he was so loyal to your father. It is our duty to feed and treasure him. We must manage somehow to find his wage and keep him here. He only lives in the loft over the granary steps, he is of little trouble to us, and cleans his own accommodation.'

Feeling more confident Mary stated, 'Please listen, I have a plan for Alfred. I have been worrying about justifying an income for him as well as not wishing for him to leave. I have spared him any land work, as he is excellent with the horses. He is diligent with the trap horses, he also turns the cart horses out for their work in amazing condition and guides me and John not to over work them. The rising cost of purchasing a horse is almost out of our limits, well certainly at the moment, so it is imperative that we take good care of our horses. We can also keep our travelling solely to the trap and sell the landau. The price of a landau is good as it will ever be, bearing in mind petrol is limited for automobiles because of the War.'

Nellie despairingly interrupted, 'But if we sell the landau, which I agreed we could do without, Alfred would feel we were pushing him out, he would feel unwanted.'

'No!' Mary said firmly as she proceeded, 'I have a new job for Alfred. He could take me to Sandbach Market where I intend to rent a stall and sell our surplus produce.'

'Mary, you couldn't possibly stand Market, you are a Walker your father would be appalled at such an idea!'

Mary trying to be gentle on her mother, but with a firmer grasp on the deteriorating financial situation of Higher Smallwood Farm, proceeded with care. 'Mother, you have done your utmost to shed staff in a dignified manner and we have managed with a few less important hands on the land. Because you do not need to provide as much daily food here it is now giving us a surplus in produce. We no longer need to make all the jams and preserves just for us, Ada and Alfred. We have not cut down on the hens. You are well meaning but give a lot of eggs away, far more than we use. I thought if I took at stall at Sandbach Market I could sell our surplus produce plus your good cheese. Therefore, I would need Alfred to help me to pick or prepare the produce, load the cart and we could both go to market. It would give him a new role here, a much greater sense of the need of his skills and it would only happen once a week on a Thursday, giving him enough time in the rest of the week to care for the horses. I have already enquired and there is a stall vacant underneath the Town Hall arches in Sandbach and I have first refusal on day stabling at The George hostelry, enabling Alfred to find cover on bad weather days.'

Mary paused at that point, to give her mother time to digest her words. Nellie said most despondently, 'Oh dear, your father would never have wanted you to do that.' Instantly Mary declared, 'With the greatest will in the world he is gone, his days here are no more but I do think father would think better of us if we tried to survive in a positive way, through these dreadful farming times, rather than steadily going down bank.' Nellie knew her daughter, with her strong character, was right and slightly nodded in the affirmative.

Mary took her mother's nod as a signal of acceptance of her words and as a sign for an opportunity to mention her proposed second change to Higher Smallwood Farm. 'Mother, there is something else.'

Nellie's eyes widened with anxiety. Mary had the knack of facing and dealing with trouble head on and Nellie thought, although she had to accept with reluctance the prudence of the market idea, she had a foreboding that Mary's next announcement would be worse.

'Because of John's age, I know you take the advice of well meaning farming uncles, particularly Uncle Lionel and Uncle Leonard, but frankly I can see Higher Smallwood sinking, despite their best efforts. They have enough to do on their own farms. As you know, we have a large acreage and we do need temporary hands to attend to the physical work of the land and the stock. Well, I plan to be in charge not the uncles, with your blessing of course, and I have made enquiries about having at least two Irish navies as hired hands here.'

Nellie took a sharp intake of breath and put her hands over her mouth for a second before exclaiming, 'Mary! Mary! What on earth would people think, you working in the fields alongside Irish men. What ever would be said about you at church!'

'I don't care.' Mary said strongly and proceeded, 'We won't be here to talk about a future at all if something radical is not done. We have very little money to pay staff and Uncle Alec says those who employ the Irish at the moment speak very highly of them regarding their work. They are paid on piece work rate and, of course, when we don't need them they can be laid off easing our stretched finances.'

'Uncle Alec! Why discuss it with him before me Mary?'

'I haven't purposely. He met me one evening last week at Keepers Cottage before I went on my nursing shift, when I was taking him a dead hen for his ferrets. He took me on one side and said how anxious he was becoming about Higher Smallwood, all our difficulties without father, the terrible farm prices and the shortage of labour. He put the idea in my head. He believes I am strong willed and would not allow any shananikins if I worked alongside any Irish labourer and I could cope with any untruths or gossip in Rode. Times are changing, mother. I think he is right and I have given it great thought before discussing it with you. I could cope and I would dearly like you to give me the opportunity to turn our fortunes around here. Please give it some thought. Don't be dismissive. Time and money is running out.'

Welling emotion misted Nellie's eyes. She had immense pride in Mary. Although slight in statue she had a physical strength to be admired but, because times were forcing country folks into unchartered waters, if Mary proceed with her course of action, it would not take her along the road of preparing to be a lady. How Nellie wished John was the elder child, not Mary and he was the one who was asserting himself in this conversation. But John was slightly too young to be totally aware of the responsibility of a big farm and here was Mary before her with the authority and competence to follow her words with dedicated actions.

Nellie stood and, holding back her tears, she leaned down to Mary and held her. Both could feel the much needed comfort of the Gentle Ribbon. The precious Ribbon cheered Nellie slightly and after they had drawn away from their loving embrace she said with sincerity, 'Which idea do you want me to agree to Mary?'

Mary's strong character shone as she stated clearly, 'Both please, mother. I can cope. I would not ask if I couldn't. Please put your trust in me. I can sort it and I will.' One lingering clasp of their hands confirmed to Mary without words that she could proceed with both of her ideas.

CHAPTER 25

LIFE IS NOT QUITE THAT BLACK
OR WHITE

Mary shouldering responsibility

The following year, around nine o'clock one chill April evening at Higher Smallwood Farm, Nellie and Mary were enjoying their usual supper time treat of diced bread with no crusts, sprinkled with newly cut sugar, covered with hot boiled creamy milk and topped with a little grated nutmeg. This combination of a food

Soldiers
Patients at Rode Hall

Mary sitting with convalescing soldiers
and a nursing colleague

and drink together was affectionately known as 'pobs' and needed a spoon with which to eat the hot soaked pieces of tasty home made bread from the small white pot basin. As well as being nutritious 'pobs' went a good way to induce sound sleep and without doubt the very best way to enjoy 'pobs' was in a twosome.

When they had finished Nellie enquired, 'How are you coping with your nursing at the Hall.'

'It's harrowing, Mother, and I wish I could do more but the Commandant is very positive and a good source of encouragement. All the nurses feel we can turn to her should situations of care escalate above our knowledge. With the soldiers' families being out of travel distance, when a patient sadly dies thankfully we only have the job of raising our own low moral and, as hard as that is, at least we do not have to deal with distraught grieving relatives of deceased loved ones. To assist people who are grieving must be a quality of character that is a gift. Mercifully, as you know, only two soldiers have died at the Hall but that's when I feel my inadequacy, depth of despair and failure the most. The poor lads managed to be rescued from the hell of war and yet we lost them despite all our nursing.'

Nellie interrupted with sorrow, 'Don't take it too much to heart. As tragic as their loss of life is, they died with dignity in the haven of the Hall. That in itself will be a source of comfort to their families and they will have a local grave at which to grieve. As we know, many of the young soldiers killed at the Front are being buried abroad.'

After a sigh and a slight pause Nellie continued, 'I'm still praying for the families of the Titanic horror. Many have no grave to give comfort or to draw a line under their grief. Not to know the whereabouts of a deceased loved one must be one of the cruelest things to bear on this earth. Grief must be endless.'

After a pause Mary flurried her thoughts into positiveness announcing, 'The Commandant does highlight all the good we do for the rest of the soldiers. Once they come to terms with their afflictions many of the soldiers are fun loving and a sheer tonic to the others. The Scottish lads are full of mischief. Let me tell you about their April Fools exploit last Tuesday.

Nellie smiled and was glad Mary was endeavouring to cheer herself and listened to her intently.

'You know how the Head Gardener is fettishly proud of his achievements within the walled garden, well Lady Wilbraham and the Commandant allow some of the soldiers to help him as part of their therapy. In the main their help is appreciated by the Gardener. However, Jock and two of his associates sneaked out of the Hall under the cover of darkness on Monday night and formed three perfectly domed mounds of soil in the freshly cultivated vegetable area. The following morning when the Gardener drew back his bedroom curtains at his cottage within the walled garden he immediately saw the soil mounds and thought he had got a mole. He was furious.'

Mary drew breath laughing at what she was about to say, 'When Jock and his partners in crime reported for gardening duty the Gardener had taken several steps as to the offending 'mole'. He had sent his lad at speed with a curt note of dissatisfaction to the Mole Catcher, high-lighting incompetence and announcing in all his experience of gardening years there had never been mole hills within the walled garden. Moles had always been apprehended in the runs outside the walls. The Gardener had also taken it upon himself to send two lads to borrow mole traps from Home Farm and Keepers Cottage.'

Mary trying to stifle more laughing continued, 'The Scottish lads kept their faces straight and even tried to assist the Gardener as he stalked about trying to trace the offending run which had given the perceived mole access to the hallowed garden ground. When the Mole Catcher arrived most insulted by the Gardeners's note, demanding an instant apology, the Scottish lads burst into fits of laughter.'

In a higher pitched voice, struggling to control her own laughter, Mary managed to say, 'The Gardener even reprimanded them for their disregard of such a serious situation and at that point they raucously announced it was All Fools day and the soil mounds were false mole hills.'

Nellie too was laughing so much that she had taken her handkerchief to her tears of hilarity and amidst her laughter questioned, 'What happened then?' With more control of her voice and as her laughter subsided Mary proceeded, 'The Gardener sat on his bottom on the edge of a small water butt and felt utterly deflated, almost limp with relief. He could hardly believe he had been taken in by such a prank. The Mole Catcher fortunately saw the funny side of the matter and playfully held the Gardener's shoulders putting him slightly off balance saying he really deserved to be dunked in the butt. The Scottish lads, amidst their laughter, shook hands in turn with the Gardener who was constantly shaking his head in disbelief.

After a slight pause Mary furthered in her mirth, 'When the Soldiers returned to the Hall and relayed their story a wave of laughter spread through the Hall. The Kitchen was in uproar and Cook had to take to a chair in case she wet herself in her laughter.'

Mary calming her voice to almost normal stated, 'The Commandant was very good. She personally went to the Gardener to apologise for the Scottish soldiers' prank but the Gardener's magnitude of character shone through, because he said he kept chuckling about the incident when it came into his mind.'

The laughing had given Nellie hiccups so she stood and took the two empty basins and spoons through to the kitchen sink and put them to soak in the bowl on the slopstone. She took the opportunity to drink water from the back of her glass which cured her hiccups. When she returned and sat in her chair again Mary said thoughtfully, 'Even though, in the main, I enjoy my nursing I do appreciate nights like this when I don't have to work a shift.'

'Good', Nellie replied. 'It is important to re-charge your energy especially with your working commitment on the farm. You must miss your father. He never would have envisaged you running the farm and managing the finances. He used to say, 'when you feel on the point of failure, you are very often nearer to the point of success' and mercifully you appear to have proved that point.'

Spontaneously Mary replied, 'Thankfully now, we are turning the crops into profit and we have been lucky with good harvests. Double summer time has been a great help. There is something very satisfying about seeing the loads of corn sheaves being carted from the fields into the stackyard and made into ricks. The Keenan lads have been invaluable and they toil hard. I have a high regard for their work. They have great skill. Uncle Alec was right, I can handle them as they have always shown me respect and they have settled as a family in Smallwood, you know.'

Nellie replied openly, 'Yes, I had heard and I have also heard of their drinking exploits on a Saturday night in Congleton.'

'I have too but, regardless of them working hard and playing hard, it amazes me that they rise early every Sunday and walk to the Catholic Church in Congleton. Their devotion is a credit to them. They never miss, unlike many of us young ones in Rode, who make work or the War our excuse for slipping the odd attendance at All Saints.'

Feeling she had digressed, Mary returned to her mother's original question. 'Yes, I do miss father dreadfully, however, I feel privileged father and I talked a lot and fortunately I was at an age to listen, understand and remember. It must be dreadful to only know your father through a photograph or to have been too young to remember your times together.'

Nellie nodded and allowed Mary to talk further.

'I hold one of his best yardsticks firmly in my mind and I live by it.'

With a glisten of pride in her eyes Mary clearly and firmly announced,

'Love many, trust a few but always paddle your own canoe.'

Nellie was saddened but pleased Mary had strong recollections of her father and said lovingly, 'He adored you

Mary. You were the apple of his eye.'

'I know', Mary replied with realism but not letting the moment get too melancholy moved on. 'I've made good friends at the Hall, although it has changed me. This War has changed many things. Well, perhaps not the War, but listening to some of the nurses and kitchen staff talking. I think quite a few of their attitudes are right.'

'Like what?' Nellie enquired with interest.

'Like not being a virgin when you get married.'

'What!' Nellie exclaimed in astonishment. 'Of course you must be a virgin. No decent husband wants a wife who is impure!'

Mary calmly continued, 'After listening to them I'm seriously thinking they have a valid point.'

Nellie rebuffed severely, 'Well, that is a very dangerous game to play. I cannot even begin to understand why you do not inform your friends they are wrong, let alone agree with them. Mary you have been reared to know what is right and what is wrong.'

'I know I have, mother, but life is not quite that black or white. Some say a few men have strange habits and it really is best to know your man before the altar. We all know once a girl is wed she has to yield herself to her man.'

'Yes I know', Nellie counter debated. 'But what about the risk of conceiving?'

'I still think they are right. I would rather walk down the aisle with child to the man I love and know, than take a chance that love might grow and I may or may not be physically compatible with him.'

Nellie sat upright giving herself time to think. Mary had struck an extremely raw nerve and she was desperately trying not to relay this to Mary in her eyes. Trying to take the moral high ground she said, 'Before he left the Rector warned of this attitude. He said on several occasions the loose ways of women from the industrial areas could over spill into our female country values.'

'Nonsense, mother. That has nothing to do with it. Times are changing fast. This War has altered things. I doubt if the

Rector got everything right. The girls say some Cardinals have mistresses and King Teddy was a rotter.'

Nellie answered sternly, 'Don't talk like that. There is a rotten apple in every barrel. There are some bad farmers and nurses. Remember bad examples can be found throughout the whole spectrum of life. The important work of the many in any profession should not be tarnished by the actions of a few. I advise you to keep a personal balanced view on life not just for yourself but for a continued respect of our good society.'

Mary realised that her last remark had been rebuked by her mother's correct point of view and decided to bring the discussion back to men. 'I do agree but I still have the strong feeling you should know your man before the altar. I hope if I have any daughters or granddaughters that they will know their man.'

In a tutting tone Nellie answered, 'I think you are treading a very dangerous path. It takes a very clever young lady to know the difference between love and lust. Men are very clever with their advances.'

'Oh I will know the difference', Mary answered very positively. 'I don't want to give you the impression that I am in floundering waters. Be assured I am good at using the word 'No'. I will only give myself to a man with love in my heart.'

Nellie wanted to steer her daughter back to the path of right and wrong and stated, 'But love is blind.'

Mary counter debated, 'Shallow or bland love is, when an uneasiness begins and your love wanes. But I am talking about true love; the real love that exists after excitement and dizziness evaporates. Pure two way love that can be undeniably felt within a kiss. True love is not blind it sees more because the head and the heart are in unison.'

'How will you know the difference?' Nellie asked harshly.

'Somehow I am very confident I will know, probably because of the very fact I am aware of the matter now. Once I walk down that aisle I will adhere to all my vows. I will never need to waiver with true love in my heart. I *will* have true love. It will be right.'

Nellie puffed slightly, blatantly aware that Mary was extremely perceptive and really would know her man and seemed on course in her own dangerous way to find true love.

Mary continued the conversation confidently, 'Besides Aunt Poll is always saying that history repeats itself. If that is the case, it is likely I will be widowed early in life like you. Therefore, it is imperative that I know my man before marriage and in turn have the sure knowledge that I love him for all the right reasons. I intend to spend my married life, no matter how short or long, with my one and only love. Therefore, I will only need to be married once. What did old Granny Bailey used to say 'make your engagement day the hardest day of your life and then your wedding day will be one of your easiest days'. No one can make a sound judgement without knowing all the facts. I think knowledge of physical compatibility is paramount, especially immediately prior to an engagement.'

Nellie was shocked and for once in her life was stuck for words and Mary sensed this and continued in a kindly purposeful manner.

'I'm not saying this to upset you, nor to antagonise you but to inform you of my thoughts.'

Nellie shook her head, her eyes slightly skimming with tears. She could not bring herself to accept Mary's point of view. It meant a great deal to her that she was pure when she took her vows in All Saints but she deeply lamented the fact that she never truly loved George. Should she have ever married him? Her head was swirling with thoughts and questions.

Mary had been honest but she was unable to reciprocate the special privilege of honesty. How could she shatter any of the good memories Mary held dear of her father? It hurt Nellie to realise she could not be as truthful to Mary as Mary was being towards her. She had never envisaged, in all her years of rearing her darling daughter, that a secret would develop to be kept from her. Nellie pondered deeply as to how could a secret appear in their very close loving relationship?

Life could be physically hard but it was just as hurtful to Nellie to feel her motherhood mental turmoil at that time. The night hours lulled Mary in peaceful sleep but the frank conversation kept mulling around in Nellie's head and gave her a restless lonely time in her bedroom.

A hard busy year ensued for all at Higher Smallwood Farm and Yuletide was once more upon them. Mary loved her Yuletide greeting cards and sent more, particularly to the injured soldiers at Rode Hall, to lift their spirits. She thought it a double blow for them, especially the Scottish lads, to be so far away from home. Nellie did not over care much for the modern custom of the cards and even less because she could not add George's name but nevertheless she continued the process of writing and posting them.

Amidst the atrocities of war Christmas at All Saints was uncheering to the worrying congregation at Rode. Would it ever end, the tragic loss that had touched most families locally and nationally? The Wilbrahams because of the War had reluctantly discontinued the tenants Christmas Eve function in the Tenant's Hall and it was sorely missed by the tenants. For many it was their only chance to share yuletide fellowship with neighbours, friends and relations at those gatherings, as well as enjoying the hospitality of the Wilbrahams.

Before the War when the Tenants Eve took place each year, a few thought they were attending out of a sense of duty but sadly realised after the gatherings had ceased they were wrong. Yes, in general the tenants yearned for the occasion to be reinstated so they could begin their Christmas in their customary way with themselves and their landlord.

Because of the demands of the War the Wilbrahams held a different Christmas gathering right in the heart of the Hall. Around the Christmas tree, in fact, in the large entrance hall where the Wilbraham family, the nursing staff and as many soldiers as could, the walking wounded, those confined to wheel chairs and some of the worse injured in their beds were shunted close together, for the carol singing.

That Christmas Miss Ffoulkes, the Commandant, had sent a postcard asking Mary to be present on Christmas Night for nursing duties and for the carol singing. Mary knew that volunteers were required to help pass round the mince pies and mulled wine and in her wisdom had decided it would do her mother good to help with these duties and had persuaded her to do so.

On Christmas evening, Mary took the reins of the horse in the trap and off mother and daughter set. Nellie thought it most odd that herself and Mary were braving the elements on that chill moonlit night without Alfred in control. However, Alfred had tacked the loyal Jack for the trap, a sound old faithful horse. Mary was unconcerned that she was in charge of the trap as they travelled down the Hall driveway at a good trotting speed. She competently turned her horse and trap off the drive to Keeper's Cottage. Uncle Alec always allowed Mary to leave her transport there when she was on nursing duty. When she had firmly tied Jack she helped her mother, who was holding tightly to her basket containing mince pies, down from the trap.

They linked arms and walked quickly, taking the short cut through the walled garden, down the cobbles to the Hall. As they were briskly walking Mary was informing her mother about the severity of the injuries of the soldiers and issued her with firm instructions not to stare at them but treat them as normally as she possibly could.

On arrival she pushed her mother forward as they entered the Hall via the estate offices for Mary to report for nursing duty. Nellie had not been to Rode Hall since it had become a hospital for the war wounded but she was greeted warmly and quickly by the Commandant, who informed her of her small catering duties.

Nellie was impressed by the charts of nursing care on the wall and the efficient air of the nurses who took charge of their patients with a slightly lighter heart, as everyone was in a mood to create a meaningful Christmas Night. In fact she felt quite humble at Mary's expertise, as she was watching her along with her colleagues, across the room dealing with the patients.

Nellie was grateful her pretty cousin, Ruby from Moors Farm, was standing with the catering corps in the Hall ready to sing the carols and Nellie tucked herself by Ruby's side. Nellie was also very touched by the stalwart efforts of the Wilbrahams who were doing their utmost to be welcoming and kind to all.

When the singing started to the accompaniment of the faithful Rode Silver Band, with the older men playing, because the younger ones were away at the war, the air of sadness but gratitude for life was extremely tangible. Tears streamed down a few soldiers' cheeks, not just in remembering their lost comrades, but wanting to be with their loved ones at home at such a precious time. It was a heart rendering sight, seeing some soldiers with mutilated bodies, singing the carols and believing in the Christmas message, even though their lives would never be the same again after they really had experienced the jaws of hell.

Nellie profoundly felt it put her own worries of life in proportion and she had many blessings to count. Thankfully, after the singing, Sir Randle recited two good monologues, namely 'Roses round the Door' and 'When I was a lad me father he was ed o'the house'. Sir Randle's excellent delivery ensured melancholy turned to amusement, making Nellie's duty of serving supper much easier. As the catering ladies threaded their way around the throng with the mulled wine and the freshly warmed mince pies the sound of moderate mirth rose to a crescendo making the efforts of everyone worthwhile.

A subdued New Year saw severe frosts at the end of January followed by heavy snow and another hard winter set in. The landscape offered no cheer, except for the skating on Rode Pool, although numbers of enthusiastic skaters had dropped because many youths from Rode were away fighting in the trenches and the dismal war news took the heart out of the merriment of skating.

The shoots at the Hall were not the same. The seriousness

of the continuous war had bitten into any misuse of ammunition, so shooting for pleasure was seriously curtailed. Officially only the killing of raptors and pests for the pot was permitted. It was imperative to exterminate the hawks to stop them killing homing pigeons carrying vital messages from behind enemy lines. Petroleum was also in short supply making it difficult for automobiles to be used and they were seen less frequently.

The farmers in Rode dug deep into their skills and culture to survive with their stock through the freezing weeks without a word of complaint, knowing any home complaint was an insult to the conditions suffered by the troops in the trenches overseas. It was a cruel winter that dragged on and strangely, the village silence on issues, even at church, spoke volumes about the harsh conditions, more than words. But as ever Mother Nature did not let the country folk down and the vernal air and the beauty of the eventual Spring was the perennial slight lifter of spirits.

CHAPTER 26

MY MOTHER NEEDS TO KNOW

The eleventh hour of the eleventh day of the eleventh month was a huge punctuation in history which affected individual lives and put an end to the ghastly, gaping, weeping wound of horrific aggression in Europe. Earl Haig, on behalf of Great Britain, signed the Armistice Agreement in that historic November of 1918. The killing guns ceased. Silence mercifully fell over the battlefields. Not one more death to add to the greatest loss of life at arms ever known. It was the end of the Great War.

Church bells rang for the first time in four years but they did not stir a wave of national rejoicing. Instead, cities, towns, villages and hamlets took the news in their own way. Cathedrals, churches and chapels were full of congregations giving thanks that prayers to put an end to the bloodshed had been answered.

But there was not one pocket of this sceptred Isle that was not suffering with the heavy heartache of loss and grief. Life would go on, of course it would. No dark tunnel takes away the will of a nation to live and survive but the knowledge of the futility of the whole black historical episode was raw and profound in dear Albion.

After a day or two of disbelief families started to put the pieces of their lives back together again to create a sense of normality. But what was normal? Social attitudes and actions had changed dramatically. The wastage of the war had been like tipping water out of a bucket and, no matter what effort was put into retrieving the water, most would remain outside the bucket and was seeping change and sadness over a wide area of society. However, because of large families, even if a mother had lost two sons to the bullet, when another returned home after the war it was a time of thankfulness to hold, if only one dear son, in her arms. As the weeks wore on, each occasion of loved ones being reunited and able to hold one another safe again, were actions which formed thousands of tiny platforms of love throughout the land and, put together as a whole, gave a vital national sense of hope for the future.

Nellie, her children and all the household of Higher Smallwood found it hard to believe they could attend All Saints released from the all consuming dark cloud of war. Rode was no different from any other village showing through the church an outpouring of gratitude that the senseless killing had ceased. Relief was tangible and it was obvious that the immense debt owed for freedom bought with the lives of some of the local lads must never be forgotten. British professional soldiers and the Nation had been used to war, the Crimean remembered by the elderly and the Boer fresh in memories. But this war was different. Youths and men who were not soldiers had enlisted because of their patriotism, knowing there was a job to be done and many paid the ultimate sacrifice.

The great British Isles had lost an incredible three quarters of a million of her sons; dead and tragically many without the dignity of a grave.

Even after that very first Peace service at All Saints the large congregation, thronging both the pathways, was earnestly discussing what would be fitting to remember the loved and lost of Rode. It seemed unanimous and imperative that some sort of stone memorial bearing their names should be erected. There was a swell of feeling that the incredible bravery of the lost and surviving soldiers, professional and enlisted, of that deplorable Great War most definitely had to be remembered.

The guns of battle had stopped but stopping the daily tasks as a result of that war particularly concerning the injured at Rode Hall went on as usual for quite some weeks. However patients' families became uneasy and decided it would be the best to take their own loved ones home to nurse and nurture them. If their injuries were too grave they wanted them nearer home in local hospitals. As the nursing at the Front ceased the doctors and nurses were able to return home to hospitals. In addition the necessary equipment, ointments, bandages and other medical supplies necessary to maintain the level of care required for the injured soldiers became available. This did not happen all at once but finally there was a will for 'the going home' to take place and eventually the last patient left Rode Hall.

The Commandant, nursing staff and kitchen staff were joined by the Wilbraham family members together with their estate staff for a special goodbye service conducted by the Rector at Rode Hall. Mary proudly stood alongside her colleagues for the last time in her nursing uniform. The Commandant thanked the Wilbrahams, particularly for allowing their family home to become hospital accommodation, as well as for their unstinting help and acceptance of the situation. She also thanked everyone in the room for their immense commitment to duty and said, although it was the official disbandment, she felt sure that the last four years they had experienced as an efficient team would be tucked into each of their hearts forever and would stand them in good stead to appreciate and treasure future joys and to cope with the inevitable heartaches of life.

Mary literally felt those meaningful words go deep within her and she made a mental note always to remember them, not to take life for granted and try to live by the Commandant's sound advice. Mary also felt privileged that she had been old enough to add, in her small way, something towards the war effort. There was no question in her mind that she had acted correctly in qualifying as a Red Cross nurse. Within the large drawing room, as the last hymn 'What a Friend we have in Jesus' was being sung, with tears in many eyes, Mary's thoughts drifted crystal clear to the faces and conditions of all the soldiers she had nursed over the war years and she could remember each one by name. She dearly hoped and prayed that her soldiers were coping well with their afflictions within the bosom of their families. Although they were young she prayed for love, kindness and understanding to always surround them throughout their lives and into their old age.

It was a turbulent time of social reshuffling. Some of the workmen, who had gone off to war and survived, dearly wished to resume their employment at Higher Smallwood Farm. Indeed, in many of their dark hours in the trenches, they had allowed their minds to dream of the beautiful peaceful meadows of Higher Smallwood in lovely Cheshire. Such dreams gave them a beacon of hope, should they survive that hell on earth, that they would one day be delivered to work again at Higher Smallwood.

The reality was brutal. Two men, on different days, had joyfully walked up the long drive, visually drinking in their old haunts which they though they would never see again, only to be told by a realist Mary and a despondent Nellie that farming had altered. Different hands had been hired and Mary would not sack the Keenan brothers. Because of the national loss of life industry was crying out for men and Nellie caringly put that idea separately in their heads. Mary and Nellie sincerely felt the returning men would be financially better off. Wages were good near the furnaces. Politely the men would nod at their words and accept the situation but their individual return journey down the drive was encircled in gloom. They were country lads, they did not want a part of the industrial scene; their hearts were in the countryside. Alas, needs must, forcing many of the South Cheshire men returning home from the war to settle, with their families, in the Staffordshire pottery towns, or the Cheshire ribbon and silk towns of Congleton or Macclesfield, hence sadly for them drawn into the associated factories and mills.

The following Spring Nellie and Mary had adjusted to their imparting of disappointing news to former good employees but Mary could see it had taken its toll on her mother. Such enforced duty had not sat well with Nellie's caring soul. Mary decided to encourage her to take her usual half yearly visit to Aunt Esme earlier than usual that Spring. Nellie was initially reluctant but her emotional tiredness indicated to her that really it was a good idea.

Normally Alfred took Nellie in the trap to Mow Cop station for her journey to be taken by train. However, with the changing times, there was a great volume of returning troops and men in general using the trains. Women were still perfectly safe using the trains alone but times had changed opinions and it was felt that, unless the journey was very important, it was not quite proper for ladies of Nellie's age, to travel on the trains on unimportant journeys.

Esme seemed to live for Nellie's visits and had provided an immediate remedy for the railway journey predicament. She had purchased an automobile and insisted that one of her sons should travel to Higher Smallwood Farm to collect Nellie for her short vacation at The Lodge at Aston. Nellie tried to impress upon Esme, in their communication by postcard, that such a way of travelling was rather extravagant but Esme brushed aside such notion by saying that, with the cessation of the war, petroleum was more plentiful and it gave her sons the opportunity of much needed practice in learning the skill of driving an automobile.

On a cold March morning at Higher Smallwood, Nellie was

ready with her necessary bags and looking very smart and trim in her best coat, hat, gloves and boots, awaiting collection for her Lodge stay. Mary did comment that her mother's skirts were too long as the modern dress was very much higher above the ankle. Nellie listened pleasantly to Mary but was in no mood to comment in depth as she was satisfied in her own mind that she suited the long skirts very well. John ran into the living room announcing excitedly that he could hear an automobile rising the drive and after a minute or two, as Nellie slightly moved the curtain with her gloved hand, she could see Cuthbert at the wheel arriving in the farmyard.

Light refreshment was taken by a happy Cuthbert before Nellie and her belongings were loaded into the vehicle and they set off on their journey to Staffordshire as the children, with Alfred and Ada, waved them on their way. On travelling only a few chains down the drive on that roaring lion of a chill March day, Nellie decided she really did appreciate the automobile as a superior mode of transport. She also mentally noted that she preferred the dark colour and style of the Lodge's conveyance compared with the flashy, cream, tub-like machine of Edgar's. Sitting, as ladies did, in the rear of the vehicle she chatted away easily to the pleasant amiable Cuthbert at the wheel and was very much looking forward to spending time with her oldest sister in law.

The following Saturday in the afternoon John ran into the farmhouse announcing, 'Mary I can hear them. Mother is arriving home.' Mary walked quickly through the doorway and as the vehicle stopped John opened the rear door and Nellie alighted in the farmyard. She was greeted with kisses and hugs from her children. In their delight at seeing their mother the children had not noticed it was Samuel at the wheel. Samuel opened his driving door and stood awkwardly on the yard. He was exceptionally smart in his attire. He knew he was much shyer than his brother Cuthbert and he was aware he slipped too easily into his shell. Nevertheless he wanted to be liked and did his utmost to be polite.

As Nellie was wallowing in her loving homecoming she remembered her manners. 'Oh children, you know Samuel, of course. He has kindly driven me home today. Aunt Esme feels he is not as competent with the automobile as Cuthbert and wished for him to travel here for good practice. Aunt Esme also feels one part of the journey is sufficient for one day so he will be sleeping in our spare room tonight before his homeward journey in the morning.'

Nellie was smiling, obviously adjusted to Esme's forceful ways and there was a reciprocal smile of acceptance by John. However, Samuel stood listening fully to Nellie's words looking most reluctant. Mary took a good look at him and did not join in the smiles. She was not sure about the arrangements and slightly annoyed at Aunt Esme for putting her son in an uneasy position. After a moment or two good manners took over Mary and she told Samuel he was most welcome and, in a light-hearted effort to erase his worried look, informed him it would soon be morning and he would be on his way home, which produced a slight smile from him.

The evening meal in the dining room was full of questions regarding Nellie's stay at the Lodge and Nellie answered fondly, recalling the incidents and happenings during her time there. Nellie was happy to hold conversation but as Mary glanced across the table to Samuel she could see he was still ill at ease and felt sorry for him having to suffer a dutiful stay at Higher Smallwood. Mary kept looking to him, hoping for an opportunity to bring him into the conversation, which she did occasionally. But even at those times Samuel used the least of words, his nervousness seemingly impeded his tongue and he had the habit of glancing at his hands whilst irritatingly twirling his cutlery with his very clean fingers.

Despite not being able to make clear eye contact, a trait for which Mary normally took a dislike to people, in Samuel's circumstances she had forgiving thoughts. After the strained meal, Mary gladly took her leave of the table with John and said goodnight to her mother and Samuel, almost feeling sorry for her mother that she had to bear the burden of politely trying to converse with Samuel.

Mary rose early for her farm work the following morning and made John get out of bed on time, as she usually did on a Sunday, enabling jobs to be finished in order that their mother could attend morning service at All Saints without a feeling of guilt over unfinished chores.

When Mary came in for breakfast in the morning room Samuel appeared still to be ill at ease. Mary could not recall anyone who had not felt relaxed at Higher Smallwood before and was sad for Samuel's sake, as it was obvious he was trying to stifle the fact he would prefer to be at home. Mary decided to brightly open the conversation as they all sat eating. 'What time are you leaving Samuel?'

'Well, err, I'm not quite sure', came his very vague reply.

Nellie intervened in a seamless manner, 'Samuel has kindly offered to take me in the automobile to All Saints for morning service and then he will continue on his homeward journey.'

Mary looked to him to see if he was in agreement, with what she felt yet another forced arrangement, but received no return look as Samuel kept his eyes down quietly eating his food. Mary was confused by his actions. She was lead to believe that out of the two brothers, although Cuthbert was perhaps slightly the better looking, Samuel was the one with a good clear mind and always sound in his judgements. He could feel Mary looking at him, Mary knew that, and yet he still did not return eye contact. How could she read him as a person without looking fully into his eyes? She was quite bewildered by him and looked to her mother who was gazing about smiling with her lovely aura of being pleased to be back home.

Later Mary was almost thankful when her mother, in the rear of the automobile, and Samuel at the wheel, disappeared down the rise of the drive of Higher Smallwood on their way, her mother to church and Samuel to his refuge of home at the Lodge.

John stood at her side as they waved in their customary manner and after their mother and her nephew had gone out of sight John stated excitedly, 'I'm sure he has a liking for you Mary. I have noticed he is certainly uneasy in your company. They say that is often a sign of affection.'

'Never!' said Mary, totally unaware of such feelings from Samuel and adding, 'I think you are wrong, but if you aren't, Samuel can forget such notions. I have no intention of courting a cousin, let alone an older cousin.' John was giggling. It was not very often he had the upper hand over his sister but he could tell he had struck a raw nerve and he was quite amused.

They both went their separate ways, Mary informing John she was going to put a parting of hay near her goose's nest and remove the freshly laid egg of the morning. Both were quite happy with their intended chosen jobs rather than enforced chores. Mary wandered across the pond croft to the goose shed and when inside she heard John shouting her name very loudly. She thrust her head out of the shed and saw John running towards her as quick as he could. 'Listen Mary, listen!'

They strained their ears and could hear the hum of an automobile. John darted around the side of the old duck pond and climbed to a vantage point in the crab apple tree and listening intently announced, 'I think it's Samuel!' Mary moved swiftly to the tree and stood on her tiptoes. 'Oh no! Has something happened? Is mother in the rear seat?' Mary anxiously questioned.

After patiently waiting for an fortunate turn in a near bend of the drive, John had clear vision of vehicle to see it was Samuel alone and called out loudly, 'It is Samuel! He is alone.' John started to laugh. 'I told you Mary. He wants to hang his hat at you. I bet he is coming to tell you his feelings now that mother is out of the way.'

'Oh no! What a stupid thing to do. He is a very nice smart gentleman but I have no feelings for him whatsoever.' John laughed more at seeing his sister in a fluster.

As he jumped down from the tree Mary engaged her brain

and gave John firm instructions. 'Go into the yard and enquire of mother's safety. If she is safe and he is simply delivering a message listen carefully, thank him and send him on his way. Tell him I am here in the croft if he wants to speak to me. If he does, at least if I talk to him here, I can see how near you get to eaves drop.' Adding in a threatening sibling manner, 'Keep out of sight if we talk John or I'll throw your catapult in the pond.'

John ran off to the farmyard quite excited by his mission. Mary kept taking deep breaths and informing herself she was going to be blatantly honest with Samuel if he wanted to speak with her, no matter what. She stood in tense anticipation and her heart sunk when she saw Samuel's brown bowler hat bobbing slightly higher than the pig cote wall as he walked in the direction of the pond croft towards Mary. When he came fully in view Mary was thankful that he was alone and she was relieved that John had indeed taken himself off in another direction.

Coming face to face with Mary, Samuel politely took off his hat, patted his immaculately groomed black hair several times to check if it was tidy and held his hat with both his hands, tensely threading it through his fingers. Mary knew ladies did not speak first and also that whoever entered a room spoke at once to the occupants. She decided in her firmness she would adopt the same code of etiquette to the croft. If he was the strong-minded man, as known to the family, then she was determined to eke some of his strength of character from him.

He took a very deep breath and said, 'Mary I need to speak with you alone.' Mary still remained silent. 'In fact my mother has informed me that it is imperative that I speak with you in this way.' Not that Mary wanted romantic words but she thought his opening was the worst of beginnings from a would-be suitor to announce he had been instructed by his mother. It smacked of his mother's conniving. She instantly decided it would be kinder to him if she did not allow him to proceed further and she would spare him from saying anything he might live to regret.

The moment had come for Mary to rebuff him. 'Stop there!',

Mary said with great force. 'I don't want hear another word.'

'But I have to speak, Mary. I really do have to tell you of the undying feelings of my heart.'

'No. No! I mean it Samuel. I do not wish to hear. Please spare me of them, please.'

'It's all too late, Mary. You must know. You must!', he stated strongly raising his voice in an inappropriate manner.

Mary equally as strong reiterated, 'No, Samuel. No! I tell you again, I want no part of your words. Keep them firmly to yourself.'

In piercing eye contact with Mary he persisted, 'You are making this extremely hard for me. Listen to me Mary! Listen now!'

Mary thought he was almost rude and she was having none of it. 'Samuel!' she roared, 'I don't want to know. That is final. Does my mother know you are here?'

'No, I am here without her knowledge. I feel deceitful with my contrived return but my mother told me it must be done in this way.'

Mary was beginning to be quite furious that he had sneaked back without her mother knowing. 'Well in that case I ask you to leave immediately', she informed him confidently.

'I need to know your thoughts, Mary. Mother needs to know', he pleaded.

'I have great respect for Aunt Esme but whatever is going on in your head Samuel I assure you I want no part in it. Please leave.'

Samuel could not take himself through the veil of pure rudeness; he was too much of a gentleman. He contemplated and composed himself for quite some time before he decided to ask, 'May I make one request of you Mary?'

'Provided it is small', Mary answered powerfully.

'Can I ask of you not to tell your mother of this', and turning his head slightly, looking for John, continued 'and I ask the same of your brother?'

Looking straight into his eyes, Mary answered immediately, 'Yes, you have my word. My mother will not know. Leave matters with me. I assure you I will take John into the same confidential frame of mind.'

Samuel's eyes did not flicker as he gazed at Mary. She could see a lot of suitability in him as a good man for a good woman. He was exceptionally groomed and wore expensive smart clothes. His face was healthy and very pleasant with his modern bushy moustache. When he really wanted to look at a woman he had expressive adorable green eyes. His body was firm and trim and he had good strong arms and hands. He was quiet, to a degree, but he held a presence of being confident and masterful should any woman take the trouble to know him better. Though a most eligible country bachelor, he was not for her and certainly not as a cousin regardless of his age. Through all these racing thoughts she kept her eyes coldly on him.

'I will take my leave. I bid you good morning Mary', he announced evenly. 'Goodbye, Samuel', Mary answered blandly, relieved that her snubbing of him had come to the conclusion she had wanted. Samuel turned, replaced his hat and walked away with not one further glance towards Mary.

She stood for a while, until she heard the engine start and from the croft watched the automobile trundle slowly down the drive. John returned with his quick gangly gait to Mary's side, watching with her as the dust followed the disappearing vehicle. March was going out like a lamb and March dust was supposedly worth a guinea an ounce to a farmer. Mary saw no worth in the dust. Her mind was not on farming matters nor country sayings.

'Gosh', John said. 'I heard you both raising your voices but I could not discern your words. Did you stop him from declaring his feelings?'

'Yes I suppose I did', Mary said rather quietly and repeated, 'I suppose I did.' Following a deep breath she stated, 'He didn't actually say a lot, probably because I spared him from saying anything he would regret in time. Well, it's over now, thank goodness. The matter will not be raised again. I definitely nipped things in the bud.'

She felt no sense of achievement as, with almost a tired gesture, she pulled her long, shining, wavy, auburn hair, behind her head with both hands, allowing the welcome spring fresh air to console her face. On remembering Samuel's final request she stated, 'There is one thing, John, and you are old enough now to adhere to a confidence, Samuel does not want mother to know he retraced his tracks back here. I did indicate we would keep his action confidential so you are not to utter a word about it to anyone. Do you understand?' she added sternly.

'Yes.' he said quite indignant. 'I can keep a secret.'

'Well make sure you do', Mary reiterated harshly as the strongest sibling. He nodded in the affirmative and said sensibly, 'If that is what he wishes, then we will do as he asks. He is no doubt embarrassed about his advances, being much older than you, thinking mother would not have approved. She is always touchy about the age gap between her and father, isn't she?'

Mary was slightly bemused with her brother's unusually mature words. She had not thought of that. She was only glad the unwanted episode was over. She hoped she had not been too rude to Samuel and had a wish that one day he would interpret her actions as just and honest.

CHAPTER 27

I Have Decided To Keep Them

Album, silk flags and pencilled message

'I'm not disturbing you am I mother?' asked Mary as she entered the drawing room. 'Of course not, dear', Nellie replied warmly, 'I'm only crocheting here by the fire.' It was the afternoon of the 11th November 1919. Mary stood with two small leather bound albums in her hand and proceeded, 'I've come to ask a favour of you. I wondered if I could keep these albums safely in your bureau?'

'In my bureau dear? You can but don't you want to keep them with your papers?'

'No, I've often thought of throwing them away but I have decided today, especially today, to keep them but I do not wish to read them anymore.'

'Which particular albums are they?' Nellie enquired. 'Have I seen them?'

'No, they are mine from the Hall.'

Nellie put her crocheting to one side and walked towards the bureau simultaneously with Mary. 'I have room for them in the third draw down on the right-hand side', Nellie instructed.

'I would prefer them under lock and key, please', Mary stated with certainty.

Nellie opened the top draw, fished out the key, carefully pulled out the lopers, unlocked the top and pulled down the lid.

'If you wish I have room here in the small draws', Nellie accommodatingly stated.

'That will do nicely', Mary answered in appreciation. With efficiency Nellie reversed the procedure of locking the top of her bureau and mother and daughter walked across the room and sat in the fireside chairs.

On recommencing her crocheting Nellie asked, 'Do you know what date it is today?' In her casual customary way Mary leaned to the knitting basket, picked out two needles pushed through a ball of wool, removed the wool to her lap, positioned one needle under her left arm and held the one in her right hand in a pen like manner and commenced knitting on the stitches of a half knitted sleeve. 'Yes I do', came her eventual reply. 'It is twelve months to the day since the Armistice was signed.' With a sigh Nellie said in slight disbelief, 'We longed for peace and I am astonished that twelve months has passed so quickly. I do not know how we all managed through those war years.'

'All the better for having our health and limbs', Mary replied in her usual mature manner.

Nellie felt humble at Mary's wise reply but continued with some local news, 'Your Aunt Poll says most Halls in Cheshire are being requested to send felled chestnut trees to help in the process of making false limbs, even now long after the war has ended.'

Mary did not want to dwell on her mother's ignorance and said softly, 'Healing takes much longer than announcing a peace agreement.'

'Yes, of course, you saw much more of the horror of nursing at the Hall.'

Mary stated, 'That is what my albums are about.'

'Oh, really', Nellie replied hoping to hear more.

'Yes. I managed to persuade the soldiers to record their sentiments. I told you I have often thought recently of destroying them. In many ways I do not want to be reminded of those times; blot it all from my memory and get on with my life. But that is easy for me.' Mary paused and Nellie detected a slight smearing of her eyes: not tears but rare emotion from Mary.

Although struggling to control her emotion Mary managed to press on. 'Well, life can never be the same for those brave, scarred young soldiers can it ?'

'No', Nellie replied with utter sincerity.

Mary took a deep breath and proceeded slowly, 'So, today, I came to the poignant decision to save the albums but I don't want to read them anymore. Although the verses are sincere and meaningful they remind me of too much pain but I do want to remember all those brave soldiers who fought for our freedom.'

'Am I allowed to read them?' Nellie asked sensitively.

'Yes, of course, they are in your bureau now', Mary replied in a very open manner. 'I have purposely asked to put them in your safe keeping in case I ever fall in love and I may feel it is time to destroy them. They should be retained safely, as if to place them aside from my life now.'

'Don't worry, Mary, I assure you they will always be kept in my bureau along with your father's phloem knife and pen knife. I have several bits and bobs I treasure from him like his field magnifier. Shall we look upon the albums as sentimentality?' 'Yes I suppose so', Mary answered.

Pursuing the sentimental thread Mary continued, 'I still have my bear father gave to me on my seventh birthday.

'Oh yes', Nellie replied, raising her voice to a tone of happiness. 'I could not understand why children would wish to posses a bear. Teddies were quite a craze and still are.'

'I like them', Mary said in her own defence. 'Much better than a hard doll. Cuddly to sleep with.' Nellie allowed their nostalgic thoughts to flow adding, 'Your father adored creeping into your bedroom each night to see you in slumber with your arm tucked around Edward.'

'Whose idea was it to call him Edward?' Mary asked lightly.

Nellie happily searching her mind answered, 'I think it was your Aunt Poll. She much preferred Edward to Teddy. Teddy was the transatlantic nickname for such toy bears. Remember some went down with the Titanic. Even at seven you were quite mature and it did seem to suit you better to have a furry companion called Edward.'

Mary glanced at the ticking clock. 'It's nearly three. I will make our pot of tea.' After neatly placing her needles together and pushing them into the ball of wool Mary left the room and in what seemed no time at all, re-appeared with a tray containing the best teapot full of freshly brewed tea with its china accessories, all on a beautifully embroidered tray cloth.

'Oh, Mary, I was coming through to the living kitchen. This fire is low.'

'No', Mary said abruptly, placing the tray on the fireside table. 'It is high time you resumed your afternoon tea in here. Please pour the tea while I fettle the fire.' Mary took the shovel out of the back of the black coal scuttle, lifted the lid and carefully placed some coal on the fire. Nellie was about to interrupt but hesitated and decided to follow Mary's instruction and not to spoil the ambience she was creating.

As both ladies were sipping their tea Nellie smiled as the fire began to burn up cheerily and the flames reflected in the brass trimmings of the scuttle.

'Mary, this is nice. You are right. I have missed using the

drawing room but of course it is extravagant to have two fires burning.'

'Was extravagant', Mary corrected. 'With the stall profits we can afford afternoon coal once more for this room and, besides, it keeps the furnishings aired and the damp hue off the wooden furniture.'

Nellie smiled at Mary's common sense, which prompted her to confess, 'I must admit I thought you were wrong taking the stall at Sandbach Market but it has been a good input into our finances and has given me a much better profit on my cheese.'

'And Mrs Thorley, Mrs Furber and Mrs Hollinshead stand market don't they?' Mary asked teasingly.

'Yes', Nellie said with a knowing smile, adding, 'quite a few good farmers wives stand market.'

'Giving credibility to standing Market?' Mary teased again.

'Yes', Nellie replied slightly laughing, feeling herself being pushed into a verbal corner with Mary's words, also admitting, 'In the times we have lived through and with hindsight I am sure your father would have approved.'

Mary noted that was praise indeed.

Nellie decided to ask, 'Now the farming wheels are turning once more are you going to stop your stall?'

'No', Mary answered emphatically.

'Good,' replied Nellie, adding freely, 'again I was wrong about Alfred. It seems to have given him a new lease of life. I think he would miss his weekly Thursday jaunt to Sandbach.'

'I am not just keeping it for Alfred', Mary announced honestly. 'I feel if I should marry and leave it could be a business I could run from any new abode.' Nellie paused for thought before she said in agreement, 'I suppose you are right. John has no time or interest in a market stall and seeing that you have made a success of the stall it seems sensible to carry it on. And of course you are twenty-three now, a perfect age for marriage. I was a mother at your age.'

Nellie sighed heavily before stating, 'Your generation gave

your youthful years to the war didn't you?' Mary made no comment.

'Well, all that's behind you now. I do enjoy seeing you dress up to attend the dances at Rode Heath.'

'Yes', Mary added lightly. 'They're so much fun. I hope I can always dance. I love the lancers and the new charleston dance.'

'With any particular beau?' Nellie ventured to ask.

Mary became unusually coy.

'There is, isn't there?'

'Perhaps there is. It is early days.'

'Do I know him?'

'I don't think so. He is from a family of butchers and cattle dealers at Brickhouse Farm Sandbach. We first met at the stall and then he appeared at the Rode Heath dances and it has grown from there. He is even attending Rode whist drives.'

'Which Brickhouse Farm? There are three together', Nellie asked knowingly.

'The black and white one. They slaughter there.'

'I know the one. I'm told the three storey Brickhouse Farm, the one facing Sandbach Heath Church, had the rinderpest in the 1880's when the Williams's lived there.'

Bringing the conversation back to the main topic Nellie decided to ask, 'What is his name?'

'William Nield. His father is Edward Nield. His mother is called Martha, known as Pat', Mary replied with ease. 'I've only known him for four months and three days.' Nellie noted that, to be aware of the exact number of days that he had been part of her life, was a tell-tale sign of her fondness for him, but kept quiet. Mary continued enthusiastically, 'He was in the war but mercifully one of the lucky ones to return unscathed. Well I say unscathed. He is convinced the war job was left unfinished and that one day we will be at war against Germany again.'

Nellie did not want to spoil the conversation but William's relayed sentiments coincided in her mind with a similar comment Polly had made. She purposely pushed her uneasy thoughts aside and commented, 'I sincerely hope not. Life is getting back to normal. I should imagine Europe has learned it's lesson not to fight again.'

After replacing her cup and saucer gently on the tray Nellie asked, 'What is he like?'

Mary replied with unusual eagerness, 'Strong blonde hair, groomed straight but could be curly if left to it's own devices. He is not much taller than me but that suits me. John's height gets the better of me at times.'

'Do I detect you want to be the boss Mary?' Nellie asked teasingly.

'No. No', Mary replied slightly laughing, 'I only want to be evenly harnessed that's all. Oh, and he adores his dog. Remember, beware the man who does not like his dog.'

Nellie drew a deep breath and announced, 'Well, you must be taken with him. You have never given me so much information about anyone before. Time will tell as to if you definitely like him. Young people are always in a win situation, they can never lose. If you stay together it is right. If you part it is right.'

Mary announced with conviction, 'Time will!' I shall marry him if we share true love. Nothing will stop me. No cousin for me or indecision. I am going to take Granny Bailey's advice and make my engagement day the hardest, so my wedding day will be easy. I don't intend to sue any man for breach of promise.' After a pause she added with certainty, 'I will definitely stand at the altar rail with true love in my heart, with or without money I will survive.'

Nellie smiled, perfectly calm and assured that Mary would achieve her wish and said, 'I remember a dear old Uncle Joe whose saying was, *'give us good health - we'll manage the rest'*. She paused wistfully before profoundly stating, 'You and your husband, whoever he may be, will be blessed if you have reciprocal love in your hearts on taking your vows. It really is the greatest gift on earth to love and be loved in return and good health is the richest blessing.'

Firmly encircled within a tender moment of the Gentle Ribbon Nellie extended her hand to her darling daughter. Mary was aware of their close love but did not need to be tactile. She left her mother's hand untouched but gave her an exquisite smile that could only come from within the bond of the Gentle Ribbon.

Thinking of William once more Mary volunteered, 'William says his family advice is to put your farm to bed, put your house to bed and put yourselves to bed together. That way you are always in one another's arms and heart.' Her words raised another smile from Nellie.

After finishing her drink Mary leaned forward and replaced her cup and saucer alongside her mother's empty cup on the tray. When sitting properly back in her chair she announced in a serious way, 'John is capable of running Higher Smallwood on his own now. It will be time for him to find a wife; he is becoming smitten with one of the Baskerville girls from Pump House Farm. When I marry and go will you remain here like Aunty Polly did once? There is plenty of room or will you find somewhere like The Oaks?'

Nellie concentrated her thoughts and took stock before replying. 'Your Granny and Grandad Bailey are delighted with The Oaks at Rode Heath after Pack Horse Farm. Never in their wildest dreams did they ever imagine retiring to somewhere like The Oaks. The money came from my Grandad Barratt from Brook House Farm, Smallwood you know. He held the enlightened view that daughters should inherit something as well as sons. He was also very proud that his daughters were blessed in dual ways, pretty and good stock women. It was really his money that purchased their retirement roof. Money was never made like that at Pack Horse Farm; not in Grandad Bailey's time.'

She took a slight pause before continuing, 'I think you are right as to John. He has altered and taken up his yoke of responsibility. I'm glad you see that in him, too. Perhaps between us we have not done such a bad job of rearing him to manhood since your father died.' Mary declared with certainty, 'He'll go on now, I'm sure, no matter what. His rapport with Uncle Alec and all the shooting connotations seems a good source of enjoyment to him by way of recreation and gives him good standing on the Estate.'

'Yes, he does seem to have achieved the balance of working hard and playing hard. You never know he may rise to your fathers status of being a gun occasionally.'

Mary lifted her head higher and gave her mother a most searching look before asking, 'But what of your future. When the time comes for John and I to marry where would your preference be to live?' Nellie gazed into the fire and held a long silence before turning her eyes once more to Mary and commenced thoughtfully, 'I've lived through many changing times but I am no different to anyone else. As you grow older you realise that the trick of life is to adjust to change no matter what change you face. If you don't, you waste your days on this earth. I still can hardly believe I am without your father but, through leaning on the good Lord in my prayers, I really do believe life unfolds. I am also a great believer that everyones' lives are in phases and whether our individual phases are good or bad, they always change. Nothing stays the same. Consequently, I feel my life will unfold somehow.'

Mary with a soft tone answered, 'I understand what you say but when John and I take our own ways in life I also know John will ask my views on your staying here and I want to advise him along the right lines. Do you want to continue living here or would you prefer to take a cottage on the Estate?'

Nellie tried to lighten the conversation by saying, 'Or perhaps you and John will purchase me a dower house and I could live as an old dowager.'

'Be serious, mother. You know we do not have that kind of money. You said earlier The Oaks was purchased out of inheritance money and besides, you can not be an old dowager you are only in your mid forties.'

Nellie smiled warmly before reassuring, 'What I am saying is you mustn't worry on worry. There is no need to force change before the circumstances arise. Folks spend too much time worrying about crossing bridges before they arrive. As a family, particularly with you Mary, we are capable of sorting matters out when it is necessary. Don't worry, don't be anxious. Life, including mine, will somehow unfold.'

Mary glanced at the ticking long case clock and said unexpectedly, 'I like that clock, it's quite neat for a grandfather clock. Can I have it and John have the long case clock from in the hall?'

Nellie really did feel Mary was entering a nesting phase in her life and replied with a smile, 'I don't see why not when the time comes.' Mary took in her mother's words and, after blinking took in the actual time of the clock, which threw her into panic. 'Goodness, look at the time. I must leave you at once to help with the milking. It's the dance tonight!'

As Nellie watched Mary make a hasty exit from the drawing room she felt pleased that her children were launching nicely into their individual lives.

After milking and when tea was over, Mary and John prepared themselves for their night out. When they re-appeared in the living kitchen they were spotlessly clean and well groomed for the dance. Nellie's pride rose to see Mary looking pretty and John handsome in their dance attire and each happy in their bloom of youth. Although Mary insisted that both John and she should use their bicycles instead of taking the trap, there was an air of excitement surrounding them both. Youthful excitement, that only encircles new adults, when they are busily engaged in organising their own night out.

Two rapid separate kisses on Nellie's cheek heralded their imminent departure into the night. They no longer asked if they could attend a dance. They just presumed they would be allowed. No noise of distant hooves on the drive as they journeyed silently on the solid rubber tyres of their bicycle wheels. Nellie reflected that, at least it was a full moon, and dances were still organised around the village lantern.

After her children had left she did not feel afraid for Alfred was in his loft on the yard, Ada was in her quarters in the attic and the dogs would bark if anything untoward happened. But as silence fell upon the room, after the shutting of the door, Nellie did feel a deep sense of her personal loneliness and pondered on how times had changed. The children out socially, George sadly dead, Polly and Rose in their own homes.

Nellie pondered deeper. She could not remember attending a dance whilst courting George. Yes, they danced during their marriage but not prior to it. How fortunate she felt Mary was attending dances and dancing with many different partners, almost having her pick of them. No wonder Mary was very confident she would marry the man she loved. Nellie allowed herself to imagine Mary dancing happily with her William. She thought in such circumstances love had more ways to send signals; in their moods, eyes, arms and perhaps through a stolen kiss. Where better to share such feelings than dancing together. Nellie did lament her courtship to George was of and belonged to the last century. The 1800's needed to change but she also realised the war had changed much.

At that point her thoughts triggered her to the presence of Mary's war albums in her bureau. She walked slowly through to the drawing room and although the fire had rendered itself to dull embers there was still a warmth in the room. On opening her bureau in her usual way, a strange feeling slowed her hand as she reached to open the small drawers to reveal Mary's sentimental treasures. She stood for a moment double checking in her mind the afternoon's conversation and satisfying herself that Mary had, indeed, given her permission to read the albums. Certain she was doing no wrong, she settled in her fireside chair and began to read each page slowly.

Mary was right: the sentiments were profound. Each individually written page was signed by the injured soldier with details of where he had been injured and with which battalion he was serving at the time. She had taken the trouble to put numerous photographs of the soldiers in the albums, taken by her with the little box camera kindly given to her by her Uncle Edgar.

Nellie was shocked and moved. It was evident they knew a lot about Mary, even giving her the nickname of Cookie, a reference to the time when she and Polly had tried to parcel Mary off to Congleton hospital to serve as a volunteer cook, in an endeavour to thwart her desire to become a nurse.

Nellie slowly read on and she was overwhelmed by some of the words:

'Trifles as well as greater things
Oft bring us on to memory's wings
The thought of those who absent are
Make them to our minds appear
As I write I wish for you in distant time
To recall these loving hours that feel sublime'

* * * *

'Though we may part and fate my sever
Love for an hour is love forever'

* * * *

'The ring is round, the bed is square
I think we two could make a pair
If you say yes then I am willing
To pay the parson seven shilling'

* * * *

'When in prayer to God above I bend my knee
Then when I pray for those I love I pray for thee
When slumber sweet enclouds my brain and thought is free
When I think of those I love I think of thee'

* * * *

'Driving dull care from my heart that pines
Often times cheering with deeds that shine
Mary you give me a belief one day for sure
I may dare to think my life will contain more'

* * * *

'I feel in my heart that which is true
There is only one I love and that is you'

* * * *

It was obvious that some of the soldiers had fallen deeply in love with Mary. Nellie stopped reading in one anxious moment. How as her mother had she not detected that Mary was handling much more than the position of nurse? She was shocked by the hidden maturity of Mary. At that point a folded envelope floated from the open album to the floor by Nellie's skirt. Nellie picked it up gently unsure if she should peek inside. Her fingers tentatively opened the envelope but it was empty. She paused and asked herself why Mary should have saved an empty envelope. Her fingers tenderly turned the envelope over to reveal a pencilled sad message:

'He is lying on his bad side now. When his breathing goes
quietly and slowly tell me quickly for I shall have a lot to do
to keep life in him. That is how the change takes place.'

After reading the message Nellie's tears flowed, so much she had to move the album slightly to protect the ink on the page, before using her handkerchief. Eventually, after frequent blowing of her nose and dabbing of her eyes, she finished reading the albums from page to page. When closing them she purposely replaced the envelope with the message written on it, between two pages for safe keeping. Again Nellie was at a loss as to how she could have shared a home with Mary through the war years and not have detected the emotional turmoil within her own daughter. She was embarrassed and sorrowful at her ignorance.

The following breakfast time was consumed by John and Mary's happy chatter relaying details of their attendance at the dance. Nellie had to force herself to pretend to be cheerful but, while John and Mary were laughing about various incidents, Nellie decided she had to speak privately with Mary again. As usual, after breakfast, John dashed off first to resume his farm work and Mary washed her hands and face again in the back kitchen and brushed her hair.

When Mary stood before Nellie about to announce her jobs for the day, she stopped her by simply saying, 'I appreciated our chat yesterday and feel I would like to talk further.'

Mary being Mary replied, 'I am busy mother. At what time of day were you thinking of?'

Nellie trying to be nonchalant answered, 'Whenever. To suit you.'

Mary huffed in thought and rechecked with both of her hands that her hair was firmly tied back for work. 'Well, if things work out, put a match to the drawing room fire this afternoon and I will try to join you in there again.'

'That will do fine.' Nellie confirmed.

In the afternoon, following Mary's instructions, Nellie had drunk her afternoon tea and recommenced her knitting, before she heard Mary hurrying towards the drawing room. On entering the room Mary announced, 'Sorry to be a bit late but I am free now.'

Nellie just smiled her knowing acceptance of Mary's work load. The fire was lovely on that dark November day, a day which had hardly managed to show any significant day light and the low cloud, for most of the time, obscured the view of Mow Cop. Mary lit the oil lamp with a spill from the fire which took away the gloom in the room.

Nellie sat in her perfect straight backed sitting pose and Mary lounged more comfortably. 'Are you troubled?' Mary asked in a caring manner.

'No', Nellie replied. 'Well, not really, as you are safe and well before me. That is a blessing to count.'

Mary thought that was quite a profound answer and decided to keep quiet and allow her mother to talk.

Uncharacteristically Nellie said abruptly, 'I read your albums when you were at the dance. I could not sleep properly during the night.'

Mary became stern, sat up straight and forced herself to speak softly. 'I did not put them in your bureau to cause you loss of sleep. I should have destroyed them.'

'No. No, Mary. You are right to keep them.'

'Not if they disturb you.'

'They don't disturb me. I suppose I am shocked, I had no idea you had to deal with the soldiers feelings as well as their bodies.'

Mary somewhat angrily retorted, 'The two can never be separated if there is hope for recovery.'

'Yes, but I feel I detect quite a few fell in love with you, Mary', Nellie stated in a very het up manner, holding her left hand fingertips to her forehead.

Mary took the tension away by keeping a short silence before she explained in a purposeful way, 'The injured soldiers arrived at different intervals. Some were mercifully slightly injured but I can't describe the depth of the despair and pain in some cases when bodies were severely mutilated. Such injured soldiers did not want to know the name of the soldier in the next bed nor indeed their own name. They somehow wanted to remain in an unknown state.

Some nurses could not handle those times and the Commandant was brilliant at nurturing the nurses into jobs in which they were proficient. I never flinched from severe injuries. With such patients I sat hours giving their wounds or the stumps of their limbs my utmost attention to ward off gangrene. I have sat all night checking, tending, caring and gently turning a silent patient to avoid bed sores. I've seen my patient sobbing on his pillow and, although I would tenderly lay my hand on his face or shoulder or hold his hand, his deep sense of realising his injuries were for the rest of his life, took away his ability to express any form of communication or gratitude.

As nurses we were always taught to talk quietly to our patients or whisper in the night to them. The Commandant would never have the soldiers treated as though they were just a number. We always had to address them by their Christian name and care for them constantly.

But mercifully, mother, healing of the injuries took place and it was wonderful to see. You know what I mean. We experience it in farming. All that tilling and working of a field and then one day a golden crop waves before our eyes. It was that sought of gratifying feeling.'

Mary continued to dominate the conversation. 'When the healing of the wounds took place then there was a window of opportunity to heal their minds. Nurses had their individual ways of finding a common interest to discuss. Agnes used to beg and borrow tiny silk flags to stitch together in the formation a soldier preferred. Betsy has a lovely voice and would quietly sing favourite songs for the soldiers to join in. My way, along with many other nurses, were the albums. You know how popular they are.

On first getting to know a patient, forgive me mother, I always told them you did not wish me to become a nurse and I was originally a volunteer cook hence, my nickname.' Nellie weakly smiled and kept listening intently.

'Oh, mother, I have quietly asked a patient when he was bodily on the road to recovery if he felt up to writing something in my album and many times I was rebuffed. It was heart warming when the same soldier eventually asked if he could add to my album. Obviously from his written sentiments I could detect if he had a love for me.'

'Were you in love with them?' Nellie quickly asked.

'Perhaps I was with a couple.'

'Two!' Nellie stated in bewilderment.

'Yes, but it was not being in love, it was having a love for them. Like I love you or John.'

'We are family', Nellie debated in an endeavour to understand. 'It is natural to have a love for us.'

Mary tried to explain, ' I know, but the love I had for them I knew was for only for as long as they would stay in hospital. When the power of love drew us together we always knew, without words, our futures would be apart. We also knew that such love would remain as a tiny speck in our hearts for ever. There was always a silent knowledge that a bigger different love would fill the rest of our hearts. It was simply the effect of the intense intimate time through which we lived, strove and pulled to together. We knew it would end but equally knew that such a love was vital at that time to sustain the precious thread of hope. Something tangible to give them back the will to cope and continue their lives despite having maimed bodies or loss of sight or both.'

Nellie sat and stared at her daughter in an enlightened way. Mary could see her mother was thankfully less bewildered. 'This is what war does, mother. It throws people together for a host of serious reasons and when it's over throws them apart again and the whole complex situation has to be accepted.'

'Why didn't I detect your turmoil, Mary?' Nellie asked in an innocent way.

'You didn't need to. You have nothing to recriminate yourself for. It was simply my role in the war and like everyone else I had to get on and cope with it. You have to cope as a widow, I'm sure I don't enquire of your welfare enough.'

'Nor do I expect you to', Nellie announced strongly with an independent streak.

After a small silence Nellie stated in a dignified way, 'Youth should be a precious time in life for enjoyment, but it is evident from your albums, you and your nursing colleagues lost your youth to the war.'

Mary replied pragmatically, 'I lost very little compared to many others. I'm enjoying myself now the war has finished. We must all move on. Perhaps I should throw the albums in the fire to spare either of us speaking like this again.'

'No Mary. No', Nellie pronounced loudly then forcing a softer tone declared, 'You are right. They are a capsule of time. They should be saved for us to understand a fragment of The Great War. You have added greatly to my understanding.'

'Thank you', Mary uttered, feeling quite drained, before adding firmly, 'I hope the albums are never taken out of context.'

CHAPTER 28

NO WORDS. LET THINGS BE

Mary in control

John as young man

One Thursday afternoon in the late April of 1920 Mary and
Alfred returned from Sandbach to Higher Smallwood after
another successful market day. The newly arrived swallows
were happily twittering and expertly checking their old nesting
haunts within the buildings around the farmyard. To first see
these heralds of full Spring after their incredible journey from
Africa makes rural folk stop to treasure the moment. The safe
arrival of the beautiful aerobatic birds always lifts country spirits

and unwraps a seasonal feeling of well being.

Mary jumped down from the trap carefully holding her stall takings in her small box. Alfred eagerly instructed her to wait a minute and after tying the horse to the wall ring he went into the workshop returning with a mallet.

'Thank you Alfred, I am most grateful to you', Mary announced in gratitude, as she carefully studied the expert way Alfred had mended her mallet.

'I've rubbed the head with linseed oil so it should be in good order for the Summer', Alfred proudly stated.

Mary gave a cheeky smile before admitting, 'He's getting closer to beating me but I don't intend to let him. He wins our skating races you know. I must never let him be a better croquet player. Having my best mallet ready for action is important to me.'

Nellie as mature mother

Alfred was chuckling. He enjoyed seeing the healthy rivalry between Mary and John and had a secret leaning for Mary's success, although he often advised John on tactics. Croquet was Mary's favourite game and Alfred missed seeing Polly, who was a good player, giving Mary a hard game. Polly had taught her well and through their games together Mary had gained vital practice making her a player to be reckoned with. Nellie usually lamented the fact that Mary's progress on the piano forte in the Winter always waned through the Spring and Summer months because of croquet.

Mary cheerily took the mended mallet into the farmhouse and after putting her money box on the back kitchen table she knelt down and carefully replaced the mallet in the long wooden croquet box under the back stairs. Ada walked through attending to her chores.

'Where is everyone?', Mary enquired raising herself from the floor.

'Your brother has spent the afternoon rough shooting with your Uncle Alec. He came back late dashing off quickly to attend to milking without his cup of tea, so I've taken it out to him in the shippon.'

After pausing for breath Ada continued, 'Your mother? I presume still sewing in the drawing room. She has asked me not to bother with her afternoon tea because of my workload. She spent a good deal of time with me at mid day making sure I know exactly what meals to prepare for several days. Your Aunt Poll is coming for dinner on Sunday after Morning Service.'

'Oh, good, thank you, Ada.'

Picking up her money box Mary, as usual, went through to the living room to count her stall takings. After counting and checking she replaced the money in the box and in her customary manner took the box and placed it in the second drawer down of the oak dresser for safe keeping. From the same drawer she removed her cash book to meticulously record her stall takings and when the book was in her hand she could feel it was unusually bulky as she took it to the table. She sat again and opened the cash book which disclosed a sealed envelope simply bearing her Christian name in her mother's handwriting. Mary was puzzled as to why her mother should be writing to her when she was sitting in the drawing room. Quite intrigued she opened the envelope roughly with her strong nails and took out a letter in her mother's hand and read:

My dear Mary

When you read this I will be far away from Higher Smallwood on a very purposeful journey. It is imperative that you remain strong. If anything happens on the farm in my absence and it is beyond you or John to sort the matter out, please lean on your Uncle Alec for help.

Also it is vital Mary for you to keep calm and use your calming influence on others. I plan to return home on Tuesday in the late morning. I do not want anyone, including yourself, to worry about me. I am safe.

Your ever loving Mother

Mary was stunned, totally stunned. She quickly re-read the letter to convince herself the words were true, but still she could not take them in. She ran into the drawing room in the vain hope of seeing her mother sewing but stopped abruptly as all she could see was an empty room, eerily different to the normal feeling of the drawing room. The fire was not lit. Mary's brain was locking and unlocking at the tell tale signs of the unused room. Her mind was swirling in her panic making it difficult for her to think straight. She forced herself to gather her thoughts and take stock. Why had neither she nor Alfred noticed an absence of smoke from the drawing room chimney on their homeward journey?

She dashed upstairs taking the steps two at a time in a most unladylike manner and ran into her mother's bedroom without a polite knock. She quickly snatched the wardrobe door to reveal a half empty wardrobe and, as her hands swiftly checked the remaining clothes hanging there, she could see they were all older clothes. The best clothes were gone. She rushed to her mother's dressing table to find her silver brush and mirror were missing. A hurried check of the small drawers revealed the hair combs and hat pins were gone. Pulling open the top drawer at speed she discovered her mother had taken her best jewellery. On further checking Mary could see the burgundy brooch box was missing. That was most odd. It contained the large cameo brooch, a treasured gift from her father. Her mother never took the brooch on any of her travels because of her fear of losing her beloved keepsake.

Mary's brain was locking again. What was going on? Another surge of thought found Mary scrambling through her mother's hat boxes. All were full with the exception of one. Mary stood with her hands on her hips trying to accurately recall her mother's hat collection. Deep concentration brought her mother's new hat to mind. Where was that? Mary continued searching to no avail. She could not even find the box. This, of course, told her that her mother was travelling in a hat and had taken her new hat in it's box.

Mary was utterly puzzled. Before she knew it, she was chasing down the back stairs shouting Ada at the top of her voice, and burst through the back stairs door to confront Ada cooking. A shocked Ada demanded, 'What ever is the matter?'

'It's mother she has gone!'

'Gone! Gone where?'

'I don't know. I was hoping you could tell me or at least inform me of the time she went.'

'Went! Went where?' How do you know she has gone?'

Mary realised Ada was as shocked as she so she gently took her arm and pulled a chair from the table indicating that she should sit. Mary sat on another kitchen chair and in a quieter tone proceeded, 'Ada she has gone. She has left me a letter informing me.'

'Your mother gone! Gone without a word, I can't take that in. Well, well, I have never heard the like.'

Mary could see tears welling in Ada's eyes and hastily informed her,

'Oh, don't worry. She says she will return on Tuesday. None of us are to worry.'

'Tuesday? Why has she gone, especially in this way?'

'I don't know', Mary answered despondently. At that moment Mary's natural sense of responsibility re-established it's self and logical questions started to flow.

'You didn't hear her go?'

'Of course not. I'm as thunderstruck as you', Ada snapped.

'Yes I'm sorry I can see you are.'

'Did you see or hear a horse or a trap, or the dogs barking this afternoon?'

Pausing and thinking very hard Ada answered, 'No, I can't say I have. No, nothing, definitely no visitors this afternoon.'

'What chores have you been attending to?'

'I've been busy. Your mother requested me to tidy the cellar and after scrubbing it, put clean newspaper on all the shelving. Usually the cellar shelves are the last spring cleaning job but your mother must have thought differently today. However, I always follow your mother's instructions without question.'

The penny had not dropped with Ada but Mary was forming the opinion her mother's departure had been well planned.

'Did mother seem agitated or upset the last time you saw her?'

Again Ada dutifully searched her memory.

'No, not at all, she seemed very matter of fact when she was insistent that I paid extra attention to forthcoming meals. She must have recognised that I had a lot to do in the cellar because of her kindness in attending to her own afternoon tea. Remember I told you that on your return.'

'Yes, yes you did, but what about mother?' Mary asked again, desperately trying not to show her anxiety.

'I can't think she showed signs of anything untowards.' Ada paused and her lip began to quiver.

'Oh Mary, I had no idea it was the last time I was going to see her.'

She began to cry. Mary leaned towards her offering a handkerchief. A grateful Ada took it and blew her nose loudly. In her tears she announced, 'This is so out of character of your mother. She would never willingly leave us all. Something must be wrong.'

In a further endeavour to calm Ada, Mary said gently, 'No, she definitely says she will return on Tuesday. In fact, in the last words of her letter she says she is safe.' Ada stopped sniffling as Mary patted the back of her hand. 'Come on, Ada. We must carry on as normal until Tuesday. Your meal smells good.' Ada tried to raise her spirits but said realistically, 'All that planning by your mother as to our meals. What a waste of time, who will feel hungry with this upsetting predicament hanging over us.' Mary again stalwartly trying to raise moral replied, 'Oh, John always eats no matter what.'

Ada's brain jolted. 'Does he know?'

A frightened glance flashed across Mary's countenance.

'No, nobody knows. Just us at the moment.'

'Oh dear, there's many to tell isn't there? Alfred will take it badly.' Another pause for quick thought by Ada prompted her to add, 'What about your Aunt Poll? She will be devastated at a Walker leaving Higher Smallwood without warning. Mary I have a foreboding no good will come from this.'

Mary could not have agreed more with Ada as to how upsetting the news would be to those who loved her mother but she had to trust her mother as to the unknown reason for her unbelievable disappearance. Yet, at that moment, Tuesday seemed too far away for comfort.

It was terrible for Mary to relay the strange news to John. She allowed him to read the letter, which he did over and over again in disbelief. Ada, unable to contain herself, informed Alfred who was as confused and upset as the rest of the household. In his endeavour to ease the situation he went in the light April evening to seek Alec and told him of the bewildering news.

Alec immediately followed Alfred back to Higher Smallwood on his horse and read his sister's letter. He was just as mystified as anyone else and hoped the news of Nellie's disappearance did not leak out in Rode prior to her return, for he outwardly expressed his fear that the news would, perhaps, be more than his elderly parents, William and Emily, could take without extreme upset. He did, however, try to console Mary and John and although he could understand their confusion and worry he told them they could only believe and follow the instructions and sentiments of their mother's letter and urged them to pull together.

Both Mary and John found it hard to pass their mother's empty bedroom that night before taking to their beds. Lying alone in her bed Mary had the haunting fear that she might never see her mother again. She almost made herself cry as her thoughts drifted to her first childhood memory with her mother. She could vividly remember standing with her little arms outstretched holding both her mother's hands, dancing to a band, in a big beautiful garden somewhere, with the sun shining. In that childhood memory Mary could see all the ladies beautifully attired in long flowing summer gowns and watching her mother's diamond smile as they twirled happily in what seemed a sea of floating pretty material. Those warm and comforting memories of her mother moved her once more near to tears. Mary had to force herself to stay positive and shun negative thoughts to stem any tears. Her pillow prayers were her only succour.

Both she and John suffered a very restless night and it was no trouble for either of them to rise to attend to the milking on the Friday morning. In fact, for the first time in each of their lives, they felt the benefit of occupying their time with work.

They were surprised to find Aunt Poll drawing up her chair

and sharing breakfast with them. Alec had risen early tending his pheasants making some time free to visit Polly's cottage and inform her of the strange news of Nellie's temporary disappearance from Higher Smallwood. Her first thought was to be with the children and she had hastily peddled to the farm on her tricycle. She knew she had done the right thing as she could see they were genuinely pleased to have her sitting there at the table. Mary naturally allowed her to read her mother's letter although Polly was aware of the contents through Alec's direct knowledge of the letter, which he had relayed accurately to her.

After breakfast Polly announced in a head matriarchal way, 'As strange and as unnatural as this feels to us all, out of love and loyalty, we must accept your mother's requests and follow her instructions, especially you Mary.'

John asked anxiously, 'What if mother is in trouble and needs help?'

Polly replied in a comforting tone, 'Her letter is quite clear John. She says she is safe and there is no need for worry.'

'She could be masking an illness and have travelled to a physician or even left us to have an operation.'

'No, John, your mother is in good health, do not alarm yourself. I am quite sure she would have told me if there was anything wrong with her health. Don't trouble yourself on that score.'

'I hope your are right', came his unsure reply.

Mary asked Polly directly, 'It's crossed my mind she may have gone to Aunt Esme's. What do you think?'

'Yes, I have considered that too, but, again, I feel she would have mentioned it and planned her trip to Aston Lodge in her usual way. No, I don't think she is there.'

'She must be somewhere', John stated in alarm.

'Calm yourself, John. I know how upsetting this is but we must rest on the re-assurance your mother conveys in her letter.'

'How could she just leave us all? I don't understand it. I don't understand it at all', John stated in a desperate bewildered manner.

Shaking her head in the negative but wondering if it should be in the affirmative Polly said kindly, 'Don't be disturbed John, she will soon be home and we shall know the reason. We must make sure her return is before any knowledge of her disappearance filters through in Rode. I am planning to miss church on Sunday morning, so I will not have to answer awkward questions, when it is noticed your mother is absent. Perhaps it would be prudent to keep Alfred and Ada away for the same reason.'

No!' Mary intervened sharply.

Polly was taken aback and paused before replying harshly, 'I think you will find it is for the best Mary.'

'I disagree', Mary said in a forthright manner, reinforcing her words with, 'I totally disagree.' 'But Mary.'

'No, I'm determined no one is to tell lies over this mysterious issue. We all must attend church in the usual way.'

Polly was quite offended and debated, 'I am not alluding to lies Mary, just to compromising situations. It will be very difficult, especially for Alfred, not to invent a white lie about your mother's non attendance at All Saints, purely out of loyalty. Perhaps we should all agree to the same white lie and stick to it.'

'No', Mary stated and firmly proceeded in monotone, 'No untruths or white lies, only the truth. Mother is away', reinforcing loudly, 'to an unknown destination, until Tuesday.'

'Oh that will fuel all sorts of village gossip', Polly argued strongly.

'It's the truth. We are all going to church in our usual manner with the truth.'

'What about loyalty and protection of your mother?' questioned Polly in an unusually high pitched voice.

Mary replied quite loudly, almost with venom, 'She should have thought of that before dropping this out of character pebble into our pool.'

Polly huffed in disagreement.

Mary did not like being at odds with her favourite Aunt but

felt it was the only way remembering her father's words 'Oh what a tangle web we weave when first we practice to deceive'. To her mind to tell no lies was clearly the only way for credibility.

On Sunday morning at church Polly found it easy to enter into her role of mother hen and sit with Mary in the Walker family pew to support the Walker name in it's strange hour of need. But, she found it extremely hard to bear the glances of the Wilbraham Family who sat in the chantry viewing any irregularities in the village and particularly anything appertaining to their tenants. Nellie's empty seat felt like a chasm to Polly.

As All Saints filled, darting glances to the Walker pew by seemingly every member of the congregation, reinforced to Polly and Mary the silent knowledge that most folks knew about the unusual disappearance of Nellie. Even the Rector gave a stark stare towards the Walker pew before commencing the service, as if to confirm to himself the news he had heard was true. The singing of the hymns, prayers and indeed the whole service meant nothing to Polly although her synchronisation of standing, sitting and kneeling with the congregation was faultless. She was totally consumed by the Walker predicament and made several prayers of her own on the issue as and when she felt the need.

Polly admired the composure of Mary as they sat together and was grateful that at least John was experiencing no shame. He was finishing his farming jobs at Higher Smallwood and besides she knew he normally attended Evensong. Polly wondered if she should attend that service also to support him although she knew he would be spared any scrutiny of their Landlord glances. Gentry never attended Evensong for it was originally meant to be an easy service for the illiterate. Nowadays, in the main Evensong was attended by the maids, labourers and servants together with the young of Rode, for this allowed them to share time together afterwards without the presence of too many prominent adults.

Another glance to Mary triggered thoughts deeper in Polly, coming to the conclusion Mary had handled the situation wrongly, coupled with Polly finding a sense of guilt, in feeling relief that the Dowager had died, thus eliminating any confession about the strange disappearance of Nellie.

Polly thought of all the sad, loving and moving times she and Nellie had shared. The genuine open way Nellie had kept Polly at the heart of the Walker family. How could she think ill of her? She found it impossible to do so. For all the Walker family turmoil, now surrounding them, deep down Polly felt Nellie was trustworthy and there must be a very good reason for her unusual absence but what?

Polly's mind was also firming over Mary, strongly feeling she should have over ruled her, out of loyalty to Nellie. Dealing with delicate village matters, being discreet and confidential and telling necessary white lies used to be a practice taken to art form by herself and the Dowager. Polly still felt that such practice would have been a better choice for the present Walker dilemma and it would have bought sufficient time for the return of Nellie.

Again Polly looked involuntarily at Mary. Mary returned her gaze with a weak smile, as if to say we are managing and Polly returned a slight smile of acknowledgement. This action eked out a pang of guilt in Polly thinking ill of Mary. How could mother and daughter be so very different? Nellie would debate, debate strongly sometimes with her, but, in the main, accept advice and pursue Polly's line on difficult issues. Mary was vastly opposite. Yes, she would listen, debate but still follow her own instincts. Mary was never for turning.

In deeper thoughts Polly realised how Mary's character was very like George's, he rarely turned. He was extremely positive and Polly remembered how George was adamant that he was going to marry Nellie. On reflection, Mary was very much her father's daughter in temperament. Her hard work and strength of character in keeping Higher Smallwood on an even keel through recent difficult farming waters had to be recognised. Perhaps Mary would always carry an inherent strength of her father throughout her life.

Sitting in the pew Polly could feel that spirit of George

in Mary now. George suffered the early loss of his father and dedicated himself to the survival of Higher Smallwood Farm and its household. Very often history did repeat itself and sure enough Mary had to cope with the death of her father at an early age. She not only kept the farm going but simultaneously conducted admirably her responsible role of a Red Cross Nurse throughout the War. Polly knew she had to give Mary credit where credit was due, probably only achieved because of a spirit equal to George's. Often, sadly those who are determined to survive and are full of self-will can be looked upon harshly by society. Polly reflected that it is easy to be an angel when nothing ruffles your wings and she did accept a focus on self-survival can unjustly put some people in a bad light. As life was unfolding it did seem that Mary was in that category.

Eventually Polly and Mary somehow achieved, with very few words, to leave the service, shaking hands with the Rector and making their way down the path but each disliking their own false fixed weak smiles. The sight of loyal Alfred, awaiting them the other side of the lych gate, holding the reins of the trap was tremendously reassuring and ensured some sort of dignity in their retreat.

Within the comfort of the living kitchen at Higher Smallwood, before the commencement of their mid day meal, Mary took the helm with ease to say grace. Polly noted Mary added the words 'and we ask for mother's safe return' to the usual words of thanks for their food, before the three of them said 'Amen'. John's 'Amen' was particularly loud before they commenced eating their food.

Prior to their Sunday meal the three of them felt they had exhausted the why's and wherefore's of the situation and Polly was pleasantly surprised to see how well the children ate in the circumstances. The only comment John forcibly made to his Aunt Poll was, that if he or Mary had disappeared, could she imagine the dire trouble they would experience on returning. However, the unanimous opinion was overwhelming that Tuesday could not come soon enough to see Nellie safe again.

Sunday night was most restless for Mary. She was reliving the events of the day particularly the morning service at All Saints. In her feather bed she tossed and turned and her thoughts gushed with memories of her father's discerning nature. She could not help thinking he would have searched his mind over a disturbing situation and formulated a pattern to resolve matters. But Mary was at a loss to understand any reason for the absence of her mother let alone try to see an outcome.

She prayed to the good Lord and asked for her father's strength of mind and whilst doing so she could hear a sharp April shower outside. After finishing her prayer she lay still on her back and listened to the rain subsiding. Her thoughts drifted to her father's simple poem about the rain and she made herself struggle in her mind to remember his sayings;

Dear England's Rain

In January if the North Wind doth blow
There may be sleet followed by driving snow

February rain or hail should fill the dykes
That is what Mother Nature really likes

March soil for farmers is their gold if dust
But rain falls if the dark clouds say it must

April sends us vernal drops in warm showers
Makes all things grow and bursts forth our flowers

When in May the chestnut blossoms are in full form
Chances are high for a loud thunder storm

Rain in June will spoil the best hay in it's row
But often provides a most glorious rainbow

At the end of the rainbow is a pot of gold
Iris is the one with trusted hands the pot to hold

In July misty rain before seven fine before eleven

August air can be muggy and stifling hot
Any thundery rain will start with a large spot

September rain tells creatures to make a Winter store
Their harvest is the gleaning from Mother Nature's floor

October rain causes cattle to ponch wet pastures and
*   makes muddy the gateway;*
By the 12ᵗʰ of October the stock are laid up and in their
*   winter housing stay*

November rain is gusty and will pelter
Storms bring the ships closer to shore for shelter

Dark depressing December rain makes us hide
In our homes dry and cosy by the fireside

Filling her mind with her father's rain sayings steadied her racing thoughts, thankfully giving sleep a better seed bed to take root, and Mary eventually succumbed to her night's slumber.

Tuesday morning arrived with extreme tension in Mary and, although the blue sky and small pure white clouds were beautiful, they were unnoticed by her. She scanned her mother's letter for the umpteenth time, taking in the return, stated as 'in the late morning'. At one point Mary's mind strangely flew out of order. Should she send Alfred to Mow Cop Station in case her mother was using the train for her return? Perhaps she should send Ada away for the day in case her return caused unpleasantness. Mary had no illusions that her mother's return would be difficult as she had many direct questions to ask her.

She managed to harness her spinning thoughts, ensuring jobs were done early and thoroughly before the impending return. After baggin time John burst through the back door startling Ada.

'Where's Mary?' he asked abruptly.

'Turning the cheeses', came an equally abrupt reply from Ada.

John shouted up the back stairs in the direction of the cheese room.

'Mary I can hear a car coming. Be quick it could be mother!'

Mary's decent of the stairs was instant as John disappeared into the yard. Her thoughts were very organised before she instructed, 'If this is mother, Ada, please take this florin and purchase six tuppenny stamps from Rode Heath Post Office. Take my bicycle. Be as long as you like and treat yourself to something with the change.' In a natural reaction Ada quickly tied a knot in her handkerchief as an aide memoire for the correct number of stamps but, before she could utter any gratitude for the surplus money, Mary curtly asked, 'Is the cold meal ready?'

'Yes ready and set in the living kitchen', Ada answered efficiently but added in a scathing manner, 'Your mother won't thank you for a cold meal on her return.'

Mary was not the least bit interested in Ada's opinion as she pressed the florin into her palm, before dashing to join John in the farmyard. An automobile was visible on the drive rise.

'I think it's Aunt Esme's car', John told Mary, keeping his eyes on the vehicle.

Mary puffed the words, 'Oh no. That's all we need, an unannounced visit by relations from Aston Lodge.'

'Wait a minute, I think mother is in the back seat. Yes, it is mother! She was with Aunt Esme after all', he said, his face lighting up with relief.

Mary was confused. Why all the secrecy for a normal Staffordshire visit. Her heart sunk when she saw Samuel at the wheel. She would have preferred Cuthbert to have been her mother's chauffeur. Samuel was the last person she wanted around to witness a frayed edge family reunion.

The gleaming car came to a halt and Samuel dutifully opened the rear door to allow Nellie to stand on the running board and he also kindly extended his hand to steady her until she was firmly on the ground. Her smile was warm and serene and seemed even more beautiful to behold. John ran into her extended arms for a long loving squeeze and a dear kiss from his mother. Whilst awaiting her turn for the familiar greeting, Mary glanced awkwardly at Samuel, only to add to her mental confusion for she noted he was busying himself, unloading her mother's belongings in an orderly manner. Normally he did not move without an instruction.

The next moment Mary was grabbed by her mother for a hug but, although Mary was extremely relieved to feel her, she could not reciprocate any tactile emotion, pulling her cheek away before her mother was able to plant her kiss. Mary's first line of defensive dissent caused no damage to Nellie's almost regal home coming, as she beamed with happiness.

Out of the corner of her eye Mary could see Ada discreetly mounting the bicycle at the rear of the farmyard, which gave her a sense of accomplishment. Alfred walked with dignity across the farmyard to Nellie and stepped forward with his right hand outstretched. 'Good to see you safe and well Mrs Walker', he said with sincerity.

Nellie shook his hand, with both of her gloved hands in a very warm way, before replying, 'Thank you, Alfred. It is good to be back.'

Alfred did not linger but he walked towards Samuel and shook his hand in a likewise manner, as if giving a grateful acknowledgment to him, although only the chauffeur, for Nellie's safe return, before walking calmly away.

Mary decided to take control a little and announced, 'All of you go into the drawing room and I will bring the tea tray along.'

'Thank you, Mary. That would be very nice', came the expected reply from her mother.

John put his hand down on his mother's shoulder in his familiar way and regretfully announced, 'I'm sorry, mother, there is a cow calving and I will have to see to her. Count me out on the cup of tea but I will catch up in a while.' Turning his gaze to Samuel he asked, 'Will you be stopping for something to eat, Samuel, before you go home?'

Nellie immediately replied for him, 'Yes, he will, John. Go and attend to your cow and we will chat later.'

Mary became agitated. Trust Samuel to be staying for his midday meal when it was a cold one.

Whilst Mary was waiting for the kettle to boil on the new black range in the back kitchen she surreptitiously set another place at the living kitchen table for Samuel, hurriedly fettled the fire and washed her hands. During these chores she was thinking deeply on how to achieve a thorough explanation from her mother about her absence especially with of the inconvenient presence of Samuel.

As she took the best tea tray, dutifully filled, through to the drawing room, she saw all her mother's belongings had been neatly placed in the hall by Samuel to be taken upstairs at a later time. Again Mary felt the pang of relief that her mother had made her return safe and sound. As she gently tapped the drawing room door with the toe of her left shoe Samuel politely opened the door with a worried countenance.

Mary put the tray down but before pouring the tea could not contain herself any longer. Contrary to what she had planned she asked bluntly, 'Where on earth have you been mother?'

'I've been away with Samuel', Nellie calmly replied directly to the point.

What! Just the two of you? How did you go? Why did you leave in such a manner? What is going on?'

Completely in control of herself Nellie answered, 'We have

decided not to answer questions nor to try and explain our time away together.'

Mary was annoyed and raised her voice. 'I deserve an explanation. These last few days have been very hard in Rode especially at All Saints. Your sudden disappearance has fuelled many rumours. Can you imagine how much you have been discussed by everyone?'

Nellie smiled and started to peel her long leather gloves from her arms and hands. Annoyingly for Mary, her mother held the pause until she had removed her gloves, folded them neatly and tossed them on to the table in an almost carefree manner. Mary's exasperation rose.

'Well?' she demanded.

Nellie in a soft triumphant voice answered, 'It's like this, Mary, everyone in Rode will just have to get used to things. You see Sammy and me were married while we were away.'

Mary involuntarily dropped in shock on to a hard chair, struggling to keep her eyes firmly fixed on her mother's eyes before asking in a slow extended breath, 'What!! Married? But he's your nephew.'

'Only by marriage. Sammy is no blood relation.'

'But you are much older than him.'

'Not too much', Nellie answered confidently.

Mary was reeling from this bolt from out of the blue. Never had she ever thought of her own mother eloping. She raised her head slightly higher and deeply contemplated her mother's words.

A long look at Samuel confirmed to Mary it was true and the love in his eyes for her mother was now obvious. A dart of guilt sprung heavily into Mary's thoughts. She blinked hard and shook her head before uttering, 'Oh, Samuel, what have I done? I was very rude to you in the croft. You were trying to tell me about your hidden love for mother, weren't you?'

'Yes, I was', he said in an understanding tone and added assuringly, 'but you were not rude to me, Mary, you were showing your strength of character.'

Nellie interrupted in a protective way of Samuel, 'However when Samuel confessed to me about the incident in the croft, it did force us to find a firm and final solution to our love. Our desire for marriage had to reach fruition in a very private way, hence the course of action we have just taken to become man and wife.'

Mary was shocked to her inner core.

Nellie allowed Mary time to digest the unexpected news. After a minute spent looking out of the window and nodding occasionally in disbelief, Mary returned her gaze to the room and stood once more. Nellie, detecting her daughter was regaining her composure, moved close to Samuel and took a deep breath before stating clearly, 'When love is fresh, unforced and true, it is like seeing and smelling an exquisite rose and it lifts your spirits like a glorious sunrise. I'm experiencing my perfect happiness. I want to hold you Mary and feel from your embrace a gladness and an acceptance that you can behold my blessing of true love.'

After a pause Nellie continued with a plea, 'Please, Mary, be glad for me. Know that I have true love in my heart and my life is unfolding in a very precious way with Sammy.'

A huge swell of forgiveness came into Mary's heart. She paused and maturely thought, did explanations really matter? True love needs to find a way and she felt she should be glad for them and be thankful for the union of their marriage, even in such strange circumstances. She slightly trembled before she said humbly, 'Oh, mother, when anyone is following a desire or firmly grasping their destiny, there is always someone around shouldering responsibility and this time I only just coped. Many times I wanted to cry but didn't; your letter asked me to be strong.'

Nellie's eyes slightly smeared with understanding tears as she tenderly comforted her exceptional daughter by saying, 'Mary, Mary, hopefully you have little need to be strong again. Samuel is with us now.'

Mary glanced to him to see him nodding in agreement with a serious sincere expression on his face. She could not speak but pleaded with her eyes for his forgiveness. He perceived her emotion and thoughtfully raised his right palm slowly towards her, clearly indicating he needed no explanation. Silence was sufficient.

Nellie held her arms wide. Mary was succumbing to rare tears. She slowly stepped forward into her mother's arms, buried her head on her mother's shoulder and hugged her round the waist. She lifted her head and closely facing her mother was about to speak through her tears. Putting a finger to her daughter's lips, Nellie instructed with immense feeling, 'Shh. No words. Let things be. Let all our lives unfold.'

She placed one hand gently to the back of Mary's head, over her beautiful hair, pulling their foreheads lovingly together. The Gentle Ribbon pulled tight. Oh so very tight!

The Family Tree of George Walker of Higher

John Walker
of Higher Smallwood Farm Rode
bn 1782 died 27th March 1863
Interred in Astbury church yard

John Walker △ md Mary Dale △
bn 1817 — of Pump Farm Rode
farmed at Higher — md 4th Jan 1844
Smallwood Farm — at Astbury Church
d. 13th Feb 1889 — d. 24th Jan 1899
both interred in Astbury Church yard

Fanny Walker
'Esme'
bn October 1844
md Robert Pointon
at Odd Rode Church
16th Aug 1871
farmed at Aston
Lodge, Stone, Staffs
'one son Cuthbert
Pointon bn 1875'
2 Samuel Pointon
bn 1880

William △ Walker
bn April 1846
d. at Higher
Smallwood
Farm
18th Oct 1871
a cripple

Hannah Walker
bn May 1847
md
Thomas
Tunnicliffe
21st May 1879
of Hilderstone
Staffordshire

John Walker
bn 9th Oct 1850
md
Keziah Yates
known as Kitty
of Hole House Fm
md 14th March
1876 farmed at
Spring Hill Fm
Totmonslow
Draycott
Staffordshire
had 13
Children

△ Interred in one grave in Astbury church yard C648
gravestone is not visible as whole grave area is
covered by a large rhodedendron

' ' adaptation for The gentle Ribbon

Smallwood Farm Rode in the County of Cheshire

Mary Walker △
bn Jan 1853
known as Polly
a spinster
lived at
Higher Smallwood
Farm for her
life with her
brother
George

Emily Walker
bn 1856
md
Thomas
Moseley
draper of
Newcastle
Staffordshire
1st Dec 1881
2 daughters
known

Sarah Jane Walker
bn July 1859
known as Sally
md
William
Croxton of
Townsend
Farm
4th Jan 1887
1 boy
1 girl known

George Walker △
bn March 1863
md
Edith Helen Bailey
known as Nellie
bn 25th July 1874
married at Rode Church
'June' 1892
farmed at Higher
Smallwood Farm
2 children

Mary
bn
24th March
1896

John
bn 1899

Compiled by Jean Williams

Family Tree of Edith Helen Bailey known as

John Bailey or Bayley
of Somerford Booths Hardwareman   married

Hannah Bailey bapt 13th April 1777	Daniel Bailey bapt 14th May 1775 at Astbury of Moors Farm Odd Rode	md Ann Shaw bn 1977 at Prestbury md 26th June 1799

John Bailey bn 6th Oct 1801   md Ellen Bostock bn Marton 1802
bapt 6th Nov 1801 at Astbury   md Swettenham 2nd Feb 1826
Gamekeeper d. 24th March 1895   died 7th Sept 1871
Aged 93 interred at Rode   interred at Rode

John Bailey	Mary Ann Bailey	Lydia Bayley	Sarah Bailey
bn 16th Feb 1829 d. 17th Jan 1906 md 30th March 1853 to Mary Ann Dale bn 8th Dec 1826 6 children Alice, Jessie, John Alec Charles, Arthur	bn 1831 md William Bostock of Buckbean Farm Goostrey	bn 8th April 1834 md 11th May 1858 James Rigby bn 18th May 1833 3 children Bertha, Arthur, Ada Helen	bn 1837 d 4th Dec 1881 md John Bostock Bank Farm Holmes Chapel no children interred at Rode

Edith Helen Bailey	Alexander Randle Bailey	George Edleston Bailey	Minnie Evelyn Bailey	Lily Maud Bailey	Lionel Harold Bailey
known as Nellie bn 25th July 1874 md George Walker bn march 1863 md 'June' 1892 at Rode Church 2 children *Mary Walker bn 24th March 1896	'Young Alec' md Mary Potts of Haslington 2 boys Alan	died in infancy	died in infancy	md Leonard Shaw 4 girls Nora Dorothy Daphne Celia	md 1. Beatric gratton 1 child John md 2 Elizabeth Holland 4 children Brian Eric madeline Raymond

John Walker md Mary Baskerville 2 sons John & Alan

* Mary md William Nield
3 girls - Edith Helen 'Nellie', Mary, Ruby Marian

(') adaptation for the Gent

Nellie of Pack Horse Farm Rode Cheshire

Sarah Booth of Astbury Parish
on 26th November 1772 at Astbury Church

Elizabeth Bailey
bapt 12th September 1779

Susannah Bailey
bapt 19th September
1819

William Bailey
bapt 24th March
1822

md Wife died
| 1by1851 census
Frances bn 1847-8

Elizabeth Bailey
bn 1842
d 9th April 1917
md
.William Berrisford
one child William
..Joseph Bostock

William Bailey md Emily Barratt
bn 1844   bn 1852 Brookhouse
d 2nd March 1922   green Smallwood
aged 77 farmed   d. 29th April 1926
at Pack Horse Farm
   both interred at Odd Rode

'Alec'
Arthur Bailey
bn 1848
md 'Martha'
Kathleen hock

Lucy Emily
Miriam
Bailey
md
Arthur
Brown
grocer
Kidsgrove
Children

John
Leonard
Bailey
md
Alice
Bailey
From Hole
House Farm
no children

William
Arnold
Bailey
md
Travelled
to Canada
Children

Sydney Herbert
Bailey
md
Nellie
Children
Marion Kathleen
John Leonard
Ronald
Irene
Sydney Herbert
Mary
Malcolm
2 died in
infancy

Percy Sydney
Bailey
md
Marie Beswick

2 boys
1 girl

Ribbon - Compiled by Jean Williams